PROOF-ROOM COPY

88

520.—

/4.

Freedom

in Agricultural Education

Freedom
in Agricultural Education

CHARLES M. HARDIN

THE UNIVERSITY OF CHICAGO PRESS

Library of Congress Catalog Number: 55–5129

THE UNIVERSITY OF CHICAGO PRESS, CHICAGO 37
Cambridge University Press, London, N.W. 1, England
The University of Toronto Press, Toronto 5, Canada

TO MY PARENTS

In this study of agricultural education Professor Hardin has
raised some notable issues and has contributed both evidence and
insight. Education is one of the great faiths of the American people.
We believe that universal schooling in literacy and social compre-
hension is indispensable to individual well-being and democratic co-
hesion. We believe that higher education should provide those able
and willing to benefit from its study with an understanding of man's
intellectual heritage. More than this, higher education is our primary
social instrument for preserving, advancing, and using knowledge.

At the same time, this faith entails some difficult issues of
public policy. In large measure universal education has been provided as a government service. Government, too, is sizably involved
in the support of higher education. It has not been easy to reconcile
governmental direction and educational administration. Mostly, we
have found our workable answers in local and state government
responsibility for education, in popularly elected and administratively
autonomous local boards of education, in state boards of trustees for
higher education, and in the development of the educational profession.

Initially, Professor Hardin began his study of the relations between colleges of agriculture and the federal government at my request. I was at that time serving as executive director of the Commission on Financing Higher Education, established by the
Association of American Universities and supported by the Rockefeller
Foundation and the Carnegie Corporation of New York. The commission
was much concerned about the increasing role of the federal government in the financial support of educational activities at the level of
higher education. Actually, the only lengthy experience in federal-
state relations in the field of higher education involved the state
colleges of agriculture. Continuing financial subsidy of these colleges
had begun as early as 1887. It was thought that it might be instructive
to examine this accumulated experience in order to throw some light
upon one or two crucial questions. Does continuing financial support

of higher education by the federal government result in an effort
at federal control of educational programs? Does federal control,
if it exists, tend to encourage uniformity of educational point of view?

Because of his wealth of background in agricultural politics, Professor Hardin, of the University of Chicago, was asked to study this
subject. From the data collected at that time, from the report prepared for the Commission on Financing Higher Education, and from
other data Professor Hardin has now written this volume. It must be
understood that this study expresses Professor Hardin's own research
findings, conclusions, and opinions. Neither the commission nor I as
its executive director has endeavored to exercise any control over
what Professor Hardin has to say. This book is his own.

While thus explaining briefly the origins of this study, I would
at the same time like to indulge in a few comments and observations.
Professor Hardin found that there was little evidence of any sustained
effort at control following in the wake of federal government financial
support of agricultural Extension, agricultural research, and the
operations of land-grant colleges. Partly, this may result from the
relatively slighter proportion of support contributed for these purposes
by the federal government in contrast with that of state governments.
Partly, it may be explained by the alert concern exercised by the
agricultural colleges collectively to preserve independence of action.
Professor Hardin goes further to point out that, on occasion, state
agricultural experiment station directors and other administrators
have used federal interest in their work as a means for preserving
their integrity in working with state government officials.

It must be remembered that agricultural education and research
have a unique characteristic in the United States. All such educational
activity is conducted under government sponsorship. In contrast
with law, medicine, engineering, science, and other fields, there
are no privately operated colleges of agriculture or agricultural
experiment stations. Thus the private activity which serves as such
a stimulus as well as a protection to state government higher education
in other fields is completely missing in agriculture. A different operating strategy has been required in this particular realm of higher
education.

Federal government participation in agricultural education has

then at times been used as a lever to pry loose hostile forces gathering around the agricultural college. But certainly this has not been
the primary purpose of federal financial support. Such support resulted
from and has been continued by the concern of farm groups in our
society to advance their educational interest. And in this process the
educational bureaucracy itself, as represented in the Association
of Land-Grant Colleges and Universities, has done its bit in watching
over federal support. On the one hand, it has encouraged financial
assistance, and, on the other hand, it has been ready to resist any
threat to institutional independence.

But Professor Hardin's interest carries him into collateral
matters. Just what is the scope of federal educational interest? To
what extent can or should the machinery of the agricultural Extension
Service be employed to inform farmers on current issues of agricultural policy? And where does information pass into advocacy, and
advocacy become partisan in spirit and purpose? Moreover, to what
extent might the broadly conceived "action" programs of the 1930's
have realized their objectives through education rather than through
direct administrative operation? If Professor Hardin does not answer
these questions with precision—indeed, is a precise answer possible?
—his study at least raises some vital questions.

In turn, this interest suggests still a further level of concern.
If the agricultural college and its affiliated educational services
are to concern themselves with current problems, how can scholarly
objectivity be defended from partisan attack in a state-supported
institution? There are examples of such partisan or special-interest
attack. Professor Hardin recites illustrative episodes. Here again
a precise answer is difficult to suggest. In general, however, experience seems to indicate that actual conflict of this kind has been
exceptional rather than customary.

Yet, Professor Hardin speculates, may not this record be merely
testimony to the conservatism of agricultural education in dealing with
problems of social conflict? Certainly the world of higher education is
essentially conservative in its traditions and attitudes, popular opinion to the contrary notwithstanding. Knowledge draws upon the past
and is ever cautious and tentative in speculating about the new and
unfamiliar. Educational institutions, moreover, were established to

conserve existing values, not to lead the advance in developing new ones. This, too, is as it should be. Nonetheless, education is dynamic, not static. It must explore all matters of life from many different points of view. Higher education is committed to freedom but is not enlisted on the side of any single group in our pluralistic society. Professor Hardin wonders whether agricultural education has always appreciated its full responsibility.

Certainly I for one find in the very issues Professor Hardin raises profound substantiation for the desirability of the prevailing pattern of higher education. Freedom in a democracy exists by virtue of competing institutional endeavors. Private and public institutions existing alongside each other have been our major guaranty of freedom in higher education. The absence of such an arrangement in agricultural education has imposed special problems for the presidents and deans of our land-grant colleges.

There seems to me to be yet another phase of the problem, however, which is only hinted at in these pages. We Americans pride ourselves with considerable justification upon the practical application of our knowledge. More than any other society, we have used knowledge for our individual and collective well-being. We do not want our educational institutions to be ivory towers. We expect them to be in and of the everyday world of practical affairs. But this everyday world is necessarily one of social conflict. Such conflict is of the essence of democracy. It can and does serve a constructive end. If our educational scholars and administrators are to concern themselves with practical matters, they are bound to become entangled in controversy. It is the spirit and manner of such entanglement which form the essence of educational management in our country. Here is a particular subject for a much more careful formulation of position than it has had up to now.

If these comments serve to suggest that Professor Hardin is concerned with important problems, then they have amply served their purpose. No one—least of all Professor Hardin, I am sure—pretends that he has spoken, or written, the last word. But he has provided us with some critical comments which should give thoughtful students and educational administrators pause for attention. This is satisfaction enough for the scholar.

John D. Millett

Miami University

On behalf of the Commission on Financing Higher Education, John D. Millett asked me to study the question whether federal grants to states for agricultural research and Extension had been accompanied by federal control of personnel or policy in these fields. The commission was interested in the answer to this question especially for the light it would throw on the prudence and wisdom of extending federal aid to higher education generally. Chapters iii and iv of this book examine the administration of federal grants in agriculture and conclude, as previous studies have, that these grants have not been a medium of federal control upon state research and education. I was anxious, however, to broaden the study, and the commission generously made this possible. I wanted to include the effect of political pressures from whatever source and exercised by whatever means upon publicly supported agricultural research and Extension. Then I wanted to reverse the coin, to study the relevant agricultural agencies as political interests, and to appraise their function respecting the making and administration of farm policy. This book thus falls in the class of studies of which Don K. Price's Government and Science (New York: New York University Press, 1954) is a brilliant example, and I should have repeatedly cited Price's work had it fallen into my hands earlier.

The present book centers upon men—administrators, researchers, and educators. What is their situation? What limits confine them? What imperatives compel them? What alternatives remain? How are the alternatives examined?—in terms of what expediency, what political calculation, and what conception of the public function of the institution? What objectives emerge? One way or another, incident by incident, such questions are being answered continuously throughout the land-grant college system and in the United States Department of Agriculture. Some of the research materials pertinent to the answering of these questions appears in print, but the great bulk of it is in the memories of the actors.

This great bulk I have tried to mine by interviews and discussions. Most of these were held during 1950 and 1951 in field trips made possible by the Commission on Financing Higher Education; but they began in 1940, when I interviewed members and guests of John D. Black's seminar at Harvard University, and they have since been continued. Numerous field trips have been made, invitations have been accepted to teach or lead seminars in several colleges of agriculture, and brief assignments have been fulfilled in the United States Department of Agriculture and the Tennessee Valley Authority. All these have provided opportunities for research.

Interviews have always been conducted with the explicit understanding that no interviewee would be quoted and identified in writing without his consent. Every effort has been made rigorously to abide by this understanding. In some of the chapters below, verisimilitude has been sacrificed in order to disguise sources; but I believe that the true meaning of the incidents reported has been preserved.

Some will charge me with gossip-mongering, reliance upon hearsay evidence, and argument by innuendo. I admit to relishing a good story as much as the next man, but, so far as this book is concerned, the charge is essentially false. I was no one-man grand jury. This book is not an attempt to ascertain the criminal guilt or innocence of agricultural researchers, administrators, and educators or of farm leaders and politicans; rather, it is an effort to understand the political process in which they operate and to appraise—and to provide some criteria for appraising—the expediency and wisdom of their actions. Legal rules of evidence are not completely transferable to the field of political analysis.

How reliable are the incidents reported on the basis of interviews? Some of them may suffer from my inability to verify them with other interviews. Chiefly, these represent incidents in which the original informant who described an attempt to influence research by bringing political pressure was the only one privy to the information except the man who was wielding the political influence. Any attempt to cross-check this kind of report would have involved disclosing sources. On the other hand, if I could publish the names of interviewees, most informed readers would recognize the overwhelming majority of them as men who would be expected to describe situations and incidents completely, accurately, and fairly. Most of my respondents were trained as scientists. Many of them warned me of their own interests, pointed out parts of their stories which they had not verified, and tried to represent different viewpoints. I have considerable faith, therefore, in the reliability of interviews for the purpose for which I have used them—to help characterize the political situation in which publicly supported agricultural Extension and research operate.

An entirely different point must also be raised: the terminology respecting governmental agencies. Even though subsequent revision has been considerable, the bulk of this manuscript was written before the reorganization of the United States Department of Agriculture in November, 1953. That reorganization abolished the Bureau of Agricultural Economics (BAE) and divided its functions between the Agricultural Marketing Service and the Agricultural Research Service. It abolished the Production and Marketing Administration (PMA) and divided its functions between the Agricultural Marketing Service and the Commodity Stabilization Service. Two of the major agencies referred to repeatedly in these pages have disappeared—the BAE and the PMA. The functions and problems, however, remain; and the writer has elected not to comb the manuscript in order to insert a thousand clarifying footnotes to explain just what these agencies are called in their current reincarnation.

In the same vein, readers outside agriculture should be apprised that a number of references in this book to the Extension Service-Farm Bureau relationship may have to be reinterpreted in the light of an order by Secretary Ezra Taft Benson which, among other things, forbade any employee of the United States Department of Agriculture to "accept the use of free office space or contributions for salary or traveling expense from any general or specialized organization of farmers" (Memo. 1368, November 24, 1954). Of the nearly ninety million dollars which the co-operative Extension program had in fiscal 1954, only 2.6 per cent came from "local nonpublic sources" (essentially, farm bureaus), and more than 80 per cent of this fraction came in three states: Illinois, Iowa, and New York. Just how Secretary Benson's order will be worked out is not clear as this book goes to press.

I am greatly indebted to the Commission on Financing Higher Education and especially to its executive director, John D. Millett (now president of Miami University), who has written the Foreword. I wish to thank D. Gale Johnson, W. E. Hendrix, and Edward J. Banfield for reading the final draft, as well as T. W. Schultz, John D. Black, M. L. Wilson, Charles E. Kellogg, and Wallace Ogg for valuable counsel on this project over the years. My appreciation is due Lewis Mainzer and Charles Macklin for research assistance, especially on chapters iv and vi, respectively. Beyond these, there is a debt of inestimable size owed to the hundreds of persons who generously shared their special knowledge of the problems under review. I am responsible, of course, for all interpretations and conclusions. Finally, I should like to thank Sallie Gibson Hardin for her encouragement and assistance in writing this book, which is affectionately dedicated to my parents, Mr. and Mrs. W. E. Hardin, of Lander, Wyoming.

Charles M. Hardin

Chicago, Illinois

Table of Contents

Can researchers and educators on the public payroll safely work on
controversial political issues? This book contributes to this grave question by examining the experience of agricultural research and Extension
work in the contemporary United States. The organizations carrying on
this work are the colleges of agriculture in the forty-eight states and
certain bureaus of the United States Department of Agriculture (USDA).
One of the serious tasks of this inquiry is to appraise the effects of
politics upon institutions which are themselves inseparably part of the
political process.

1. Political Characteristics of the Colleges of Agriculture

Late in 1952 President-elect Eisenhower named a fourteen-man com-
mittee to help draft the nation's farm program. Members included Dean
W. I. Myers, of Cornell University's college of agriculture, as chairman;
Dean Harry J. Reed, of Purdue University's college of agriculture; and
G. Burton Wood, head of agricultural economics at Oregon State College.
Such recognition of agricultural colleges by Washington powers-that-be
has been traditional since the term of James Wilson of Iowa (and Iowa
State College) as Secretary of Agriculture (1897-1913). The ties between the
USDA and the colleges have been strained but never broken. Prompted by
common interests and objectives, college and USDA leaders have period-
ically reconciled their differences and turned the bilateral actions to
which they are legislatively enjoined into free and fruitful co-operation.
Out of this experience, a number of salient political characteristics of
colleges of agriculture have emerged.

The colleges are recognized political interests.[1]—Some readers may
feel uncomfortable about the designation of research and educational agencies as political interests. Their doubts may be relieved by an immediate denial of anything inherently evil in political interests, which have
always been the acknowledged dynamics of the American Constitution—

and which have embraced virtually every kind of organized activity, sacred or profane. Members of colleges of agriculture share common purposes and show a common determination to advance them, among other ways, by securing financial support from government. Individually and collectively, they are well organized and have excellent access to both national and state governments.

The colleges of agriculture are representative institutions. —State agricultural Extension directors recognize this fact when they confer with county agents about rural opinion. Congressmen and officials of the USDA recognize it in counseling with agricultural college leaders about farm policy. It is acknowledged in the numerous forums where "business," "agriculture," and sometimes "labor" meet—with college participation and often under college sponsorship. Standing between the farmers and the rest of us, agricultural college leaders inevitably are among those who speak for agriculture—but they also speak to agriculture. It would be difficult to exaggerate the potential importance of this representative function, properly conceived and carried out; through it, agricultural researchers, educators, and administrators can make major contributions to the preservation and strengthening of American constitutional democracy.[2]

Agricultural college officials can appropriately share in the resolution of public policy issues of a controversial (and thus political) nature. — The essence of constitutional democracy is discussion, which implies appeals to reason. Rational analysis can be supplied in part by democracy's own research and educational institutions. The broad language of the basic laws of the latter provides ample scope for the participation of institutionalized reason in the political process.[3] Of course, no verbal magic can eliminate the travail of public educational and research institutions which tackle political issues.

The colleges of agriculture exemplify the primary American answer to the problem of bureaucracy. —Our government is heavily obligated to defend the country, to keep order, to regulate and promote the economy, and to provide social security and other services. To fulfil these ends requires a formidable organization of power that is symbolized in the term "bureaucracy," a swear word in several languages.[4] How is this power to be controlled? "Ambition must be made to counteract ambition," wrote James Madison,[5] and the permanent friction between the colleges of agriculture, essentially state institutions, and the USDA represents a practical application of his precept.

The colleges of agriculture display an "attitude, a temper, or an approach"[6] to politics which (with some misgivings) the writer will designate as "conservative."—The interests of agricultural colleges prompt them to favor decentralization of government to the states and critically to scrutinize those functions which, if continued by government, must be nationally administered (like price supports and production control). Whatever explains it—the age of the colleges, their roots in rural society—agricultural college leaders are usually suspicious of proposals to expand governmental activities in social security and welfare legislation, in market regulation and control, and in the development of natural resources. But perhaps this is sufficient preparation for a more formal introduction.

2. Agricultural Research and Extension in the United States

Chiefly, this book studies the colleges of agriculture which are established in the forty-eight states as divisions of land-grant colleges or universities which, in turn, are members of the Association of Land-Grant Colleges and Universities.[7] The land-grant colleges and universities are fundamentally state, rather than national, institutions. In accepting the Morrill Act of 1862, however, the states acquired certain obligations. The act provided land grants, income from which must go "to the endowment, support, and maintenance of at least one college where the leading object shall be, without excluding other scientific and classical studies and including military tactics, to teach such branches of learning as are related to agriculture and the mechanical arts, in such manner as the legislatures of the States may respectively prescribe, in order to promote the liberal and practical education of the industrial classes in the several pursuits and professions of life."[8] Under this broad charter, land-grant colleges are established and regulated by state law. They are headed by presidents or chancellors, directed by governing boards, provisioned largely by state legislatures, and subject in varying degrees to state governors and other officials.

Within the land-grant colleges and universities are colleges, schools, or departments of agriculture, headed by deans. The colleges of agriculture include agricultural Extension Services,[9] experiment stations, and divisions of resident teaching (of which little will be said).[10]

The Extension Service, headed by a director or an associate director, commonly administers the agricultural Extension and home economics programs. Typically, his administrative staff includes the state county agent leader and the state leader of home demonstration work, as well as district agricultural agents and home demonstration agents, each responsible for supervising the work in several counties. State Extension Services also employ subject-matter specialists in field crops, soil conservation, animal husbandry, agricultural economics, and so on; the number and titles vary considerably. On June 30, 1952, the state Extension staffs numbered 2,994 workers, of whom 788 were state supervisors, 1,694 were full-time specialists, and 512 were part-time specialists. At the same time, county Extension staffs numbered 4,866 county agricultural agents, 3,285 home demonstration agents, 645 special boys' and girls' club agents, and 803 Negro Extension agents.[11]

State Extension workers are co-operative employees of the state and federal governments; so are county Extension workers, but, in addition, the latter are typically selected by (and therefore, in some degree, responsible to) county governing boards. Qualifications for Extension workers are established by state laws; and county governing boards make their selections from qualified nominees submitted by the state Extension office. Naturally, some modifications of the foregoing general pattern are found.

In round numbers, total Extension funds in 1952-53 were $84,670,000,[12] derived as shown in Table 1. Only 1.3 per cent of the total was spent by the federal Extension Service; 76 per cent was spent for county Extension work. The program is heavily decentralized to the states and—even more so—to the counties.[13]

TABLE 1

DERIVATION OF AGRICULTURAL EXTENSION FUNDS, 1952-53

Source	Per Cent	Source	Per Cent
Federal government.	38	County governments.	23
State governments...	36	Other*....................	2.6

*Chiefly the farm bureaus in a few states.

State agricultural experiment stations, headed by directors or associate directors, are divided into departments—animal husbandry, dairy husbandry, agronomy and soils, agricultural economics and rural sociology, plant diseases, and so on. In 1952 the federal government provided some $12,500,-000 to the stations in grants-in-aid; some $57,000,000 was furnished, largely by state appropriations. The stations had 7,270 research workers, about half devoting full time to research, the rest dividing their time between research and teaching or Extension.[14] Research is further decentralized in that many states have established substations, experimental farms, or outlying fields.

In the USDA the federal Extension Service had 249 employees on November 30, 1952, compared to 12,600 state and county Extension workers. This office administers the federal grants-in-aid for Extension, provides liaison between Extension and other federal agricultural programs, and offers assistance to state Extension Services. On the same date the federal Office of Experiment Stations (OES) had 143 employees (compared to some 7,270 in state experiment stations). The OES administers federal grants-in-aid for agricultural research and helps to co-ordinate research among the stations and between the stations and other research agencies. It reports through the Agricultural Research Service (ARS). The ARS, established on November 2, 1953, as part of a general reorganization, includes six major USDA research bureaus, which spent nearly $30,000,000 for research in the fiscal year 1952, much of it in co-operation with state agricultural experiment stations.[15] The ARS also includes research in farm management and costs, land economics, and agricultural finance from the Bureau of Agricultural Economics (which was abolished in the reorganization), as well as certain research heretofore conducted elsewhere. Not quite all USDA research, however, has been consolidated in the ARS.

Among the USDA agencies, this book treats primarily the federal Extension Service, the OES, and the Bureau of Agricultural Economics (an especially significant subject for the study of research in relationship to politics). These organizations provide our subject or, rather, the human beings that staff and deal with them provide it—university presidents, college deans, Extension and experiment station directors, department heads, USDA bureau chiefs and scientists, state legislators and congressmen, college trustees, and farm leaders. For we are studying men as they go about their business (individually and in groups), abstracting as best we can from what they say and do that part which is political. Our subject is thus invested with the infinite variety that humanity bestows—these people are selfish and magnanimous, fearful and courageous, thoughtful and emotional, impulsive and phlegmatic; they are prestige-conscious and aware of the norms of behavior appropriate to their stations; they have their hostages to fortune, their conflicting group loyalties, and their loves and hates. If they sometimes seem to be only cardboard figures, the fault is in the writing.

3. Assumptions

Can these public agencies for research and Extension effectively examine the controversial issues which multiply in our society? American governmental forms and procedures open many doors for interest groups to urge or protest public action. Modern communication and transportation facilitate the activating and empowering of political groups. The appearance of some groups able to affect public policy prompts others to organize around opposed interests. The controversiality of public issues thus arises largely from the demands and counterdemands of organized groups.

If controversy abounds, American political processes and ideals require the resolution of issues largely through debate and discussion, in which appeals to reason are made. We may suspect the rationale of the positions taken on controversial issues by interested groups to which we do not belong, but we still expect it.[16] When divisive issues emerge, we look to "disinterested" sources for analyses in which group interests will be less prominent (or, at least, less apparent) and in which a more "public" interest will be represented. Such sources are pre-eminently our research and educational institutions.

By examining controversial matters, however, these institutions lay themselves open to political attack. No analysis of divisive issues will please everyone. To employ an imperfect analogy, the Supreme Court's decisions, however judicious, are commonly condemned by the losers; the court's defenders today are often its detractors tomorrow. Even more than the justices, researchers and educators can expect criticism of their conclusions on the part of disaffected interests—and the frequent projection of the attack from the individual researcher to the institution which he serves. For publicly supported research and educational institutions, political pressure presents special problems. To say this is not to disparage the pressures that affect private foundations and universities.[17]

Nevertheless, the public institutions are peculiarly vulnerable in attacking politically controversial issues, for they must look for financial support to the same public that is divided into interests whose agitation makes the issues controversial. The flow of legislative largesse to the colleges is watched by a sleepless Argus with as many eyes as there are affected interests.

The special sensitivity of the public's research and educational institutions means that, if pressure upon them is to be resisted, it must be by a force of its own kind. Political power is countered by political power, influence by influence—here as elsewhere. Therefore, we need to know how politics affects these institutions, as well as what kinds of "situations of strength" or "postures of defense" can be built. If an overt attack is made upon freedom of research and education and if the issue can be squarely raised and the aggressor clearly identified, a formidable body of public opinion will often rally behind the college.[18]

4.   Relevance of the Agricultural Experience

The foregoing assumptions are properly generalized, since the question whether publicly supported research and education can attack controversial issues is one for our entire civilization and not for just a segment ot it. The secular trend suggests that a larger and larger share of the bill for all kinds of education and research will be met by the public. If the problem is not confined to agriculture, however, this book is; thus some appraisal of the relevance of the agricultural experience is needed.

The relevance of this experience is qualified as follows: Agricultural research and Extension workers operate in relation to their clientele with an intimacy which is difficult for their more cloistered colleagues to understand. Agricultural scientists often carry on experiments with farmers literally peering over their shoulders. Sometimes ingenious stratagems have to be devised to keep untested results from premature application. Extension specialists from the state colleges find their local meetings blazoned in press headlines, and the county farm and home demonstration agents are continuously on the firing line. It would be hard to imagine a more striking contrast to the experience of the typical academician, whose influence works slowly (if at all!) through his library and study, his classrooms and publications, and perhaps enjoys a perceptible effect in a generation or so. The extreme proximity to action of the agricultural worker makes him understandably more wary than, say, his

liberal arts colleague and makes him perhaps a little less appreciative
of the values in abstractions about academic freedom. The agricultural
worker, moreover, is used to searching for specific practical answers
to specific practical questions. The urge is toward the practical, the
immediate, the concrete, and away from the abstract, the long-range,
the systematic, and the theoretical. Thus the agricultural experience may
not tell us much about the problems of public research and education in
dealing with theoretical systems and models which powerful groups
come to regard as dangerous to themselves and, by an easy projection,
as inimical to the nation.

On the other hand, agricultural research and Extension have some
characteristics which recommend them as case studies for the general
problem. Both the federal and the state governments have developed and
financed these agricultural agencies. Any tendencies for federal political
control to follow the federal grant-in-aid dollar should be discernible
in a study of them; but so also should be the effect of state and local
political pressure. Moreover, the relative age of the experiment stations
and Extension Services and their proximity to their farm clientele take
on another meaning when one recalls that these same farmers have organized and successfully demanded governmental action. As these agricultural educational institutions have evolved, so have controversial issues
affecting rural America. The former have been repeatedly tested by the
latter. How have our public research and Extension institutions in agriculture behaved under these tests?

Along with food and fiber, American farmers have traditionally raised crops of public issues. This "political husbandry" has severely tested the ability of agricultural research and Extension to work on controversial matters. How has this test been met? Both that question and its answer will be clearer for readers with perspective, which this chapter proposes to supply, upon the issues involved.

1. Before the New Deal

Our focus on recent years by no means disparages the earlier significance of agricultural issues in American politics. The drive to ease credit for agriculture, to prevent farm mortgage foreclosures, and to secure taxation systems more satisfactory to rural interests pervaded the new-born states and came sharply to a head in Shays's Rebellion in Massachusetts (1786). Reaction to rural discontent was one of the stimuli to the formation of the federal Constitution.[1] Again, rural political issues have prompted some of the great decisions interpreting the Constitution. The panic that ended the western land boom in 1819 brought state reprisals against the Bank of the United States and eventuated in McCulloch v. Maryland,[2] in which Chief Justice Marshall laid down the celebrated doctrine of implied powers. In finding that the United States could charter a national bank in the absence of a specific grant of power to do so, Marshall declared: "Let the end be legitimate, let it be within the scope of the Constitution, and all means which are appropriate, which are plainly adapted to that end, which are not prohibited, but consist with the letter and spirit of the Constitution, are constitutional."

It is inappropriate here to trace the effect of farm politics upon constitutional decisions, upon the extension of the suffrage, or otherwise upon state constitutions as the nation moved west. Nor need we tarry over the Granger movement of the 1870's. When Populism arose in the late 1880's and 1890's, the colleges of agriculture were old enough to figure in farm controversies.[3] After 1896, the farmers' economic situation improved.

Agricultural rents doubled in Iowa every ten years from 1890 to 1920.
The years 1910-14 were sufficiently favorable to serve as the base for
"parity" legislation in 1933. Using 1910-14 as 100, prices paid to farm
producers rose to 117 in 1916, to 176 in 1917, and to 209 in 1919; land
prices climbed to 169 in 1920.[4] The period from the decline of Populism
to the end of the first World War saw the conservation movement, the rise
of Progressivism, the Country Life Commission with its disheartening
report on rural social conditions, creation of the co-operative agricultural Extension Service, establishment of the federal land bank system,
and the first vigorous development of farm co-operatives.

In 1920 farm prices broke. The index of prices paid to farmers
dropped ten points in July, fifteen points in August, and fifteen points again
in September. The modern farm problem took its place high on the agenda
of American politics. Congress created a Joint Commission of Agricultural Inquiry in 1921, and national agricultural conferences were held under
administration auspices in 1922 and 1924-25. Economic disadvantages of
agriculture prompted farmers and their representatives to organize. The
"farm bloc" (1920-23), in close alliance with the newly formed American
Farm Bureau Federation, pressed successfully for such laws as the Packers and Stockyards Act (1921); the act regulating grain exchanges (1921);
the Capper-Volstead Act, which substantially freed farm co-operatives
from the antitrust laws (1922); and the Agricultural Credit Act (1923).
Finally, in 1926 the South and the West began to form that uneasy combination which has largely dominated recent American farm politics.[5] In
1927 Congress passed the McNary-Haugen Bill, defeated twice before;
and President Coolidge vetoed it. An amended bill was repassed in 1928
and again vetoed; the Senate failed to override by only four votes.

The McNary-Haugen Bills, though modified considerably over time,
consistently proposed to separate the domestic market from the foreign
market and to collect "equalization fees" from farm products sold domestically. These fees would be used to subsidize exports. Another proposal
to "make the tariff effective" for agriculture was the export-debenture
plan, offered by Professor Charles L. Stewart and backed by the national
Grange. Bounties on farm exports were to be financed from the sale to
importers of "debentures" which could be used to pay customs duties.
Another proposal made an allotment to farmers of their share of the domestic consumption of farm crops; the prices for the domestically
consumed portion of crops would then be raised by the amount provided

in the tariff, and what was not used at home would be sold on the world market at world prices. Finally, the Simpson Plan of the National Farmers Union proposed to guarantee farmers their "costs of production."

The Republican administration opposed all these and preferred the "orderly" production and marketing of farm products through co-operative action. To these ends, the Agricultural Marketing Act of 1929 created the Federal Farm Board, with a $500,000,000 revolving fund. The board lent money to farm co-operatives to withhold produce from the market and established its own stabilization corporations for wheat and cotton. But the depression inflicted heavy losses on the board, which began to urge that orderly marketing without production control was not enough. Farm income in the United States, $11,900,000,000 in 1929, had shrunk to $5,300,000,000 in 1932. In February, 1933, twice as much farm produce was required to buy a given amount of industrial goods as before World War I.

Thus the period from 1920 to 1933 began with one depression and closed with another. The first decline brought agriculture sharply down from the peaks of the boom that was the culmination of twenty years of farm prosperity. Many farms had been bought at inflated prices. Many farmers labored through the 1920's in an effort to save their heavily mortgaged farms and still to provide their families a share in the currently rising level of living. If 1926-29 saw farmers sharing in the general prosperity, many of them were unable significantly to decrease their mortgage debt. Then came the great depression.

During this period many issues emerged. Aggregative analyses were advanced which seemed to show that farmers as a group were at a disadvantage compared to other great social groups. Were the findings sound? Farm groups sought legislation to support agricultural prices and farm incomes. Would such laws constitute "class legislation"?—unconstitutional price-fixing? If constitutional, were the actions sought prudent? If industry and labor profited from the protective tariff (as the argument ran), should not its benefits be extended somehow to agriculture? Collective action was urged and practiced through farm co-operatives. Were special favors for co-operatives, in taxation and otherwise, in the public interest? The issues helped farmers to organize, and the organized groups pressed more and more vigorously for resolution of the issues on the farmers' terms.

As the issues crystallized, conflict over them rose, subsided, and

surged up again. At the same time, public institutions were being created rationally and systematically to examine the farmers' economic
problems. The Bureau of Agricultural Economics was established in
the USDA in 1921; many colleges of agriculture established departments of agricultural economics. Agricultural outlook work began in
1923 to probe the economic future. In many states agricultural plans,
made essentially by colleges of agriculture, became the vogue. In 1925
Congress authorized federal grants-in-aid for research in economics
and rural sociology by state experiment stations. In 1927 the Association of Land-Grant Colleges and Universities published a committee
report on the agricultural situation as its contribution to the numerous
analyses, more or less rational, of the farm problem. When the depression came and deepened, political opinion in agriculture became impa-
tient of the research and educational approach to the farm problem. A
readiness for sterner measures was manifest.

2.   The New Deal and After

Of the numerous agricultural programs of 1933 and after, the most
important for our purposes is that first administered by the Agricultural
Adjustment Administration (AAA) which was replaced in 1945 by the
Production and Marketing Administration (PMA), which, in turn, was
broken up and distributed in 1953, chiefly in the Agricultural Marketing
Service and the Commodity Stabilization Service. Since the events referred to in this volume fall almost exclusively in the pre-1953 period,
these agencies will be designated as "AAA" or "PMA" or, sometimes,
"AAA-PMA." The AAA and its successors have administered the agricultural adjustment acts, the first being passed in 1933, with numerous
significant amendments and re-enactments in subsequent years. The
main features of these programs are to be sketched. (Important changes,
especially the lowering of price-support levels on basic commodities
to 82 1/2 to 90 per cent of parity, were enacted in August, 1954; however,
the controversies with which this book deals stemmed from the earlier
legislation.)

The AAA and the PMA were charged to help farmers to get parity
prices or income. Parity is a ratio. Present prices which farmers re-
ceive are supposed to bear the same ratio to prices farmers pay that
obtained in the years 1910-14. (The base period for tobacco is 1920-29,

and there are certain other departures from the 1910-14 base.) Thus on
January 15, 1953, the weighted average prices received by farmers
were 267 (1910-14 equals 100). The parity index (that is, the prices of
a bundle of goods farmers buy) was 282. Dividing 267 by 282, we get .95,
the "parity ratio." Parity is also figured by commodities. A bushel of
wheat in 1910-14 sold for an average of $0.88. On January 15, 1953, it
sold for $2.10. Thus wheat was 238 compared to 1910-14; dividing this
by 282 shows that wheat was selling for 84 per cent of parity.[6]

The USDA helps farmers get parity by supporting the prices of
agricultural commodities. Cotton, corn, wheat, rice, and tobacco were
to be supported at 90 per cent of parity through 1954. Discretionary
support has been available for a list of other commodities, including
perishables. Thus the Secretary of Agriculture has had to support
butterfat at some point between 75 and 90 per cent of parity, making
his decision by April 1 for the ensuing twelve months. In addition,
30 per cent of the customs receipts are available for surplus removal
operations, e.g., by purchase and distribution to the school lunch program. Further, under the Agricultural Marketing Act of 1937, federal
marketing orders were in effect for 49 fluid-milk markets on September
15, 1953, and 25 different marketing agreements or orders were in
operation for certain fruits, vegetables, Irish potatoes, and tree nuts.

Merely to list these price-supporting functions suggests how many
farmers are directly involved in AAA-PMA operations and how many
consumers are indirectly affected. For the basic, storable commodities
the USDA makes loans to farmers. The loans are made, or the paper
is discounted, by the Commodity Credit Corporation (CCC). To be eligible for loans, commodities must be in proper condition and storage.
If the price rises above the loan, the farmer may pay the government,
sell his crop, and realize the gain. If the price does not rise above the
loan, the government eventually takes over the commodity, and the loan
becomes, in effect, the farmer's price. The CCC also purchases, stores,
and disposes of other farm commodities. The federal marketing orders
work differently; for example, under the fluid-milk orders, milk is
classified according to its uses, minimum prices are set for each use,
and an administration is provided to insure that dairy farmers are paid
accordingly.

Except for tobacco, peanuts, and (in 1950) cotton, the basic agricultural commodities were not subject to marketing quotas, i.e., controls

enforced by penalties, from the beginning of World War II until quotas
for wheat and cotton were announced for 1954. The prodigious involvement of the federal government at the farm level is worth illustrating.
As for other basic crops, the law directed imposition of marketing quotas for wheat under certain conditions. Not later than July 15, 1953,
the Secretary of Agriculture had to decide whether the total supply of
wheat exceeded the normal supply by more than 20 per cent. Normal
supply was composed of normal domestic consumption (ten-year averages,
adjusted for trends), normal exports, plus 15 per cent of the total of
these. If the Secretary found the total to exceed the normal by more
than 20 per cent, a referendum in which all wheat growers were eligible
to vote had to be held. If two-thirds of those voting favored quotas,
the Secretary might impose them. If he did, the quotas became effective for wheat marketed in the year beginning on the following July 1.

Under the quotas, the amount of wheat production planned for the
following year was calculated in bushels, and this figure was converted
to acres on the basis of average yields. The national acreage allotment
was divided among producing states, largely on the basis of their historical production; state allotments were broken down to counties and
county allotments to farms, largely on the same basis. Appeals provisions
were provided for farmers who thought their allotments inequitable. A
farmer who exceeded his allotment when marketing quotas were in effect
incurred severe penalties on the wheat grown on the excess acreage, even
though he fed it on his own farm to cattle that he was preparing to market.[7]

If this seems complicated, it is only the beginning. The PMA told
the subcommittee on agricultural appropriations of the House of Representatives that it needed $13,781,000 for fiscal 1954 to prepare and
administer the 1954 wheat-marketing quota. Sixteen steps were involved.[8]
They would have to be taken for an estimated 2,100,000 wheat farms. At
the same time, the PMA requested $15,469,000 to prepare and impose
marketing quotas on some 1,350,000 cotton farms.

One can hardly exaggerate the importance of the AAA-PMA programs
in the eyes of American farmers. This has been the farm program. Parity,
which has been its aim, has often been synonymous to farmers with simple
economic justice. The operations required have been formidable. The
CCC, first created in 1933, was made a federal corporation in 1948.

In 1954 its borrowing authority was increased from $6,750,000,000 to $8,500,000,000, and a supplemental request was made to increase it to ten billion. The PMA, like the AAA before it, rested on community and county committees elected by co-operating farmers and state committees appointed by the Secretary of Agriculture; usually, under the Roosevelt and Truman administrations, state committeemen were chosen from county committeemen. Moreover, many men from state committees were brought into the USDA—Claude Wickard eventually became Secretary of Agriculture and both N. E. Dodd and Al Loveland reached the post of undersecretary. At the end of 1952, the PMA had 11,257 full-time employees, and there were some 9,000 county and 103,000 community committeemen.

Not only has the AAA-PMA carried on price-support and production control; in World War II it was primarily responsible for administering the production-goals program, for making production payments to farmers, and for rationing producers' goods in agriculture. From 1936 to 1953 it administered the Agricultural Conservation Program (ACP). When the Supreme Court invalidated most of the first Agricultural Adjustment Act,[9] Congress passed the Soil Conservation and Domestic Allotment Act, which authorized $500,000,000 annually to make conservation payments to farmers. Initially, this act was primarily an income-raising, production-controlling measure, using payments as an incentive rather than using penalties. When the war changed the agricultural problem from one largely of regulating production to one of promoting selective increases in production, the character of the ACP program changed considerably. Congress has continued to appropriate large sums to this controversial program. In 1940 payments were made to more than 4,300,000 farms; in 1947 the number had declined to about 2,700,000; but in 1953 it had risen again to nearly 3,000,000. During 1940-52, inclusive, appropriations totaled $4,487,000,000.[10]

Congress also provided another major federal soil conservation program, that of the Soil Conservation Service (SCS). Established in 1933 and shifted to the USDA in 1935, the SCS has given farmers technical assistance in making and carrying out soil conservation farm plans. The SCS co-operates with soil conservation districts organized under state enabling acts. Appropriations for SCS increased from some $24,000,000 in 1943 to nearly $60,000,000 in 1952. At the end of 1952 the SCS had 11,584 employees, and, by then, the SCS had given technical assistance to some 1,250,000 farmers in about 2,500 soil conservation districts.

Another significant program was the Farm Security Administration (FSA), 1935-46, preceded by the Resettlement Administration and succeeded by the Farmers Home Administration. The FSA was created to help low-income farm families. It established resettlement projects and carried on subsistence homesteads inherited from an earlier agency. It also operated a tenant purchase program (later called a "farm ownership" program) to help tenants become owners. Five-year loans to farmers, once renewable, at low interest rates, were made. These "rural rehabilitation" loans were based on written farm and home plans which sought to bring the income and outgo of the farmers into balance. The FSA's county farm supervisors and home supervisors helped the families plan their operations and often supervised the carrying-out of the plans. How many farm families were reached by the FSA? The vilified resettlement project program, which Congress ordered to be liquidated in 1943, provided approximately 15,000 family units. By 1946 the tenant purchase program had made loans to 39,000 families. But the rural rehabilitation program had reached about 1,000,000 farm families. These were families that could not get credit from any other source, public or private. While a few of them had been successful once, most of them, especially in the South, were and had been desperately poor. They were poor in material goods, in education, and often in health. To its everlasting glory, the FSA reached a helping hand to those who were sore in need.

Among other agencies was the Rural Electrification Administration (REA). Established by executive order in 1935, by statute in 1936, and transferred to the USDA in 1939, the REA made loans for bringing electricity to rural people. By the end of fiscal 1952, REA borrowers had energized 1,210,473 miles of transmission lines serving 3,769,426 consumers. In addition, the Farm Credit Administration's activities were expanded during the depression. A program of purchasing "submarginal" land was in operation. A federal crop insurance program was begun in 1938-39. An act of 1937 provided federal aid to forest farmers as well as to farms with wood lots. In the Great Plains the reclamation law was liberalized, and a water facilities program was established. Farther west the public domain was closed to further homesteading, and the Taylor Grazing Act of 1935 introduced the first systematic management of the public range.

3. Emergent Problems of Relationships

With the rapid development of federal activity to aid the farmer, problems of administration and relationship emerged. Previously, the USDA's activities, with the exception of some of its regulatory work, had been largely co-operative with the colleges of agriculture. In 1933 state and local agricultural Extension Services contributed heavily to the success of the first AAA program. But, as the emergency stretched out and the AAA developed its own administrative organization from Washington to the grass roots, it tended to draw further away from the agricultural colleges in general and the Extension Service in particular. Other USDA agencies showed similar tendencies; thus both the SCS and the FSA established large regional offices which the colleges of agriculture detested and from which these agencies tended to work with local administrative units, by-passing the state level, at least to some degree. At the same time, some friction developed between USDA agencies at the farm level. Farmers occasionally received conflicting advice from the AAA, the SCS, the Extension county agent, and possibly others. Greater integration of public programs in conservation and agricultural adjustment began to appear highly desirable.

In the thought that was lavished upon the problem of relationships, a distinction emerged between "action" agencies and others. Since we shall repeatedly follow this usage, the distinction must be explained. Representatives of the Association of Land-Grant Colleges and Universities have defined "action" programs as those making use of the police power, the power to tax, or the power of eminent domain and as including those extending credit or grants-in-aid or subsidies.[11] Generally, college spokesmen have wanted to avoid administering this kind of program; but they have steadily claimed a dominant role in administering other kinds of programs—in research, demonstration, education, or Extension. And a vexing question has repeatedly arisen: Where shall the line be drawn between "action" and "education"?

The Mt. Weather Agreement of 1938 [12] was the only major effort by the USDA and the colleges to reach a general settlement of the problems of formulating and administering farm programs within the legislative framework laid down by Congress. The agreement underwrote the established relationships between the USDA and the states in research and Extension. It then acknowledged problems inherent in correlating subsidy and other "action" programs to achieve stability of farm income and the best use of farm resources. Therefore, it provided for "land-use planning" in which local committees of farmers were to be enlisted at once and, in time, to take over more and more responsibility for program formulation. These committees were to be paralleled and served by official committees with federal and state agencies participating. A balance was sought between farmer appraisal of farm problems and inititative of proposals for programs, on the one hand, and, on the other, an effective advisory function by experts and administrators who would also co-operate in bringing public programs in line with what the farm committees wanted, so far as authority permitted. Later in 1938 the Bureau of Agricultural Economics (BAE) was reorganized and designated the USDA's partner in the co-operative state and local land-use planning program, envisaged by the Mt. Weather Agreement. The BAE signed memoranda of understanding with most of the colleges, and by January, 1942, nearly 1,900 counties were in some stage of the planning process. Vigorous critics of the program had their way, however, and Congress liquidated it in the appropriation for 1943.

Meanwhile, growing international tension was reflected in the defense program of the United States, which meant in agriculture the creation of a network of defense boards—later, war boards—that were built upon the nuclei of the AAA committees. While the war years were not without their problems in intra-agricultural relationships, the close of hostilities precipitated a rise in conflicts among these agencies. Friction grew between the SCS and the agricultural conservation program of PMA (which had replaced the AAA in 1945). Differences between these USDA agencies and many of the colleges of agriculture, especially the state Extension Services, sharpened. The American Farm Bureau Federation (AFBF) continued its criticism, begun in 1940, of "duplication and overlapping" in federal agricultural programs. The AFBF is a federation of state farm bureaus, many of which enjoy close informal relationships with state agricultural Extension Services (although in 1954 the once common legal tie between state Extension Services and state farm bureaus continued to exist in very few states).

After the surprising Democratic victory in 1948, Secretary Charles F. Brannan brought out his famous plan. It expanded the old category of "basic crops" in agriculture. It substituted an income standard for parity, and the effect was considerably to increase the level at which farm prices would be supported. For storable commodities Brannan proposed continuation of loan and storage programs; for perishable commodities the market would have set the price, and the difference between the market price and the price needed for farmers to realize the income standard would have been made up by production payments. Initially, the plan provided no payments to farmers with gross incomes of $25,000 or more from agriculture.

The Brannan proposal precipitated a sharp break between the USDA and the AFBF, a break which lasted throughout the Truman administration. The proposal, along with other things, caused further deterioration of relationships between Secretary Brannan and many of the colleges of agriculture. In 1951 Secretary Brannan initiated the Family Farm Policy Review, in which colleges of agriculture, among others, were asked to co-operate with departmental agencies in appraising federal farm programs. The AFBF bitterly criticized the review, and its position was shared by many college officials.

4.   Controversial Issues

This historical outline suggests many, though not all, of the agricultural issues generated in recent years. The magnitude of the departure was recognized by Speaker Bankhead's comments on the bill to apply penalties to the overplanting of cotton in 1934:[13]"Now, this does look like compulsion. It is compulsion. But what difference in principle, gentlemen, is there in this other program [the National Industrial Recovery Act?] Why, a few years ago, if you had said, 'Why we are going to set up a system of codes, requiring every industry to regulate injustice, shop practices, cut-throat competition, by the strong arm of the Federal Government,' why, you probably would have balked at that. The truth is, gentlemen,we are living in a different age from what we did a few years ago." Should government fix farm prices? If so, by what means for different commodities? Should government support farm incomes? If so, how? What principles should govern the distribution of governmental income supports among farmers? How could feed crops like corn be supported without subjecting dairy and poultry farmers, for whom feed is a cost of production, to inequity? If price supports required production controls, how would the right (or was it a privilege?) to grow the controlled crops be assigned? If the right to grow controlled

crops went to areas, regions, and farmers according to their history
of growing such crops—and this, in general, has been the principle
employed—how would shifts of production take place? Would acres
taken out of the production of some crops be used to produce commodities which were not controlled?

Should the federal government help to plan individual farms, run
terrace lines for farmers, help them with erosion-control practices,
and pay them for liming their fields, plowing under green-manure crops,
building stock-water ponds, and so forth? Should the federal government
offer credit to farmers not deemed sound risks by commercial banks?
Should it insure crops that private companies would not? Should it extend
favorable loans to farm co-operatives for general purposes as well as,
through a special program, for electrifying farms? Should federal orders
be applied to metropolitan milk sheds if two-thirds or three-fourths
of the dairy farmers concerned approved in referendums? Should bona
fide co-operatives be allowed to vote their membership in such referendums? If so, what was a bona fide co-operative?

All these questions and many more can be derived from the history
briefly sketched above. Numerous other issues emerged. What kind
of tenurial arrangements were equitable among owners and tenants
under varying circumstances? Even with the expansion of government
credit for agriculture, was enough credit available of the kind best
suited to the needs of differently situated farmers? How much public
subsidy was justified for the domestic sugar industry? What were the
impacts of tariffs and quotas upon farm imports on foreign economic
policy and on foreign policy generally? What principles should govern
the use for grazing of public lands? How much could the government
reasonably invest in developing land for agriculture in the arid regions
under reclamation law? How should federal and state taxes on colored
margarine be evaluated?

Clearly, if publicly supported research and Extension in agriculture
were to examine and discuss questions of this sort, the personnel of
these agencies had their tasks cut out for them. This personnel traditionally worked under the closest scrutiny of farm groups. Moreover,
the agencies in which they were employed—the experiment stations and
Extension Services in the colleges and the research bureaus in the USDA—
were often directly interested in the outcome of the issues which they

might be studying. If their agencies were not directly interested, their farmer personnel would likely be.

With this background, we can begin our examination, the first part of which is concerned with the political influences which operate upon agricultural research and Extension and especially upon the colleges of agriculture.

Since 1887, federal grants-in-aid have been available for agricultural research in state experiment stations; since 1914, similar grants have been made to state agricultural Extension Services.[1] Have these grants resulted in federal domination, coercion, or overreaching control of state personnel and policies in research and Extension? Emphatically, the answer is "No." Indeed, as this and subsequent chapters show, federal grants have on occasion helped the state experiment stations and Extension Services to resist political influence, especially of the state and local variety.

1. Federal Supervision of Research Grants

The small staff of the Office of Experiment Stations (OES) must approve all experiment station projects which use federal funds, but scrutiny is essentially limited to making sure that federal funds have not been used for unauthorized purposes. Perhaps the most important item is to insure that research workers whose salaries come in part from federal grants do not spend undue amounts of time in teaching. In 1887 the Hatch Act permitted the Secretary of Agriculture only to advise the state experiment stations on research. But the appropriation act of 1894 authorized the Secretary to prescribe forms for the annual financial statement of the experiment stations, to ascertain whether expenditures are in accordance with law, and to report to Congress.

The OES has asserted some authority over personnel actions in state experiment stations[2] and has exercised it since 1920 by withholding funds from four states, the last being Mississippi in 1931.[3] The OES acted because of dismissals or forced resignations of personnel which it deemed qualified or because of the appointment of unqualified personnel. The states accepted the action. The Survey of 1930, which was published during the period in which the OES was most active in withholding funds, held that the OES had consistently maintained a policy of "participation rather than control."[4]

The best testimony on the question whether the OES has sought to

22

control experiment station research policy or personnel recruitment
through manipulation of federal grants is the opinion of state agricultural research administrators. Conversations with research administrators in some thirty states, chiefly, but not exclusively, in 1950 and
1951, elicited absolutely no complaint that the OES had attempted to
control these matters. Indeed, some experiment station directors
thought that the OES should provide a more searchingly critical analysis
of state programs.[5]

2.   Other Federal-State Research Relationships in Agriculture

Many co-operative research projects are undertaken by research
bureaus of the USDA and one or more state experiment stations. Others
are joint projects between state experiment stations and the Bureau of
Agricultural Economics (BAE) or the Soil Conservation Service (SCS).
Such relationships are generally satisfactory. A midwestern agricultural college official told the writer that in some far western colleges
of agriculture, with less money for research from state sources, the
BAE was exercising considerable, and perhaps undue, influence on
college agricultural research programs (1951). An inquiry in several
far western states produced no criticism of the BAE by agricultural
research administrators; on the contrary, most of them warmly approved
of their relationships with the BAE. More recently, some criticism has
been directed at the BAE's supposed tendency to follow the principle
that one federal agency should not criticize another (see chap. xv below).
Whereas many colleges of agriculture have had strained relationships
with the operations program of the SCS,[6] co-operation with the SCS in
research has been uniformly satisfactory to the colleges in recent years.

Respecting co-operative projects between USDA research bureaus
and state experiment stations, the director of one state station criticized
what he called "hidden domination." He cited the negotiation of a co-
operative agreement between his station and a federal research bureau
which later suffered a cut in research appropriations and proposed to
withdraw money from the ongoing project. The effect would have been
to use federal money for salary for researchers but to require the state
to make up the loss in maintenance expenses. Under such circumstances,
a state station might feel that it had lost some control of a joint project,
in that the federal government now would pay the salary of research

workers (and therefore might command their loyalty) without paying an appropriate share of the maintenance. Further questioning indicated that the chief complaint arose from what the state director deemed to be high-handed action by the federal administrator involved. The latter was quoted: "If you want to continue this project, you must take care of all maintenance expenses; otherwise, it will have to be liquidated."

Friction between personalities appeared to underlie this complaint. Such frictions are bound to occur in co-operative arrangements between federal and state agencies. Often they can be sustained with no greater damage than ruffled feelings. A more serious problem, of course, is the reliance of publicly supported research upon annual appropriations, whether federal or state. Since definitive research results cannot be guaranteed to coincide with the ends of fiscal years, administrators have their annual anxieties.

Many interviews with state research administrators produced strong criticisms of the administration of section 9(b)(3) of the Research and Marketing Act of 1946, which authorizes appropriations for co-operative research among two or more state experiment stations, with or without the co-operation of a federal agency. Complaints were aimed at the cumbersome procedures, however, and not at federal domination. More generally, the Research and Marketing Act has led to increased scrutiny by Congress not only of Research and Marketing Act projects but also of projects undertaken with federal grant funds under the Hatch and subsequent acts. Some anxiety was evident that this development might upset the well-liked federal-state relationships that have obtained in research.

In summary, traditional grants-in-aid and co-operative relationships in agricultural research are eminently satisfactory to the states. Some state experiment station personnel might welcome more constructive federal critical evaluation than that now forthcoming—but not if it meant federal control. Other federal-state research relationships create occasional frictions, but these are overshadowed by the gains that most states report from such joint activities.[7] Over the years, and especially during the 1940's, state research in agriculture fared rather well, comparatively, at the hands of Congress and state legislatures.[8]

3. Federal Administration of Grants-in-Aid for Agricultural Extension

The Extension Service of the USDA administers federal grants for agricultural Extension. The basic statute vests more power in the Secretary for supervision of Extension grants than he has respecting research grants. The Smith-Lever Act provides for "agricultural extension work which shall be carried on in cooperation with the United States Department of Agriculture." The federal Extension Service approves state plans and programs and certifies to the Treasury authorizations to make grants-in-aid payments to states. In 1914 a memorandum was jointly developed between the USDA and the land-grant colleges. The memorandum, signed by the USDA and individual colleges, provides (among other things) for the establishment of an agricultural Extension Service in the college "with a responsible leader selected [by the college] satisfactory to the Department of Agriculture."[9] State agricultural Extension programs financed in part by federal grants are to be planned jointly by the college and the federal department. All agents who carry on such work are declared to be joint representatives of the college and the USDA. These provisions, of course, reflect the congressional injunction to "cooperate."

As with the administration of grants for research, the Secretary of Agriculture may withhold grants for Extension from states which misapply federal funds or fail in some other statutory obligation. Such withholding is only temporary, however, until the legislature of the state concerned has had an opportunity to appeal to Congress.[10] A search of federal Extension Service reports during 1920-52 reveals no record of grants withheld except for the failure of states to appropriate offsetting funds.[11] Withholding aside, the federal Extension Service has effectively remonstrated with states respecting a number of personnel actions—Mississippi and North Dakota in the 1930's and Texas and Pennsylvania in the 1940's.

Discussions with state Extension administrators (including college deans with responsiblity for both Extension and research) reveal considerably greater awareness of problems of relationships in Extension than in research. One president emeritus of a land-grant college could recall no disagreements with Washington over research in nearly a score of years—"but we had dozens of difficulties over Extension." Similar statements recur,[12] but they have to be evaluated carefully. They are

ordinarily made by convinced "states' righters," of whom colleges of
agriculture have many, and they usually stem from the post-1933
period, when Extension was heavily engaged in administering the AAA
program. Since no personnel or policy changes have been forced by
Washington Extension on the states concerned and since most state
college administrators are agreed that the federal Extension Service
has never sought to "coerce" the states, such expressions can be
properly discounted.

Indeed, only one serious allegation of federal coercion of a state
Extension Service via the grants-in-aid program has been made. In
1943 some Pennsylvanians were fearful that federal domination might
be inherent in the administration of Extension grants.[13] In 1950,
during a debate with Senator Lucas in "America's Town Meeting of
the Air,"[14] President Lawrence M. Gould of Carleton College asserted that federal domination of the Pennsylvania agricultural Extension
Service had occurred. The following chapter is devoted to the Pennsylvania case, which proves to be no example of federal domination
of a state Extension Service by means of the grants-in-aid program.

To summarize this and the preceding section, the evidence
available to the writer indicates that there is neither any objective
basis in the facts for supporting the proposition that federal domination
of state agricultural research and administration has been incident to
the administration of federal grants-in-aid nor any significant subjective feeling on the part of relevant state officials that this has occurred.[15]

Actually, the influence of the colleges of agriculture appears to
have been very strong in the OES and the federal Extension Service
throughout most of their histories. Thus J. S. Jardine, director of the
OES from 1931 to 1946, characterized himself as the representative
of the state stations.[16] An incident may also be cited in connection
with the administration of the co-operative state and local land-use
planning program (1939-42), which was a co-operative venture between
the USDA and the land-grant colleges, the specific co-operating agencies
being the BAE and the several state agricultural Extension Services. Rid-
ing together during a midwestern farm tour were officials of the BAE
and the federal Extension Service and representatives of a college of
agriculture which had not signed the memorandum of understanding
with the BAE for the conduct of the land-use planning program. The

representatives of the college of agriculture and of the BAE argued
over the failure to sign the memorandum; the latter finally declared
that the program was not financed according to the typical grant-in-
aid formula and that the BAE was not compelled to co-operate with
a state college, regardless of whether it chose to sign the memorandum. The college official retorted, in effect: "See here; I know that
my prosperous state pays much more in taxes to the federal government than it gets back. Maybe you can talk that way to the 'foreign
missions' in the South, but don't try to tell us how to run the home
church." The BAE representative angrily left the car, whereupon the
man from the federal Extension Service slapped the college official
on the back and congratulated him.

Now this story raises the question about the "foreign missions."
It is reinforced by the statement of a college official in 1951: "If it
were not for nine or ten powerful states that would tell the federal
government to go to hell if they started getting funny, there might be
federal domination." What of those states, with lower per capita incomes, in which the federal government has continued to provide the
greater proportion of Extension moneys? For fiscal 1950, although the
total state contribution was 57 per cent of total Extension funds within
the states, Alabama contributed only 46 per cent of its agricultural
Extension budget, Mississippi only 44 per cent, and Arkansas only 41
per cent. Ten years earlier the shares of the same states had been
only 28, 34, and 36 per cent, respectively. Yet conversations with
Extension personnel in all three states at various times from 1941
through 1950 support the conclusion that the federal government has
not tried to dominate Extension work in these states.

4. Federal Grants as a Source of Strength to State Agencies

Instead of constituting a threat to state agricultural research and
Extension, federal grants help to strengthen these institutions against
political threats from other sources and against the vicissitudes of
changing economic fortunes within their own states.[17] Many Mississip-
pians welcomed the USDA's refusal to accept the Bilbo appointees
in agriculture in the early 1930's. An excellent illustration of resistance
to political pressure upon the basis of the federal grants is found in the
Kentucky tobacco story of 1950 (see chap. vi below). Numerous state

college adminstrators declare that the system of federal grants provides support against political pressure from whatever source.

Indeed, the most bitter complaint against the federal office was that it failed to protect state Extension Services from intrastate political pressures.[18] In the state primarily concerned, the board of regents gave the president of the land-grant college powers of reorganization. Three weeks later the president summarily discharged certain officials, including the directors of agricultural research and Extension. The dismissal may have violated the state law regulating such terminations and providing for a right to be heard before the regents. Agitation in favor of the discharged men grew, and two weeks later the president withdrew his charges against the two directors and resigned his own office. Considerable annoyance was expressed because the federal Extension Service failed to intervene vigorously and promptly within the state on behalf of the state Extension Service. Federal action would have had to be of the hair-trigger variety to affect the situation during the two weeks between the discharge of the state Extension director and the resignation of the president.

5. Conclusion

Why has federal domination failed to follow the federal dollar in the administration of these grants? Of great and perhaps primary importance is the conviction which many influential Americans share that research and educational functions shall not be politically dominated or controlled, especially by the federal government. The well-known jealous regard for the maintenance of local control over primary education is accompanied by a determination to keep public control of publicly supported higher education from gravitating to Washington. Any serious effort by federal administrative agencies to exercise undue influence over such state institutions would have to be overt. It would be publicized immediately and countered by the enormous resistance which land-grant institutions, some of them already in their second century, can muster in the general public, alumni, and supporting groups.

Among these groups, the state farm bureaus and the American Farm Bureau Federation (AFBF) can be counted upon to defend the colleges of agriculture from any imaginable federal encroachment.[19] Farm bureaus exist in all states, and the membership of the AFBF has recently reached 1,600,000 (chiefly farm families). Farm bureaus and Extension Services grew up together. Intimate association and mutual helpfulness exist between strong farm bureaus and the Extension Services in twenty-five to thirty states. The Farm Bureau has traditionally supported agricultural colleges and especially the Extension Services, seeking to augment their appropriations and to transfer programs into their hands. In these actions the Farm Bureau has protected its own organization and its system of alliances; but no explanation is adequate unless it goes beyond this self-seeking to acknowledge the dedication of many farm bureau members to the strengthening of research and educational services to American agriculture.

Collectively, the land-grant institutions are organized in the Association of Land-Grant Colleges and Universities, formed (under another name) in 1887.[20] By 1890 the association was effectively urging its view upon Congress;[21] by 1904 it was strong enough to eliminate from an appropriation bill an authorization to the Secretary of Agriculture to "coordinate the work of the several [experiment] stations . . . and unify and systematize agricultural investigation in the United States."[22] Time and again, the association has promoted congressional action on behalf of its members.[23] Through its powerful committees on organization and policy and, since 1940, its Washington office the association has looked after its members' interests; no federal abuse of grants-in-aid to encroach upon the traditional prerogatives of the state institutions would escape its vigilance. Instead, the federal grants strengthen the association. Through it, the colleges can presume to speak for the entire agriculture of the country. Without federal aid, some states would doubtless have established colleges of agriculture (some, indeed, were doing so before 1862); but it is extremely doubtful whether all states would have founded similar institutions. Moreover, the grants create an interest which the several institutions can unite in their association to protect and extend.

It should also be stressed that federal personnel in the Extension Service and the OES have traditionally looked after the interests of the colleges of agriculture, in which most of them have served. Thus the States Relations Service of the USDA (forerunner of the present federal Extension Service and the OES) prepared the original memorandum of understanding to be signed with the states, pursuant to the Smith-Lever Act of 1914.[24] The first sentence declares that the state college will "control Federal and State funds for extension work." The memorandum further obligates the USDA to carry on in co-operation with the state college concerned "all demonstration and other forms of extension work in agriculture and home economics which the Department is authorized by Congress to conduct in the state."

Further, both parties agree that Extension work in question "shall be planned under the joint supervision of the Director of Extension Work of the College of Agriculture . . . subject to the approval of the Dean . . . and of [the appropriate federal officials] ." While this language might include the seeds of federal control in the eyes of determined states' right-ers, it clearly vests the senior partnership in the state Extension Serv-ices; and federal administration has continuously been in the spirit of this interpretation.

Finally, federal statutes authorizing grants for agricultural research and Extension provide that any withholding of funds by the Secretary of Agriculture from any state shall not be final until the state has had an opportunity to appeal to Congress.[25] These sections have never been used; so long as they remain on the books, however, they should be men-tioned.

What is the significance of the history of federal grants-in-aid for agricultural research and Extension for the general problem of financing higher education? The agricultural experience suggests that federal grants could be safely and profitably expanded to aid other kinds of research and higher education. Similar state and local political forces—both organized groups and public opinion—would insure the recipients of such grants against federal domination. To be sure, the colleges of agriculture have been heavily involved in politics, as following chapters show; but the inference is not permissible that they have been subject to federal domination. Quite the contrary: the federal grants-in-aid for agricultural research and Extension have strengthened the colleges as institutions with interests opposed to the centralization of power in the federal government. The history of agricultural policy in the United States since 1933 demonstrates that the colleges of agriculture have been the organ-ized critics, the watchdogs, and almost, indeed, the political "opposition" of the United States Department of Agriculture.[26]

1. Strained Relationships, 1940-42

In 1940 the Extension Service of the USDA refused to approve certain plans of work of the Pennsylvania Extension Service and considered whether to withhold certification to the Treasury for Pennsylvania's grants-in-aid for the remaining six months of the 1941 fiscal
year. Voluminous correspondence between the federal Extension Service and the president of Pennsylvania State College (since 1953 the
Pennsylvania State University) produced a gentlemen's agreement. The
federal grants were made available. In 1942 M. S. McDowell, Pennsylvania's veteran Extension director, retired. The USDA withheld approval
of J. M. Fry as his successor. S. W. Fletcher, dean of Pennsylvania
State's school of agriculture and director of its experiment station,
assumed the directorship of Extension. In 1943, Fry was appointed
director of Extension and was accepted by the USDA. During this period
Pennsylvania was not deprived of federal grants for Extension or
ultimately prevented from appointing Fry as director.[1]

Negotiation and compromise, in which Pennsylvania won its major
points, solved the problem. Still, it might be urged that Pennsylvania
was induced to co-operate through its Extension Service with federal
agricultural action programs. Perhaps this "inducement," while not
"coercion," was rather strong. Perhaps it marked a step toward eventual federal coercion. Further inquiry is clearly needed.

The dispute between the USDA and Pennsylvania arose directly out
of the development of New Deal programs for agriculture. In 1933 the
dominant political opinion supported the New Deal programs, drastic
though they were. Popular support was so great that 1934 provides the
only mid-term election from the Civil War to 1950 in which a party that
had won the last presidential election increased its margin in the House of
Representatives. But to reach farmers effectively with the New Deal
program, especially the Agricultural Adjustment Administration (AAA),

31

was a staggering task. Only the co-operation of state and local Extension Services enabled the first AAA to reach 3,000,000 farmers. In the early years the AAA provided some $8,000,000 annually for Extension budgets to augment salaries and often to re-employ Extension agents (chiefly in the far Midwest and the Great Plains area) whom economy-minded county governing boards had dismissed in the depression.[2]

Then came the Bankhead-Jones Act of 1935, one of the earliest practical admissions that the AAA was not a short-run emergency operation. The Bankhead-Jones Act provided $8,000,000 in permanent annual appropriations for Extension immediately and authorized additional appropriations of $4,000,000. Unlike previous Extension grants-in-aid, these sums required no state matching. The total of $12,000,000 approximately doubled what Congress had previously authorized for agricultural Extension in the acts of 1914 and 1928. The new money was authorized in recognition of the vastly changed role of Extension as a result of the radical shift in agricultural policy caused by the great depression. Director W. A. Munson of the Massachusetts Extension Service described the activities which the additional money would finance—all of them incidental to helping farmers meet economic and social problems and most of them designed to facilitate the work of action agencies. There can be no question that Congress passed the Bankhead-Jones Act essentially to provide money for work in connection with the full-scale governmental attack upon the depression.[3]

The AAA was the main governmental effort for agriculture in these years—by 1940 some 6,000,000 farmers, including 70 per cent of the farmers in Pennsylvania, were AAA co-operators. But the AAA was by no means alone. Chapter ii has sketched the development of other programs and shown how thoughtful persons in both the USDA and the colleges wanted to improve their integration. The Mt. Weather Agreement was reached in 1938, and the co-operative federal-state-local land-use planning program was initiated.[4]

Pennsylvania State College, however, through its board of trustees, rejected the memorandum of understanding upon which the land-use planning program was based. The board held that participation in the program would involve the college in the use of the police power and in policy-making rather than in its accustomed and appropriate fields of education and research. If the board applauded the sentiment that "farmer thinking should dominate the work" in land-use planning, it also was convinced that the real dominant influence would be the technical experts and officials of the several action programs. Finally, Pennsylvania State College was already engaged in land-use planning through committees long established in each county.[5]

It was against this background that the federal Extension Service seriously considered withholding its approval for federal grants-in-aid for Pennsylvania. The original Smith-Lever Act provided: "In order to aid in diffusing among the people in the United States useful and practical information on subjects related to agriculture and home economics, and to encourage the application of the same," agricultural Extension work may be inaugurated in each state. But if such work is inaugurated it "shall be carried on in cooperation with the United States Department of Agriculture."[6]

The first underlined phrase above indicates that Congress intended more than the mere diffusing of information—"to encourage the application of the same." The second underlined phrase suggests that the Department of Agriculture would be derelict in its responsibility to Congress if it acquiesced in a state's refusal to co-operate in carrying on a program which Congress itself had authorized.[7]

Convinced "states' righters" might well stress these statements. They might grant that federal aid to states for agricultural Extension would involve no federal control, if Extension and research were the only public programs in operation. But when agricultural action programs are multiplied and when the administration of these programs is closely associated with Extension's operations, they would argue that federal grants for Extension might involve federal control of state and local programs.

These arguments cannot be lightly brushed aside. Indeed, the following chapter will return to an examination of the political influence of action programs upon agricultural Extension and research. So far as the Pennsylvania incident is concerned, however, the arguments have two answers. The first has already been given: Pennsylvania suffered no loss in federal grants and was able to get its choice for the Extension director approved after a little delay.

The second answer is that all other colleges of agriculture, except California, did co-operate with the USDA in the land-use planning program. Illinois did not sign the basic memorandum of understanding for the land-use planning program, but the work went on there much the same as it did elsewhere. The Mt. Weather Agreement, it should be em-

phasized, was the basis of the land-use planning program, and this
agreement was not a unilateral act of the USDA but a joint act of the
USDA and the land-grant colleges and universities. Indeed, one of its
major architects was Milton Eisenhower, then in the office of the
Secretary of Agriculture but later president of Kansas State College
and, since 1950, of Pennsylvania State College. Moreover, the complaints
of Pennsylvania were not echoed by other colleges of agriculture. Pennsylvania based its case upon academic freedom. The implication of the
Pennsylvania argument, as set forth by Dean Fletcher, was that colleges
of agriculture which co-operated with action agencies or in the land-use
planning program had sacrificed their academic freedom. Judging by
their actions, representatives of other colleges of agriculture did not
agree. These representatives apparently felt that they could negotiate
with the USDA from "situations of strength" and could safely co-operate
in joint programs produced by negotiation.

Pennsylvania's stand during these years seems to find an explanation in the aloofness and individuality of its Extension Service. The
following section attempts to show these qualities.

2. Pennsylvania Agricultural Extension Service, 1920-41

The period under discussion begins with the emergence of the "farm
problem" in modern United States politics; it ends with the incident just
described. During these years, M. S. McDowell was director of the
Pennsylvania Extension Service. The unusual qualities of his leadership
and of the agency he administered were expressed (a) in the centralization of Pennsylvania Extension, (b) in a certain aloofness from the
activities of the Association of Land-Grant Colleges and Universities,
(c) in a pronounced aloofness from the USDA, and (d) in an unusual
emphasis upon self-help during years when farmers (along with others)
were generally turning to collective action to solve or ameliorate grinding economic problems.

The centralization of the Pennsylvania Extension Service. —Typically,
state laws vest selection of county agricultural Extension staffs in
county governing bodies, with approval by the state Extension Service.[8]
But Pennsylvania provided in 1913 that "the trustees of the Pennsylvania
State College may employ and maintain resident county advisers and
travelling experts in farm management."[9] This set the stage for a
centralized organization, responsible (in effect) to the state Extension
director. In 1920 Director McDowell emphasized the importance of

county agents' being employees in the state organization."Can the United States Department of Agriculture [he asked] and the colleges carry this responsibility if the county agent does not regard himself as part of the extension organization in the same way that the specialist does?" He added that "this does not mean that the local people have no control over what is done."[10]

Local financing of Extension work has its problems, particularly when workers' salaries derive in whole or in part from local funds.[11] McDowell's position implies, however, a more centralized control of Extension personnel than is commonly conceded to be desirable.[12] To put the interpretation somewhat bluntly, McDowell's attitude of independence from Washington was apparently combined with a belief in strong hierarchical authority within the state Extension Service.[13]

Aloofness from the Association of Land-Grant Colleges and Universities.—In 1920 Director McDowell was a member of a committee of seven Extension directors to confer with H. C. Taylor, of the Farm Economic Association, and members of the USDA respecting the establishment of a program of work in marketing. In 1926 he was secretary of the section on agriculture. In 1927-29 he served a term on the Extension committee on organization and policy, reporting for the committee in 1929 in the absence of its chairman, Director A. J. Meyer, of Missouri. In 1931 he was a member of the committee on nominations; but from then until his retirement no further formal participation is recorded.[14] Further, although McDowell read several papers at association meetings before 1920, he apparently presented papers subsequently only in 1920 and 1922.[15] In contrast, Director H. C. Ramsower, of Ohio, had five papers in 1927-37; Director R. K. Bliss, of Iowa, had six papers from 1920 to 1939; and F. W. Peck and P. E. Miller (Peck's successor in Minnesota) had five papers between them in 1921-40.

Aloofness from Washington.—The refusal of Pennsylvania to co-operate in the land-use planning program had its precedents. In the early 1920's McDowell rejected proposals by representatives of the federal Extension Service that Pennsylvania develop a strong state farm bureau. Of Pennsylvania's sixty-seven counties, sixty-five had farm bureaus, which, Director McDowell stoutly maintained, had been organized to co-operate with the USDA and the college in developing Extension work in agriculture and home economics. So far, they had "devoted themselves to this purpose."[16] Pennsylvania had no state farm bureau until 1951.

A comparison of "Pennsylvania Extension Circulars" with "New York (Cornell) Extension Bulletins" during 1920-41 is instructive. Almost no mention is made in the Pennsylvania series of operations of various federal agencies; on the contrary, the New York series has many such notices. For example, Pennsylvania Circular 215, by John R. Haswell and V. S. Peterson, Electric Wiring for the Farm (1939), contains no mention of the Rural Electrification Administration (REA). New York Extension Bulletin 339 (1935), by L. D. Kelsey and H. W. Riley, How To Get Electricity on the Farm, lists the REA as one of five reasons stimulating current rural electrification; it also noted the assistance of the Production Credit loans of the Farm Credit Administration.

Again, Pennsylvania Circular 212 (1939), How To Reduce Soil Erosion Losses by Strip-cropping, did not mention the federal Soil Conservation Service. Contrast this with New York Bulletin 347, Soil Erosion in New York, by F. B. Howe and H. R. Adams, which stated: "In this area [150,000 acres in Steuben County] the Soil Conservation Service of the United States Department of Agriculture, with the coopera- tion of farmers, is putting into practice the different erosion-control methods described in this bulletin." Pennsylvania's indifference toward Washington agencies is demonstrated. [17]

Economic attitudes. —The Pennsylvania Extension Service consid- ered that the economic problems of the farmer were largely to be met by self-help; Extension, however, had an obligation to assist him to help himself. The 1922 Annual Report noted that "the impression persists that 'educational work' means more production without regard to other factors which necessarily influence production; that the securing of better markets and fairer prices is in no way connected with an Extension program. This view is erroneous." But it was immediately stated that Extension can do no more than advise farmers respecting co-operative buying and selling. The purpose was to encourage and advise existing organizations and to foster the formation of new organ- izations for specific purposes, where needed. Nevertheless, a review of the decrease of numbers of farmers and the increase of farms with mortgages led to the belief that "farming today is pretty much a 'sur- vival of the fittest.'" Hence great emphasis was placed upon reducing farm costs and getting farmers to keep farm accounts.

The analysis of F. P. Weaver, in The Prices of Farm Products in Pennsylvania (Pennsylvania Extension Circular 101 [1923]) argued that the control of credit through the Federal Reserve System might well provide both for the needs of business and the maintenance of fairly stable buying power. It noted that "the prosperity of Pennsylvania farmers is very closely tied up with the prosperity of her industries and vice versa." But it finally advised individual action: "It is the psychology of the crowd that makes cycles. The individual who increases production when the prospects seem bluest to people in general and decreases when everyone wants to produce his absolute maximum, is likely to profit oftener than he loses thereby."

These examples of fundamental orientation toward enlightened individualism are counterbalanced somewhat by the analysis of the Philadelphia milk marketing plan by Professors F. F. Lininger and F. P. Weaver[18] and J. E. McCord's Farm Tenancy and Lease Forms in Pennsylvania.[19] The former praised the base and surplus plan which had been developed for the Pennsylvania market. The latter advocated preparation of farm leases which would change with the times, provide for sharing risks and profits between owners and tenants, and stimulate the best farm practices while keeping open "the steps on the agricultural ladder leading from hired man to owner." These two circulars (in common, indeed, with the references to assisting farmer co-operatives in the annual report of 1922 already noted) acknowledge considerable value in collective action. A successful marketing scheme for a large city milk shed requires co-operation of many groups, organizations, and (usually) public agencies. Likewise, really effective programs to reform farm leases require more than operations by individuals acting in their "enlightened self-interest."

Nevertheless, the general orientation of Pennsylvania Extension work during these years appears to have been essentially confined to encouraging and improving the self-interest concepts and operations of the individual. This interpretation finds some supporting evidence in the apparent failure of McDowell to participate formally in the numerous discussions in the Association of Land-Grant Colleges and Universities on such subjects as state economic programs for agriculture, redefinition of Extension's job in view of the development of action programs, changes in Extension operations suggested by the depression in agricul-

ture, the agricultural conservation program, and federal-state relationships in Extension work. Such discussions rest upon common acknowledgment that economic problems of farmers and the public action consequent upon them have presented agricultural Extension with a profound
task of self-examination and reappraisal. The Pennsylvania Extension
Service apparently did not share in this common acknowledgment. Indeed,
an examination of the "Pennsylvania Extension Circulars" in the 1930's
discloses virtually no recognition of the depression or of the various
public programs designed to meet it. Again, New York provides considerable contrast.[20]

In sum, a remark by La Rochefoucauld comes to mind: "All women
are beautiful, but God spent more time on some." Each state agricultural
Extension Service is different from all the others; but in some the
art of being unusual is highly developed—and Pennsylvania is one of
these. Relationships between Pennsylvania Extension and the USDA were,
indeed, almost unique. The strained relationships of 1940-43 are readily
understandable, given the history of exchanges between Pennsylvania
and Washington in the preceding generation; but they cannot be justly
used as an example of federal dictation. Finally, Pennsylvania Extension's extreme orientation against USDA agencies was opposed within
the Keystone State itself.

3. Intrastate Pressure upon Pennsylvania State College

In 1945 the Pennsylvania legislature revised the State Soil Conservation Commission, which administers the state soil conservation district
law.[21] The Pennsylvania School of Agriculture and particularly the
Extension Service have been among the strongest land-grant college
critics of the federal Soil Conservation Service (SCS). Apparently
friends of the SCS became unhappy about the administration of the
state commission, which, under the 1937 law, was located in the state
department of agriculture and was composed of the state secretary of
agriculture, the secretary of forests and waters, the secretary of high-
ways, and the director of the agricultural experiment station. The 1945
law kept the first two ex officio members but eliminated the others and
provided that the governor appoint three farmer members from a list
of six nominees of the Pennsylvania Council of Farm Organizations. It
is probably significant that the representative of the school of agriculture was eliminated.

In 1946 the Pennsylvania State Council of Farm Organizations unanimously indorsed a statement which declared, among other things:

"The School of Agriculture of the Pennsylvania State College . . . has not received the consideration its importance demands. The result is that the farmers of the State are being deprived of services which they greatly need.

"We have given serious consideration to the . . . activities of State college. The committee has spent many hours discussing the many complaints which came to its attention. Our conclusions are that the general situation at State college is one which merits immediate attention by the farm groups. . . .

"An illustration of one of the problems confronting agriculture has to do with the State Soil Conservation Act. . . . We are informed that there has not been forthcoming from the State college the assistance which is necessary to make the Act truly effective."[22]

The incident suggests that persons sensitive to federal encroachment may be sniffing the Washington wind suspiciously when the breeze is really blowing from their own grass roots. Certain federal agricultural action agencies have been skilful in building local group support; but the organizations that are thus created are no more artificial than the farm bureaus which agricultural Extension Services helped to start. The upshot is that local pressure is generated upon colleges of agriculture. College leaders may accurately attribute this kind of pressure to federal agitation; but the agitation would never be successful unless there were some dissatisfactions or some unfulfilled wants to which to appeal. It may be that the programs used in these appeals are inexpedient, unwise, untimely, or that they have some other fatal drawback. If so, analysis should be able to show it, and superior alternatives should be discoverable. Except for propaganda purposes, however, it is insufficient merely to condemn the phenomena as "federal encroachment" or "bureaucratic socialism." But this leads us into the next chapter.

"In dealing with these federal agencies, I am continuously forced
to risk my professional career," said a land-grant college president
in 1943. An agricultural college dean's remarks were more morbid:
"Why, if I said what I really think about these federal outfits, I'd be
shot."[1] Eight years later an eminent agricultural college dean told the
writer that the then Secretary of Agriculture was a ruthless politician
and that a series of moves had been taken to build up the Production
and Marketing Administration (PMA) at the expense of research and
education both in the USDA and the states. What (if any) political influence upon agricultural research and education has been exercised by,
or channeled through, federal agricultural action agencies?

1.   Nature of the Inquiry

Such agencies have been defined.[2] Their programs embrace price
supports, commodity loans (as well as purchase and disposal), administration of acreage allotments and marketing quotas, administration of federal marketing orders and agreements, rural elctrification and tele-
phones, provision of credit (co-operative or direct), federal crop insurance, market regulation, administration of subsidies and agricultural
conservation payments, promulgation and administration of land-use
regulations, rural zoning, grading and inspection, administration of the
wartime farm labor program,[3] flood control, real estate assessment
and taxation, and building and maintaining public markets and roads.
Action programs of paramount concern to this chapter are those in
agricultural price support, production control, commodity loans, surplus
removal, subsidization, soil conservation, crop insurance, market regulation, and agricultural credit—in all of which the USDA has an important role.

Considerable difficulty plagues the inquiry into possible political
influence by agricultural action agencies upon research and Extension as
well as the interpretation of whatever the inquiry discloses. The difficul-

ty stems from the dual character of agricultural research and Extension organizations—the reader is referred to the political characteristics of the colleges of agriculture, described at the beginning of chapter i, characteristics which include both the traits of the interest group and also those of the university oriented toward study of public problems. Conflicts between colleges of agriculture and federal action agencies may be manifestations of profound political struggles or realignments. The tension existing between state Extension Services and the federal Soil Conservation Service (SCS) involves the question: Which agency can best carry much the same program to much the same people? It also involves a power struggle, of course! And this bald statement of the controversy obscures some subtle but extremely important differences concerning emphasis and techniques. Nevertheless, the SCS-Extension controversy is simpler politically than the struggle between the old Farm Security Administration (1937-46) and the agricultural colleges and Farm Bureaus in certain southern states. Here some participants on both sides felt that the rural class structure and its relationship to the structure of political power were deeply involved.

A somewhat similar interpretation is applicable to the friction between the Agricultural Adjustment Administration (AAA—later the PMA), on the one hand, and colleges of agriculture and often the Farm Bureaus, on the other. This friction was most obvious in the Middle West, probably because it involved partisan politics there (the AAA-PMA being oriented toward the Democratic party, the agricultural colleges and Farm Bureaus toward the Republicans).

Light can be thrown upon these intra-agricultural conflicts by reference to a general and ancient theory of political behavior—the view of political activity as corresponding to a series of more or less concentric circles. The innermost circle is composed of intensely and consistently active politicians; other circles include progressively less active persons, until eventually the indifferent and apathetic are reached.

The relevance of the concept to the problem of this chapter is that the political appeal and support of the agricultural research and Extension programs tends to be in smaller, more active political circles— the Farm Bureaus, commodity organizations, farm business survey organizations, seed-improvement associations, cow-testing associations, and so on. The SCS appeals to farmers who are similarly active politically; men prominent in soil conservation district programs are often active in other agricultural group enterprises; often they have been among their state Extension Service's prized Extension leaders or master farmers. (A number of state Extension directors have been rather bitter about the SCS's proselyting their farm leaders.) On the other hand, the Farm Security Administration and its successor, the Farmers Home Administration, appeal by definition to a low-income farm group which has had the vote, of course, when it could qualify and cared to use it but which has been poor in other political assets—poor, that is, in status, in organization, in leadership, in resources, in experience, and in expectations. Some would add "poor in native ability," but the writer believes that native ability is one kind of wealth which is distributed with considerable impartiality in each new generation.

Again, the appeal and support of the AAA-PMA has been in the same circles as agricultural research and Extension but also in larger circles. These larger circles include many farmers who are less active in formal organizations (even though they may be nominal farm bureau members, for example) but who still are actual or potential voters.

An illustration of the concept of concentric circles is found in the vote of the House of Representatives on June 30, 1952, to extend agricultural price supports on basic commodities through 1954. This action was actively opposed by the Farm Bureau in the Middle West and was contrary to the weight of analyses of colleges of agriculture in the same area; nevertheless, rural middle western congressmen voted quite solidly for the bill. They were anticipating a larger vote in November than that represented by the Farm Bureau leaders and the college spokesmen. They thought that this large vote would be antagonized by a stand against 90 per cent of parity on such commodities as corn and wheat. It seems more than a coincidence that the PMA had stood for 90 per cent of parity in the Middle West as against flexible price supports.

Thus an inquiry into action agency influence upon agricultural research and Extension is not a simple search for scapegoats in the federal bureaucracy or the colleges of agriculture. The nature of farm politics— in both its organizational aspects and in the character of the policies it has produced—affects the inquiry. Moreover, general theories of political phenomena are needed to explain the politics of agriculture. But let us turn now to questions of overt coercion by action agencies, reserving the examination of the more subtle influences.

2. Allegations of Direct Pressure on the Man or on the Product

Political influence upon research and education may appear as pressure upon the researcher or teacher or the administrator of his institution or upon the product (the bulletins, articles, books, and lectures). Although it is somewhat arbitrary to separate pressure upon the man from that upon the product—often both are involved, and political groups would rarely worry about the man if they found his work acceptable—convenience advises their separate discussion.

Pressure on personnel.—Most significant here are college and university presidents, agricultural college deans, and directors of Extension and research, in that order. Appointments and removals of presidents of major colleges or universities, land-grant or otherwise, are significant political actions. Agricultural college deanships are also political offices in the sense that farm and related groups are extremely sensitive to them. To the writer's knowledge, however, no federal agricultural official has ever sought directly to control the appointment or dismissal of an agricultural college dean, much less a president of a land-grant institution.

Indeed, the only known examples of alleged action-agency influence respecting these important personnel decisions have been reports that action agencies obtained the dismissal of agricultural Extension directors in three southern and western states and prevented the appointment of a candidate in a fourth state. One of these allegations has some color of truth; in fact, a federal action agency official told the writer that he had secured the dismissal; but other inquiry disclosed that the Extension director in question had made himself so widely unpopular that the claim cannot be justified. Respecting the other dismissals, the informed consensus within the states concerned was that intrastate politics was really responsible. Respecting the failure of the candidate to be appointed Extension director, the writer's inquiries have produced nothing beyond the initial allegation. This completes the record,[4] so far as the writer has been able to uncover it. The conclusion is that, with the possible exception of the dismissal of one state agricultural Extension director, federal agricultural action agencies have not directly influenced personnel actions at this level.

It should be realized that Extension directorships in a few southern and western states have been rather precarious because of intrastate politics. At least five state Extension directors who lost their jobs after 1933, always, it is believed, because of intrastate politics, found new employment with federal agricultural agencies—three of them with action agencies. For these men the existence of federal agencies meant the availability of alternative employment. Presumably, their example was not entirely lost upon their colleagues in other states. One might interpret federal agricultural agency influence upon state Extension directors as providing them with a little job insurance that would stiffen them somewhat against intrastate political pressures. On the other hand, one might argue that the possibility of sanctuary in federal agencies shows that the federal agricultural programs exercise a real, if subtle, domination over state agricultural Extension directors, who do not want to antagonize the federal officials who may some day be their employers. The second interpretation would appeal to states' righters; but it has no support, so far as the writer can discern, in either the actions or the expressed attitudes of state agricultural Extension directors.

The question of action agency influence upon personnel in the colleges of agriculture must be extended, however, to the professorial level and even to the county agents' offices. Had action agency pressure operated like typical intrastate pressures, the jobs of such research and teaching personnel would sometimes have been directly threatened. So far as can be ascertained, this has not happened. The apparent exceptions can be explained away. The Kentucky low-nicotine tobacco case, discussed in the following chapter, might appear to be an exception—until it is noted that the pressure on the professor involved was generated by intrastate groups. Other examples are furnished by the SCS, which in the early 1940's complained that economists jointly employed with state agricultural experiment stations failed to produce unequivocal evidence that farmers co-operating in the SCS and the soil conservation district program rapidly reaped large cash benefits. Soon the SCS drastically reduced such co-operative research in economics. In recent years, however, state experiment station directors interviewed by the writer have been virtually unanimous in their satisfaction with research relationships with the SCS, including the joint economic research then remaining in Illinois and Wisconsi

Finally, with a single exception which will not be discussed, the writer has seen no evidence of efforts by agricultural action agencies to cause the removal of federal research or Extension personnel.[5] Rather than seeking dismissals, action agency officials have acted in other ways.

Sometimes they have ignored research and Extension as businessmen occasionally brush aside college professors. Sometimes they have gone a little further in efforts to exclude researchers and Extension workers from the important centers of policy formation and implementation. (A former high official in the New Deal remarked: "When I was in the USDA, we kept the damned scientists in their offices.") Sometimes they have conducted their own research and educational programs. And always they have competed vigorously for appropriations.

Pressure on the product. — Turn now from pressure on the job of the researcher or educator to efforts at control of what he produces. Iowa provides the primary example of overt federal action agency pressure upon agricultural college research and Extension known to the writer. In the 1930's, Iowa State College's department of agricultural economics and rural sociology counted a number of researchers who were busily inquiring into controversial issues, some of which involved federal action agencies. When critical statements were written and distributed, officials of the AAA protested that the college should not employ the United States frank to mail out attacks upon federal programs. The protest was ineffectual and was soon withdrawn, but it stimulated the most searching examination of the issues made by a land-grant college.[6] It should be added that the Iowa State group kept its critical function undiminished. Indeed, the "Farm and Food Policy Bulletins" of 1942-43 were often quite critical of federal programs; but the controversy which one of these bulletins touched off at Iowa State in the summer of 1943 involved intrastate pressures and not pressure by federal action agencies.[7]

In one other state, an experiment station researcher reportedly developed a strain of Burley tobacco which was resistant to black shank disease. Wishing to avoid testing the tobacco on the university farm, thus getting the disease into its soil, he proposed to test it in co-operation with a farmer who would plant it on soil already infected and then sell the crop on the open market for whatever it would bring. The local PMA committee objected to the farmer's experimenting with the disease-resistant strain outside his acreage allotment under his marketing quota. The farmer did not want to risk his allotment on the experiment, and it was called off.

With the exception of some SCS pressure reportedly upon work produced by joint employees (again, this was a number of years ago), the writer has heard of no other attempts by action agencies of the USDA to influence research or Extension policy in land-grant colleges by suppressing publication or by insisting on censoring it. On numerous other occasions, college workers have been apprised of the preferences of action agency officials among research results and of their objections to certain results. Mere notifications and protests, however, need not concern us.

On the federal level the writer knows of only one concrete example, an effort in 1941 by an official of the AAA to have an article, prepared for publication by a ranking official of the Bureau of Agricultural Economics, suppressed; the effort was unsuccessful.

How does one appraise these bits of evidence, which are exhaustive so far as the writer is aware, of efforts by federal action agencies to control research and educational policy of agricultural institutions? Examples are extremely few—in striking contrast to the numerous examples of intrastate pressures upon research and Extension personnel reported in chapters vi-ix. And even those few federal action agency efforts at control have almost always been unsuccessful. If it is argued that only the unsuccessful efforts were told the writer, he can only reply that a rather large number of highly successful intrastate pressures were described to him.

How to explain the relative absence of overt, direct federal agricultural action agency pressure on the job or the product of research and Extension workers? First should be stressed the self-restraint[8] of many federal administrators who have acted in accordance with their belief that research and education should be untrammeled by politics. Second should be mentioned the anticipation by federal officials of the uproar that would accompany federal interference. Third, the manner of organization of federal action agencies does not facilitate their bringing pressure upon state colleges of agriculture. To elaborate the last point: the sometimes considerable influence of agricultural action agencies and their allies has commonly been organized to affect action in Washington rather than in state capitals. But research and Extension workers in state colleges of agriculture are more vulnerable to direct political pressure which operates through state channels—legislatures and institutional governing boards.[9] To confine the analysis to direct political influence, however, would be to neglect the more subtle—and more significant—effects of action agency programs.

3. Indirect Influence

It is one thing to search for identifiable action agency officials
who have exercised direct pressure upon the job or the product of researchers or of Extension workers. It is quite another to appraise the
indirect and subtle influences of the changed situation upon agricultural
research and Extension. The action agencies are important elements
in the new situation, but they are neither its essence nor its cause. The
full force of the great depression was measured in falling farm prices
and rising numbers of farm foreclosures before the AAA and the other
agencies were created. As the new situation crystallized, however, new
influences, in which the action agencies were at work, began to affect
agricultural research and Extension by changing (a) the distribution of
power between the states and the federal government, (b) the scope and
orientation of research and education, and (c) the control of public
opinion in agriculture.

The distribution of power between the states and the federal government. —Federalism forces two organized governments to live together
in the same house, as it were. It is thus a natural breeder of political
suspicion. Under the best of circumstances, agencies of the member
governments and those of the central government which must co-operate
with each other do so with misgivings and some sense of risk.

The best of circumstances for the colleges of agriculture in their
dealings with the USDA ended in 1933. Earlier, agricultural research and
Extension personnel were in a fairly satisfactory political situation that
was rather well settled, predictable, and understood; but the new agricultural action programs changed all that. In the first year of the New Deal,
agency and partisan loyalties were forgotten in the common effort to help
a stricken agriculture; but in much of the country this honeymoon was
soon replaced by a political situation more normal to a democratic
society. The new federal action agencies acquired large staffs; a number
of them worked through regional offices; increasingly, they reached
directly to the farmers; and, finally, they developed or called forth organizations among the farmers themselves or formed alliances with existing
farm organizations.

These developments changed the distribution of political power
adversely for the colleges of agriculture, many of which have since been
sometimes in conflict with one or more action agencies. Examples are the

friction in Alabama between Extension and, first, the Farm Security Administration and, later, the SCS; in Missouri, between Extension and the SCS; in Pennsylvania for a number of years between the school of agriculture and federal action agencies generally; and pretty well throughout the Midwest in and after 1942-43 between Extension Services and the AAA-PMA.[10]

The colleges of agriculture have tried repeatedly to redress the balance which, they felt, had unduly shifted in Washington's favor or to get control of the new instruments of power. Illustrations include participation in 1936 in drafting the original soil conservation district "standard act"; an unsuccessful effort in 1938-39 to get the SCS transferred to the colleges; co-operation with the TVA and vigorous recommendation of the joint program as a model for the United States; the Mt. Weather Agreement; the Report on Post-War Agricultural Problems of a Committee of the Association of Land-Grant Colleges and Universities in 1944; support of the Aiken Bill of 1948; influence upon the recommendations of the Hoover Commission's Agricultural Task Force in 1949; and influence in the reorganization of the USDA of November 1, 1953.[11]

An apparent result of this heightened political activity is its consequence for the reputation of the colleges of agriculture. Many college personnel will consider it indecent to suggest that their objectivity as researchers and educators may have been affected in the slightest. But numerous subjects which touch college interests are appropriate for research and Extension work.[12] As the colleges move into the political spotlight, such work will have a question mark attached to it. Those who deal with the colleges will have to be repeatedly convinced of their objectivity. Unlike Caesar's wife, the colleges cannot hope to be above suspicion, which is now their natural lot and can be counteracted only by the most scrupulous propriety.[13]

Furthermore, the road to a general reputation for objectivity may have been made virtually impassable because of partisan politics. A conscious effort was made to advance the interests of the Democratic party in the Middle West by means of the AAA-PMA committee system. In consequence the strong Republican predispositions of midwestern agricultural colleges were brought into bold relief. Since the writer discussed these phenomena in 1952,[14] the Republican victory has brought certain immediate gains to midwestern agricultural colleges through shifts in political power.

The PMA was abolished in November, 1953, its major functions being divided three ways: marketing to the Agricultural Marketing Service; production control, storage, and related activities to the Commodity Stabilization Service; and the Agricultural Conservation Program to the Federal-State Relations group. Reorganization of the PMA committee system (since renamed the "Agricultural Stabilization and Conserva- tion" [ASC] committees) had begun in March, 1953, with the separa- tion of their "policy-making" from their "administrative" functions (the latter to be placed in the hands of professional administrators). A policy of rotation for state committeemen was announced at the same time; a similar policy for county and community committeemen was pro- claimed in June, 1954, together with a prohibition of officers of general farm organizations from serving as members. Meanwhile, state commit- teemen from the previous administration were being replaced, commonly by Republicans with political clearance. In the administration of the USDA, patronage purposes, which had not been strongly emphasized in 1953, came to the fore in 1954.[15]

Meanwhile, agricultural college leaders (and some from the Farm Bureau and allied interests) had moved into USDA positions of eminence— and exposure, for the gains involved certain risks. Much of the dissat- isfaction of friends of the SCS with the administration of the USDA was vented on the colleges. More ominous for them was the growing (apparent) dissatisfaction of many farmers and farm congressmen with Benson's farm policy. If this policy were repudiated, the leadership of the Farm Bureau and of the agricultural colleges which had become identified with it would also be adversely affected.

The scope and orientation of agricultural research and Extension.— The foregoing changes in the distribution of political power are clearly full of potential influence upon agricultural research and Extension— influence none the less profound because of its indirection. Other indirect influences are inherent in the same situation, as can be seen, first, by focusing upon the budgetary squeeze suffered by agricultural research in competition with action agencies for congressional appropria- tions. The contrast with the states is striking. State expenditures for agricultural research, exclusive of federal grants, increased from $12,635,000 to $50,972,000 in 1940-51—or 130 per cent, if one deflates the figures in accordance with the buying power of 1935-39 dollars. During the same period, the USDA expenditures for research, exclusive

of federal grants to states, increased from $21,806,000 to $43,118,000—
a gain in deflated dollars of only 13 per cent.[16] In 1940 federal expenditures for agricultural research accounted for nearly 60 per cent of all
federal expenditures for research, excluding the military. In 1951 agricultural research accounted for about 2 per cent of all federal research,
exclusive of the military and atomic energy.[17]

One cannot demonstrate, of course, that less money for action
agencies would have meant more for agricultural research; but the
increase of only 13 per cent in deflated dollars during these unprec-
edentedly prosperous years seems very small to agricultural researchers. This "niggardliness" is sometimes attributed to the difficulty of
increasing federal funds for agricultural research in the face of a
federal agricultural budget which persistently allocates large funds for
action programs.[18] Strong beliefs exist in powerful quarters that action
programs are more immediately and practically helpful to farmers than
are research and education. On April 13, 1954, Congressman H. Carl
Andersen said of the money bill for the USDA for the fiscal year 1955,
then before the House:[19]"The budget request was so lopsided in favor
of research and extension, and so deficient in support of our great
action programs, that we could see that here was a proposal of men who
were prejudiced against much that Congress favors and ignorant of
what we term a balance between research and the act."

The budgetary squeeze has been accompanied by stimuli to change
the orientation of research and Extension work. Here the initial impetus
came from the effect of the AAA program upon Extension, which played
a heroic role in the original reductions of acreage and distribution of
benefit payments during and after 1933. When the AAA developed its own
administration sufficiently to move apart from Extension (except in a
number of southern states, where the two programs have retained considerable integration), demands were multiplying for Extension to assist
many other federal agricultural programs, in soil conservation, credit,
rural electrification, crop insurance, and, in certain localities, forestry
or reclamation. Where there was no co-operation, there often was friction,
which was also time-consuming. In addition, there was the effort to provide
a planning and co-ordinating framework for farm policies in 1938-42, in
which the land-grant colleges were partners with the USDA. There were
accretions to Extension from action agencies—the migratory farm labor
program from the Farm Security Administration and certain of the
information activities of the AAA both in 1943. In 1951 there was Secre-

tary Brannan's Family Farm Policy Review, which many of the colleges disliked. It was followed in 1953 by Secretary Benson's "grass-roots" inquiry, which was cordially received.

These illustrations convey both the persistence and the magnitude of the demands which in one way or another the action programs have caused to devolve upon the colleges of agriculture. Much time and effort have been invested in explaining programs, helping to administer them, evaluating them, seeking co-ordination among them, and—sometimes—rebuffing them. The major effect of these influences has been upon Extension; but, where communication is properly organized in colleges of agriculture, demands upon Extension are rapidly conducted to the experiment stations. Sometimes the experiment stations have been directly involved, as in the wartime capacity studies, the capacity study of 1951, and the technical consultation to agricultural conservation programs. Resident teaching has felt the influence as reflected in courses for soil conservationists or in agricultural policy.

In some ways the most striking evidence of the changed orientation of the colleges is the Extension program in public policy (see chap. xvi). This program is a logical[20] consequence of the questioning and demanding mood of many farmers since the price break in 1920. Its purpose is educational in the sense that it aims at improving the ability of farm and rural people to choose among alternative courses of action.[21] In 1954 forty-four states had formally adopted this program; informally, of course, the professional personnel of agricultural colleges has often heavily—if frequently quite uncritically and even unconsciously—engaged in what might be called "public policy education." When farm prices or incomes fall faster than farm costs, the county agent who can escape searching questions about farm policy is rare indeed. The same is true of agricultural researchers who visit substations or farms which are co-operating with the station in applied research.

To its credit, the formal Extension public policy program has reached beyond immediate farm policy problems to the larger questions of inflation, deflation, fiscal policy, foreign trade, and even to problems of domestic and international politics. But much of the impetus for Extension work in public policy clearly came from the agricultural action programs. Behind the action programs, in turn, it must never be forgotten, was farm unrest. Behind the farm unrest was the embittering struggle to pay off an inflated mortgage at deflated farm produce prices or to

educate the children and provide the family with some of the expanding
amenities of life while the economic "terms of trade" were turned
persistently against agriculture.

These experiences affected the farmer's beliefs and values—beliefs,
for example, about how the market worked or failed to work, and values
respecting what government should do to counterbalance his apparent
economic disadvantages. Quite concretely, wheat sold for 94 cents a
bushel in 1922. But farmers were shown that the general price index
that year was 152, compared to 97 in a ten-year prewar base period.
During the prewar period, wheat had averaged $1.02 a bushel. Therefore,
the argument ran, it should have sold for $1.60 in 1922.[22] If farmers
believed this kind of analysis of the facts, they would easily conclude
that they were entitled to a "fair exchange value" for their crops or to
"cost of production" or, later, to "parity." Such beliefs and values
became crystallized into attitudes of willingness for action; in other
words, farm public opinion was ready for the agricultural action programs.

Public opinion in agriculture.—Presumably, however, public opinion
in agriculture has not stayed the same since 1933. What are the political
demands which the bulk of farmers in various sections are now willing
to support by action—specifically, by switching their votes from one
party to another? This question may be scientifically unanswerable;
but the politicians have to answer it. The question is also most pertinent
for agricultural Extension's public policy educational program. Can
education affect political demands so strongly rooted in immediate
economic self-interest as the demands for price floors at 90 per cent
of parity appear to be? Education can reach farm leaders; as an outstanding example, President Allan Kline of the American Farm Bureau
Federation was not born with his preference for flexible price supports
and the economic rationale to sustain it. He acquired these by study, in
which he was helped by professional economists.

But what of the 1,600,000 families who belong to Kline's organization, to say nothing of other farmers? Clearly, they are not so many
blank pages for Extension workers in public policy to write on at will.
Many of them have strong convictions about the economic facts of
farming and about what they want and deserve. Some college officials
believe that farmers' convictions are generally so strong on these subjects that they are out of reach of the Extension public policy program.
Asked whether a vigorous program of research and education can be

combined with the agricultural adjustment effort so that commercial farmers can become economically sound enough not to need price supports and production control under ordinary circumstances, they throw up their hands. "All this is too complicated, too time-consuming, too full of apparent risk for farmers," they say; "it cannot compete with the simple appeal of 90 or 100 per cent parity guarantees."

The "simple appeal" after 1948 was made by Secretary Brannan and some of the PMA committeemen. Flexible price supports had been advised by the USDA in October, 1947, supported by the American Farm Bureau Federation in December, 1947, and incorporated in the Hope-Aiken Act of 1948, which provided that the transfer from fixed to flexible supports would be gradual. Mr. Truman promised 90 per cent of parity supports to farmers, however, and the Brannan Plan of 1949, among other things, sought to fulfil this pledge. The Brannan Plan was not enacted, but the issue was drawn in many areas, as illustrated by a handbill distributed to farmers by PMA committeemen in the senatorial election in Iowa in 1950: "Vote Democratic for 90 per cent supports— or take the consequences of 60 per cent Republican supports."[23]

This is the final example of influence of action agency programs upon agricultural research and Extension—a conscious effort to structure farm opinion. The Extension public policy program and its supporting research, assuming that they are aimed at improving farmers' ability to choose rationally among alternative public policies, would be frustrated in the important field of agricultural price policy if the PMA effort succeeded. For the range of real alternatives would be drastically reduced.

To probe further would set off some explosive questions. In order to carry forward the argument of this chapter, let us merely assert that there is a widespread belief in the existence of a structured farmer opinion in favor of 90 per cent supports.[24] Let us further assert that a consensus among informed persons in agriculture holds that the PMA organization, at least at some times and in some areas, has made important efforts to firm up and spread the acceptance of this kind of opinion. To say that an opinion is believed to exist and that an agency sought to establish it, however, is not to say that the opinion really exists or that, if it does, the agency was the chief, or even a major, cause of its establishment.

It is vital to understand the qualifications of the last sentence. They are not offered to excuse the PMA from censure for its propagandistic efforts. But what we are interested in are the influences which make rural public opinion inhospitable to efforts to promote rational choice among alternative policies. A thorough search for these influences would raise profound scientific and philosophical questions which are beyond the scope of this work. Crude observation of the PMA's activities, however, tells us that, if we want to diminish this influence, the PMA is one place to start. In chapter vi, more crude observation tells us that the same influences stem powerfully from other sources, including the Farm Bureau and commodity organizations and, most probably, informal but very effective groups such as the family and the neighborhood. It is easy to exaggerate the ability of a central bureaucracy to manipulate opinion in a free society—or to underestimate the confining influences of beliefs and customs upon freedom of thought and expression.

4.   Conclusions

In this examination of the political influence of agricultural action agencies upon research and Extension, some evidence was found of direct pressure against the job or the product of researchers and Extension workers. Sometimes this direct pressure has been exasperating and perhaps, in a very few examples, successful. On the whole, however, direct pressure by federal action agencies is much less significant than pressure by state and local political groups (chaps. vi-x below). This is especially true of pressure upon the colleges of agriculture. (It has been less true on important occasions of pressure on the Bureau of Agricultural Economics, a federal agency (see chap. xiv below). State and local political groups are well organized to influence the colleges, specifically, by working through state legislatures to which federal action agencies have little access.[25]

Moreover, the widespread predisposition against political control of research and education is much stronger against federal than against state or local control. To illustrate, Earl C. Smith, in his presidential address of 1945 to the Illinois Agricultural Association (the Farm Bureau), referred to the prize-essay contest on the subject of agricultural price policy, sponsored by the American Farm Economic Association. He condemned the winning papers and called upon agricultural economists in "our land-grant colleges" to refute the heresy that they contained.

One finds it hard to imagine the head of a federal agency speaking of the colleges of agriculture in the proprietary tone that Smith assumed as a matter of course.

When the examination turns, however, to indirect and subtle political influences upon colleges of agriculture, much more significant evidence appears. Public agricultural research and Extension have found themselves in a new situation since 1933, a situation characterized by greater competition for funds, by strong demands especially on Extension for assistance to various action programs, and by recurring struggles for the loyalty of various farm groups. Not only have the colleges been impelled to increase their activities as interest groups, but they probably have been more clearly identified as interest groups by a wider public. The colleges, moreover, have been drawn into a study of public policy itself, a far cry from "making two blades of grass grow where one grew before." And as the colleges address themselves to public policy issues, they find that public opinion in agriculture seems to be firming up in support of a number of policies which appear ill advised to the college analysts. Or, at least, they find that this construction of public opinion is widely accepted among farm politicians.

In every one of these influences the action agencies figure importantly; yet their operations are sometimes less significant than those of other groups, and both are perhaps less meaningful than trends in public opinion. The following chapter on the low-nicotine tobacco incident illustrates these qualifications.

In the examination of political influence upon agricultural research ·and Extension the search is about to shift from national to state and local pressures. The unsuccessful effort in 1949-50 to circumscribe tobacco research in Kentucky will serve as a bridge as we move from one side of the federal system to the other. For here the pressure upon research was organized by state and local groups and operated through state channels; nevertheless, its aim was to insure the Burley tobacco market by protecting the system of production control upon which it rests—production control through marketing quotas established by national legislation and administered by a national agency, then the Production and Marketing Administration (PMA) of the USDA.

1. Low-Nicotine Tobacco in Kentucky

Professor W. D. Valleau, plant pathologist of the College of Agriculture, University of Kentucky (Lexington), conducted research for some fifteen years on low-nicotine tobacco. He developed a strain with less than 0.4 per cent nicotine as compared to 2-5 per cent in Burley. According to accepted practice, seeds of the new strain were given limited distribution in the United States and abroad. Upon request of a Mr. Salmon, who had leased a large Kentucky farm and was producing Burley tobacco, Valleau gave him some seed. Salmon increased his acreage of low-nicotine tobacco, which he grew for use in cigars, cigarettes, and pipes, and made arrangements for its manufacture and distribution in John Alden cigarettes. During 1949 low-nicotine tobacco was grown on 400-500 acres in Kentucky, of a total acreage of all types of tobacco (but mostly Burley) of some 400,000.

Meanwhile, low-nicotine tobacco, at the instance of Valleau, was classified as a separate type of tobacco by the PMA.[1] The object was to protect both buyers and sellers of Burley from complaints arising from the purchase of tobacco classified as Burley but differing from it in taste and in nicotine content. One effect, however, was to remove low-nicotine tobacco from the application of Burley marketing quotas.

56

The classification was first protested by a member of the PMA committee in Woodford County, where some of Salmon's operations were located.[2] On October 19, 1949, Burley tobacco growers, in a PMA meeting called to discuss acreage reductions, adopted a resolution requesting the USDA to classify any tobacco similar to Burley in a manner "to stop and to prevent the growing of any type tobacco similar to burley except under the same rulings, regulations and restrictions as applied to growing and marketing of burley tobacco." The resolution also requested that "the activities and services of Dr. Valleau be limited to his technical field." The Burley Tobacco Growers Association, a cooperative, resolved through its board of directors that low-nicotine tobacco be reclassified as Burley. The Kentucky Farm Bureau unanimously adopted a resolution that low-nicotine tobacco should be reclassified as Burley and subjected to marketing quotas (Louisville Courier-Journal, December 27, 1949). In February the Kentucky legislature unanimously memorialized the PMA to reclassify low-nicotine tobacco (Kentucky Farm Bureau News, February and March, 1950).

On February 7, 1950, a bill was introduced in the Kentucky senate to prevent the growing of any type of tobacco which would "jeopardize the profitable production of tobacco now being grown and marketed in Kentucky under and pursuant to quotas" by tending to create "abnormally excessive supplies of tobacco." It limited experimentation with other than the Kentucky types (Burley, fire-cured, and dark-air-cured) in various ways. Seeds of other types were to be prevented from getting into the hands of "any person other than the Dean of the College of Agriculture or his duly authorized agents." The dean and the university's board of trustees were instructed to enforce the limiting provisions. Penalties for infractions ranged from one to five years in jail and from $1,000 to $10,000 in fines.[3] The bill was prepared for the Kentucky Farm Bureau by a Frankfort attorney.

On February 11 the Louisville Courier-Journal editorialized against the measure. The Fayette and Clarke County Farm Bureaus strongly resolved against the senate bill, and it was publicly opposed by Dean

Thomas P. Cooper of the Kentucky College of Agriculture.[4] The executive and legislative committees of the Kentucky Farm Bureau then jointly repudiated the senate bill, and all county farm bureaus were so notified. Nevertheless, the Kentucky Farm Bureau News for May, 1950, recorded support for the measure.

Meanwhile, the bill had been amended to permit some experimental growing of non-Kentucky types. It provided for permits issued by the Kentucky department of agriculture for the experimental growing of such types by persons over whom the university would have no control and stipulated the conditions under which permits might be granted. The amended bill sought to protect the federal marketing-quota program by providing that no person might grow the authorized types in excess of federal quotas and that no tobacco grown in violation of the bill (either in the future or in the past) should be considered in the establishment of a quota. The Kentucky senate passed the amended bill on March 14, by a vote of 20 to 2, but the bill died in the house.[5]

2. Interpretation

Freedom for research was threatened in Kentucky in 1950; but the threat was successfully turned back by prompt, vigorous action in which Dean Cooper and Professor Valleau were prominent. Significantly, both men argued that, since the federal government contributed to the research, the latter could not be circumscribed by the Kentucky legislature acting alone. The existence of federal research grants helped the Kentucky experiment station resist the political demands of state and local organizations and of the state legislature itself. Other factors which contributed to the result were editorial opposition to the bill, the internal division in the Farm Bureau, friction between leaders in the Kentucky senate and house, and the confusion at the end of the legislative session.

How deeply involved in politics a typical college of agriculture becomes is illustrated here. So are the virtues of political courage and the need to use it at times on behalf of physical and biological scientists (some of whom believe that no such disturbing questions would arise if only the economists would keep out of trouble). Not so obvious, but implicit in the situation, is the importance of the cultivation over the years of political strength, so that, when the issue arises, courage will have a suitable position from which to counterattack.

The incident shows the possible importance of federal production-control programs to the political life of colleges of agriculture but also the need to search behind the federal agency itself for the source of political influence which the college feels. The issue could hardly have arisen without a price-support and production-control program for tobacco. Private efforts (including co-operative efforts) to control production had proved insufficient even when reinforced by some private violence (the "night riders"). If production was to be controlled, governmental power would have to be used—federal power, since tobacco is grown in many states. The forces which sought to restrain research on tobacco were rallying to protect the federal marketing quotas. Significantly, the initial complaint came from the local PMA; but, even more notably, the PMA in Washington did not classify the new strain as Burley, as it would have done had it been completely integrated on the proposition that any threat, however slight, to the marketing-quota system should be suppressed. Moreover, even when division appeared in the Kentucky Farm Bureau on the issue, the PMA did not seek to exploit it, as theoretical analysis of the friction between the PMA and the Farm Bureau might lead one to expect.

Behind the obvious significance of production-control programs is the even more important fact that the pressure upon the experiment station came from state and local sources and almost took effect through state legislative action. Here is food for thought on the part of all those who are anxious to define and maintain a sphere of freedom for agricultural research and education. The open, direct, even brutal character of the attack in Kentucky is also worth noting. In many states, college administrators have been subjected to the table-pounding approach—"Do this; refrain from that—or else!" Probably such overt threats to educational freedom are more vulnerable to counterattack than are the more subtle varieties of influence. Even if the attack is rebuffed, however, and the battle lost, the attacker may have won a victory. In the first place, the successful defenders may feel that the risk was so great that it should not be incurred again; openly or tacitly, the staff may be urged henceforth to put a premium on caution. In the second place, physical fatigue and emotional strain are considerable costs of such defenses, even successful ones.

But political analysis cannot stop with the visible, organized groups and with legislatures, courts, and executives. Continuing questions in the

evaluation of the demands of group leaders are: Will his membership
support him? Beyond the membership, what of the large numbers of
people who seem to have a logical interest in the matter and who at
least may vote in elections? Analyses of the political relationships between visible governmental officials and organized group leaders is
tentative enough; when the study reaches out to the potential groups or
to public opinion, the difficulties become staggering. Yet it is precisely
this kind of political force that politicians must appraise.[6]

Still, our appraisal can be a little more confident than usual, even
though the evidence, as is common, is inferred rather than explicitly
observed. It is a fact that some 149,000 farmers in Kentucky had Burley
tobacco bases in 1950. Informed persons believe that these farmers and
many others who supply them or trade with them are convinced that
their economic future depends upon the maintenance of the Burley program, including marketing quotas.[7] As long ago as 1938 a producer
referendum among Burley growers (the bulk of them in Kentucky) recorded 154,208, or 87 per cent of those voting, in favor of marketing
quotas. In 1949 nearly 90,000 Kentucky Burley growers voted in a similar
referendum; only 3.5 per cent rejected quotas. In 1952, of nearly 118,000
Kentucky votes, only 1.3 per cent opposed quotas. It follows that any
attack upon marketing quotas will probably provoke an adverse political
response from a very large group. Apparently, the experimentation with
low-nicotine tobacco was construed as such attack. This analysis would
account for the initial action of the Farm Bureau and would help explain
the passage of the bill by the Kentucky senate.

The implicit threat to Burley marketing quotas was not the only basis
for an appeal to a wider public, however. Frontal attacks upon research
and educational freedom usually mobilize their defenders. In Kentucky in
1950 leading college personnel and newspaper editors denounced the
attack upon freedom of research, probably with considerable effect. The
split within the Farm Bureau turned largely on this question. The fact
that, after passing in the state senate by an overwhelming margin, the
bill failed even to come to a vote in the house suggests that the legislators
heavily discounted the demand for its passage. Very likely they sensed
the growing hostility to the measure, hostility apparently based upon strong
values placed by the community on educational freedom.

It would be wrong, however, to picture the underlying political situation
in terms of one large group tacitly demanding that marketing quotas be

protected at all costs, an even larger group that was muttering louder and louder against interference with educational freedom, and another group torn between these two but edging more and more into the camp of the opposition to the bill. Presumably, by far the majority of Kentucky citizens could not have identified the low-nicotine-tobacco controversy had their lives depended upon it; and, if they had been able to, many of them would still have been indifferent about its outcome. Moreover, the issue between educational freedom and restrictive legislation to protect the tobacco program was not drawn in a definitive way. For the issue to have been definitive—to have really tested the strength of those who favored the tobacco program against those who supported freedom of research—the apparent threat of research to the tobacco program would have had to be much larger. Yet the experimental acreage in low-nicotine tobacco outside quotas was only about one-tenth of 1 per cent of the current tobacco quotas in Kentucky.

Where so microscopic a threat to the tobacco program could cause a row of these proportions, the incident becomes especially interesting. If the powers of resistance in the college of agriculture are suggested, so is its vulnerability. So is the importance to the college of accurate political analysis to show precisely where the threat comes from;[8] what resources it commands; what motivates its adherents (so far as this can be shown); and then, in turn, the location, strength, and motivations of the forces of resistance. Finally, the college probably must count in part on the resource constituted by the acceptance by a considerable body of citizens of the principle of freedom of research and education.

VII / Intrastate Politics and the Land-Grant
Institutions: Background Sketch

Visit a state university campus, a land-grant university, if you please, and visualize its emergence from the legislative chambers — even out of the "smoke-filled rooms." Ask: What has politics done to public university education? And be answered: Politics has created, sustained, and expanded it. Politics has also disciplined its youth and harried its maturity. And, in this alternation of nurture and pressure, politics has blown its own spirit into the university, which is no longer merely in politics but also of it. The center of learning is now a locus of influence. A rightful claimant of public funds, the university has achieved a certain autonomy characteristic of major political associations in pluralistic democracies. But, if it takes, it gives. A wealthier economy and a richer culture flow from the university, and something more, something that sustains the commonwealth itself—or fails it in a difficult hour.

Now to return to the pedestrian business of describing political influence upon agricultural research and Extension. Several chapters will explore the state and local politics in which the land-grant institutions find themselves, beginning with their matrix.

1.   The Struggle for Establishment

The land-grant colleges are state institutions. Federal support (chiefly for agricultural research and Extension) rose from $5,000,000 in 1915 to $13,308,356 in 1928; meanwhile, state funds increased from $19,731,132 to just under $70,000,000.[1] "The ordinary assumption is that the agency controlling an educational institution contributes the major proportion of its support. The land-grant colleges are state-controlled."[2] But state support had to be secrued by political activity, often against considerable opposition. "Farmers, the especial 'industrial class' for whom the new training was designed, were generally lacking in appreciation."[3] As late as 1903, only 2,405 students were enrolled in colleges of agriculture.[4]

Organizational periods were full "of doubt and discouragement."[5]
President Clark resigned at Massachusetts College in 1879, which
"then entered on a period of difficulty and uncertainty regarding the
future." Legislation indirectly forced liquidation of much college property. The governor and council, created as a committee of investigation by the legislature in 1879, recommended abandonment of state
assistance. "This proposition, although strongly advocated by Governor
Long, was so radical and so subversive of the integrity of the State
that it gained no favor at the hands of the public, and no effort was made
by the legislature to accept this report."[6] In 1864 Pennsylvania State
College retained its land-grant fund with difficulty, and it experienced
more hardship "in establishing itself firmly and getting adequate
financial support."[7] Even Cornell, while the benefits of its founder's
plan for favorable disposal of its scrip were still in abeyance, suffered
reverses. "Friends of the university kept it from going into bankruptcy
until the great land sales of 1881-82 made its financial status stable."[8]
Struggles occurred over the locations of the new colleges, over their
method of government, over their secular nature, over their course
offerings (especially the classical-versus-practical debate), and over
their relationships to the several state governments, many of which
were loath to support them. Sometimes a "famous victory" helped, as
that of the "aggies" of Massachusetts State over Harvard in a boat race
in 1871. Sentiment against state assistance to the college had been
strong, but "This event did much to give the agricultural college standing as a real college. That year the legislature (appropriated) $50,000
for its debts and other expenses. . . ."[9]

The Minnesota College of Agriculture grew so slowly that, with only
one graduate in each of the years 1884 and 1885, a movement was
fostered by farm organizations and grew swiftly in the legislature to
separate the agricultural college from the university. The issue was
close in 1887, but it was settled favorably to union in 1889, when the legislature accepted a large gift from J. S. Pillsbury, former governor,
who had prevailed on an earlier legislature to accept the Morrill Act.
The condition of the gift, the continued union of the college of agriculture
with the university, was accepted by resolutions of both branches of the
legislature. This timely measure of avoiding partition seems to have
been promoted by President Cyrus Northrop.[10]

a) Missouri

More detail on experiences in a few states will lend weight to the
analysis. In Missouri the university was governed by a board of curators
which was the focus of conflict as early as the 1840's. The Democratic,
cabin-dwelling,. Methodist, Baptist, or Campbellite pioneers opposed
the immigrants from the Kentucky blue-grass region into Columbia,
Boone County—Presbyterians, Whigs, and slaveholders. John Lathrop,
first president of the university, identified himself with the latter.
At first the difficulties of transportation meant that curators were
concentrated in Boone County and hence were friendly to Lathrop; but
in 1849 the legislature spread the curators over the state at large,
thus insuring a Democratic triumph. Lathrop resigned amid mutual
recriminations.[11]

University fortunes then reflected the "irrepressible conflict" and
its aftermath. Professor Viles called 1862-67 the "Time of Troubles."
Despite Missouri's early acceptance of the Morrill Act, Columbia was
not designated as the seat of the qualifying college thereunder until
1870.[12] The board of curators was reorganized,[13] but the university
was fortunate in the chairmanship of James S. Rollins (1869-86).
The Missouri constitution of 1875 pledged the state legislature to aid
the university. On the other hand, President Read had to contend with
opposition from a minority of the board and legislative attacks engen-
dered thereby.[14] When Read left in 1876, he could take pride in achievements, but for at least twenty years "politics and partisanship" never
ceased "to be important handicaps, and at times serious handicaps."[15]

As happened in many states, the college of agriculture became controversial. In 1874 the state horticultural society "resolved that 'A prompt
reorganization of the agricultural college is needed.'" In 1875 the state
board of agriculture, "dissatisfied but eager to help," listened to a
curator expound the college of agriculture's weaknesses as part of the
precarious position of the entire university and urge greater support of
the university as a whole, as part of which agriculture should get its
due share: "'That is good,' responded a member of the Board of Agriculture, 'but what are they going to do about hog cholera?' A revealing question." An investigation prpduced a "blistering report" but little else.[16]

The administration of President Samuel Spahr Laws (1876-89) was
harassed by the agricultural question. In 1882 an issue developed over

George C. Swallow, dean of agriculture, who had the support of the board of agriculture and the Grange. The board of curators dismissed him; but by 1885 President Laws became convinced that his "chief difficulty in dealing with the legislature and the people was failure of the college of agriculture to develop." So he rechristened the school the "Missouri Agricultural College and University" and evolved a system of bookkeeping in which all "science and art departments were to be administratively 'Academic Schools of the College of Agriculture' and frankly financed from agricultural funds." The alumni protested, and students paraded with signs: "Agricultural Medical Students," "Agricultural Law Students," etc. The board rejected the proposal. Agricultural issues helped precipitate an investigation in 1888, whereupon President Laws was forced to resign.[17]

Richard Henry Jesse's presidency extended from 1891 to 1908. He characterized his task as follows: "Then, too, I am always mindful of what labor and care fall daily upon the administration of a great University, especially when it is within the reach of politicians. You see I had six years' experience of it (in Louisiana)—when I had not only to manage the University itself and foster and develop it, but also to keep both eyes constantly on the Legislatures, City Councils, and politicians outside of both. Were I to become President of your University, I should be obliged, so soon as I possibly could, to visit every decent High School in Missouri, from which pupils either did or did not come, and to win over their authorities, if possible, to greater or less loyalty. While making these Diocesan visits, I should not fail, as it were accidentally, to meet personally the chief local politicians, and do what I could to impress them with a certain respect for me, my administration, and most of all for the University itself. It would be especially important to know personally, so far as possible, each and every member of each and every legislature."[18]

President Jesse needed the kind of political sixth sense which he so well describes. The agricultural school was still a major problem when the new president took power.[19] Then came the great fire of 1892, which burned down much of the university's physical plant and destroyed the classic argument for the site at Columbia. Meanwhile, another kind of fire—the Farmers' Alliance-Populist movement—had flamed up. A special session of the legislature had majorities of dissatisfied farmers in both houses. Would a "real farmers' school" ever develop in the shadow of the university? For six weeks "the fate of the University hung in the balance." The battle was won for Columbia, only to be renewed when, in 1895, a Republican-Populist fusion controlled the lower house of the legislature and passed a bill to create "three mutually independent schools, the University, the College of Agriculture, and the School of Mines." But then came William Jennings Bryan, a bracing stimulant for unification of the conservatives. Afterward, while there "was plenty of 'sniping' at Jefferson City in later sessions, . . . never again was there the need for determined resistance to the dismemberment of the University or to its removal."[20]

b) Iowa

"As in every other public institution there was the ever-present danger that having freed itself from sectarian control, the College would be dominated by political influence."[21] State administration was in its "dark, benighted days." The spoils system, differences over aims of the college, and absence of organizational support—all made for political difficulties.[22] Much of Iowa State College's history has turned on the question: Is it a "School of Technology," or is it a university with full recognition of the "liberal and practical education" prescribed by the first Morrill Act? Early presidents, particularly Adonijah S. Welch, favored "liberal" education; but most of them knew when to trim their sails, and their interests did not exclude the "agricultural and mechanical arts." The issue figured in the removals of Presidents Welch and Seaman A. Knapp, and it flared in the Populist period.

In 1890 a committee of the Farmers' Alliance visited the college at Ames and consulted with the board. Subsequently, the Alliance attacked the college through Henry Wallace's Homestead.[23] The drift away from the teaching of practical agriculture was criticized; so was the handling of experiment station funds under the Hatch Act. Henry Wallace and "Tama Jim" Wilson, later Secretary of Agriculture, led the Stock Breeders' Association in demanding a "distinctly agricultural and mechanical course in which no place will be found for purely academic and scientific subjects."

In 1891 the Alliance, the Dairymen's Association, the Improved Stock Breeders, and the butter, cheese, and egg associations indorsed resolutions presented by a committee of the Alliance. Among other things, the group demanded and got a new president (Beardshear, the Alliance's candidate), creation of a dairy school, re-establishment of a full agricultural curriculum with a two-year short course, and the appointment of "Tama Jim" as professor of agriculture.[24]

Issues over the objectives of Iowa State College reappeared intermittently.[25] However, Professor Ross, whose wide researches in this area lend much weight to his judgments, declared that "factional, partisan, and personal divisive and disruptive influences, sufficiently pronounced in all conscience, were still not nearly so prominent and determining [in Iowa] as in many other states."[26]

c) Illinois

John Milton Gregory, first president of Illinois Industrial University and a Baptist minister,[27] faced the familiar accusation that the university was a classical college masquerading in false colors. In 1870 delegates of various agricultural societies met in Bloomington "with the avowed purpose of arresting further abuses in the disposition of the University funds, and of having it removed where they might keep a watchful eye over it." Gregory attended the convention and calmly explained the purpose of the Morrill Act as preventing the exclusion of classical studies. The convention then appointed an investigating committee whose report "was a complete vindication of the University"—and a subsequent convention not only adopted the report but "appointed five men to enlist support for the institution. The vindication practically ended the harsher criticism and greatly strengthened the school.[28]

Yet difficulties remained: "From the point of view of administration the college of agriculture had as uneven and dismal a history as from that of enrollment and State confidence." In 1885 the word "Industrial" was dropped from the university's title. The Iowa Homestead remarked that "the sensibilities of the dude students were now cushioned, and that it only remained to substitute for the motto of 'Learning and Labor' the words 'Lavendar and Lilly White.'" But the farmers "who had lost faith in the University in 1885 were much assisted in regaining it in 1887, when plans were promptly drawn up to erect a true agricultural experiment station with the funds carried by the Hatch Act." For several years agricultural societies were to have a dominant role (later advisory) in directing the station.[29]

Financially, agriculture helped the entire university. The legislature had been stingy. Indeed, the "turning point in the University finances

came less through State than through Federal appropriations"—
the Hatch and Second Morrill acts of 1887 and 1890.[30] Other states
had left Illinois behind, but real and continuous recognition began in
Governor Altgeld's administration. Under President Draper, about
the turn of the century, the University of Illinois "passed from a shrinking
pretender to State favor to an institution whose power was recognized
from Chicago to Cairo." Agriculture played a significant role in this.
The year 1900 ended a decade in which from "the weakest division
of the University the agricultural departments came to constitute in
many ways the strongest."[31]

Dean George E. Morrow, whose name is perpetuated in the famous
"Morrow Plots" at Urbana, had resigned. His abilities were ill designed
to advertise the college or to recruit organized support: "Governor
Tanner had stated that someone was required 'who can chase members
of the legislature over a stake and rider fence.'" Dean Eugene Davenport
qualified. He developed new courses, attracted able associates, initiated
a building program, and acquired direction of the experiment station.
A number of agricultural societies were marshaled to help get appropriations. For 1901-3 the legislature granted $108,000 for agricultural
research—the first sizable grant in any state. Other and larger appropriations followed. To the president's dismay, the funds for the station
and the college of agriculture were "set wholly apart from those given
the rest of the University." Each farming interest which had helped gain
the grants shared in an advisory committee to the station: "Thus the
Livestock Breeders' Association was to appoint a committee to offer
advice upon experiments affecting the feeding and marketing of cattle;
the Corn Growers' Association, the Corn Breeders' Association, and the
Grain Dealers' Association were to assist the station in devising experiments upon the best methods of producing corn; the State Farmers'
Institute was to appoint a conference committee upon the analysis of
the soils of the State and their maintenance; the State Horticultural
Society upon experiments for the improvement of orchard treatment;
the Illinois Dairymen's Association upon the investigation and improvement
of dairy conditions; and the Illinois Beet Sugar Growers' Association
upon the investigation of the best methods of beet sugar culture."[32] How
well this illustrates the skilful use of political support! Other groups
(engineers, for example) imitated the farmers. Yet the agricultural

college grew so rapidly after 1900 that the president admitted "in tacit reference to it, that 'the University of Illinois is a one-sided institution.'" But Dean Davenport explained the sturdiness of the growth in that Illinois farmers had determined to make the college of agriculture a leading institution—"special funds were appropriated for each special purpose, and back of each was an organized group of agriculturalists interested in that field; . . . the college was organized with few departments, each with its own funds and a large measure of administrative independence." There had been a "substantial service to State agriculture." Moreover, the group support in agriculture was helpful to the entire university.[33]

d)   Kansas

Since the Populist movement foreshadowed the rural discontent in the 1920's and after, experience in Kansas is extremely interesting.[34] In 1892 Populists and Democrats combined to elect a Populist governor and a favorable senate, but they lost the house to Republicans. Since regents of Kansas State College were appointed by the governor, with senate confirmation, some anxiety was felt in college circles about the views of new board members named by Governor Lewelling. But "rather conservative counsel prevailed," and no one lost his position. The main effect of Populism was to increase the college work in economics, in which, by action of the board, thirteen weekly lectures were required. A full and dispassionate treatment was directed; the lectures, non-partisan, "shall not ignore nor unfairly treat the positions taken by what is commonly known as the new school of political economists. . . . The principles maintained by the advocates of land nationalization, public control of public utilities, and the reform of the financial or monetary systems shall be fairly stated and candidly examined, with a view of leading the students to grasp the principles involved in the science of production and distribution without bias or prejudice." The board, in 1894, brought in Thomas E. Will from Boston as professor of political economy.

In 1897 a fusion-dominated board (Populist and Democrat) demanded the resignations of the entire faculty. Will was made president; but the partisan lines were clearly drawn, and nearly every appraisal of college actions in this period was politically motivated.[35] Nevertheless, J. T. Willard thought that, so far as selection of the faculty proper was con-

cerned, "there is no basis for a charge that party politics had any
important influence. . . . President Will . . . and the Board of Regents
doubtless also, intended that in the members who taught history, sociology, and economics, the point of view that the majority of them held
should be sympathetically presented, but other aspects were not excluded.
The men chosen . . . were scholarly, and while favoring extension of
governmental social control, were not radical in their beliefs. Extreme
views on the money question were not held, and that most typical feature
of populism received little or no advocacy."[36]

Later the board legislated widely and minutely for the college and
issued a "Statement Relative to the Recent Reorganization of the Kansas
State Agricultural College," all without a quorum. Willard characterized
the statement as "a plausible, skilfully expressed, closely knit presentation of truth, half-truth, and error in respect to the past, which can be
analyzed only by one having comprehensive knowledge of the antecedent
facts and circumstances."[37] An effort was made in the days of waning
Populist control to re-enact the "midnight judges" episode by means of
contracts between the board, President Will, and the others—
contracts intended to maintain the faculty, at current salary and in
current positions, until 1901. But a Republican, W. E. Stanley, was now
governor, and he acquiesced to a petition for an investigation of the
board of regents under a law of 1889. Subsequently, removals were made
which brought the board under Republican control. "In view of the charges
of overloading the curriculum with economics, and the faculty with
teachers of economics and sociology," the board now appointed a faculty
committee on revision of the course offerings and requirements. There
was no general faculty review of the committee's findings, which were
in the form of a majority and minority report. The latter (in which
Willard participated) was, on the whole, accepted: "This reduced the
required work in history and political science from nine terms to five,
but the opportunity for choice in electives was increased."

The board also canceled the invitation previously issued to William
Jennings Bryan for the annual commencement address, an action "quite
generally condemned as bad taste, bad tact, and bad business for Manhattan." Next followed the "severance of relations" with President Will
and four colleagues, including Professor Ward. The action "illustrates the
fact that those who support an educational institution will not accord to
a college professor freedom to teach that which tends seriously to contro-

vert their own views. He is on shaky grounds who even discusses as impartially as possible a subject on which there are serious differences of view."[38]

2. Politics Continues

This section might be headed "politics after establishment," on the grounds that land-grant institutions generally had matured quite well, say, by 1915.[39] Thus the University of Wisconsin developed the "Wisconsin Idea" of an institution in service to the state:[40] "By 1910, . . . thirty-five professors . . . were giving part time to some branch of the state service." This work paid dividends in legislative appropriations, e.g., in 1911. Then came the conservative reaction of 1914 and what Pyre called the "notorious Allen 'survey.'" But the university weathered the storm. G. H. Mead remarked: "It is in the study of such incidents that we realize the growth that is going on underneath the surface of society. The University has become a part of the people of the state." Favorable conditions, attending its remarkable expansion, "have merely given it the opportunity of developing. And the unfavorable political conditions of the last year could not materially affect this life and growth."[41]

Not all institutions were thus "established," however—as Allan Nevins noted in describing the fortunate situation that had developed in Illinois: "no one at the University or in the State is apprehensive lest political currents unduly affect the institution. The State has moved beyond the stage at which, as in Oklahoma, the Trustees could wantonly turn on the President and the best faculty men to replace them with arbitrary appointments; or, as in Florida, political pressure and desire for size could drive out an excellent President against the wishes of Trustees and faculty; or as in Kentucky, a President of fine training and intellectual grasp could be replaced by a petty politician."[42] Nevins declared that the natural function of the university is leadership, "and it cannot too thoroughly fulfill it." Nevertheless, state universities may go headlong into activities which endowed institutions develop more cautiously, as Illinois "rushed precipitately into the establishment of a school of commerce." In view of the controversy over the school of commerce of the University of Illinois in 1950-51, these remarks acquire added interest. A major issue was joined within the school of commerce itself, in part over the relative merits of different schools of economic thought; but the struggle also involved certain groups in Illinois politics.[43] Precisely the same kind of phenomenon occurs in conflicts over the role of colleges of agriculture, where the issue is frequently joined within the walls as well as among outside groups.

Furthermore, Illinois experience illuminates the great significance of governing boards in academic controversies. Nevins recorded that the relationships between the board of trustees and the presidency in Illinois had been "altered throughout its history." In early decades a board of unwieldy size fell under the influence of the regent (as the president was then called). In 1887 the board was made elective, whereupon the tables were reversed and the board became unduly influential, until President Draper obtained in 1898 a definition of the board's function: "to obtain the needed revenues for the University, . . . to determine the way in which the funds should be applied; . . . to map out University policy but to leave the execution of that policy to its executive agents." President James continued Draper's policies. A notable tendency emerged for the board "to accept the expert judgment of the President. . . even when it is opposed within the University." Though trustees were nominated by state party conventions, alumni played a quietly effective role in their selection: "Politics have played virtually no part in the proceedings of the Board; on the other hand, sectional affiliations and various economic interests have sometimes played a disagreeable part. . . . The members have usually been very fit, and though nominations may be careless, none is ever wilfully bad. . . . The asylums and charitable interests have sometimes been the football of partisan interests; the normal schools, very seldom; and the State University, never."[44]

In the light of events in 1953 these remarks are ironical. Late in July the board of trustees suddenly voted "no confidence" in George D. Stoddard, who immediately resigned as president of the University of Illinois. Harold (Red) Grange, former football star and one of the regents, made the motion. According to the Chicago Daily News, he had gone "on the board with the backing of downstate politicians to get Stoddard." The Chicago Sun-Times declared: "The Statehouse politicians have been after George D. Stoddard's scalp almost from the very day he took over as President of the University . . . in . . . 1946. After seven years of stalking, . . . the men who want to use the state's university of higher learning for political advantage got him." President Stoddard reported that twenty-one department heads at the university had protested the board's action. The late H. P. Rusk, dean emeritus of the college of agriculture, commented: "There is no question in my mind that politics was involved."[45]

In Kansas the board of regents was replaced by a state board of administration in 1913, supervision of which was extended in 1917 to some twenty institutions (educational, penal, and charitable). The board was appointed by the governor and was subject to his removal, a circumstance (in Willard's opinion) making "grossly partisan action possible." In 1925, a nonpartisan board was provided with supervision over five Kansas educational institutions; it was freed from summary removal by the governor and from senatorial confirmation. Willard's enthusiasm for this arrangement, "the best we have ever had," was dampened by a law of 1939 requiring senatorial confirmation and thus reintroducing "all the disadvantages previously described, in respect to uncertainty of tenure."[46]

The first board of Iowa State College had thirteen members, two ex officio and eleven named from the judicial districts by the legislature for four-year terms. According to Ross: "Selections too often were made for political expediency, especially with the appearance of pressure groups in the farmers' movements." In 1873, following a legislative investigation, the board was reduced to five members, still named by the legislature. But "open and well-nigh scandalous factional divisions and political bargaining" developed, eventuating "in the abrupt change of administration in 1883." So the board was reconstituted in 1884; and, in 1909, a board of education was created to supervise the university, the teachers college, and Iowa State College. The governor chose the nine-member board, of whom three might be alumni of the institutions named. In turn, the board chose a three-member, full-time, salaried finance committee. In 1912 the board directed certain reforms to end "duplication" among the institutions, all three of which fought back. Both candidates for governor repudiated the board's order, and it was withdrawn in 1913, pursuant to a request by a joint session of the legislature. In his final report President R. A. Pearson of Iowa State College (1912-26) praised the "devotion and sacrifice of the Board." But he denounced the finance committee, which (he thought) might well become the real president, replacing the "nominal" chief executive of Iowa State College. Professor Ross wrote: "From their side the Board no doubt found it difficult to view the retiring executive, or either of his fellow executives, in the role of a 'nominal president.' Their records, verified by their

personal experience, made abundantly evident that he had sought tire-
lessly . . . to be every inch a president. The Board had had occasion to
feel, too, that apart from the matters with which ⌈the finance⌉ committee
was concerned the President had not always acted in accord with their
policies and declared desires. While, as the 1915 survey had emphasized,
there were grave difficulties involved in the financial administration,
the differences of issues here presented extended to questions of fundamental policies and jurisdictions quite beyond these concerns."[47]

In view of such experiences, the Survey of 1930 thoughtfully examined
the composition, organization, manner of selection, and role of governing
boards.[48] Forty-five land-grant institutions reported a total of 644
board members. Five of them had boards of from 31 to 50 members:
"These boards are unwieldy." Poor attendance at meetings meant that
a handful of interested members conducted the affairs of the entire
board. Twelve institutions had boards of from 10 to 15 members; twenty,
of from 5 to 10 members, "a far more advantageous number."[49] Of the
total of 644, some 37 per cent were former students in 1928—evidence of
the influence of alumni groups.[50]

Governors enjoyed important roles in selecting board members in
thirty-six states; in three states, members were popularly elected; in
four states, the legislature chose all or part of the board. Agricultural
societies played a formal role in board selection in only two states.[51]

The Survey applauded the terms of five years or more in thirty-one
institutions as assuring "the elimination of political and partisan influence to a considerable degree." But it did not acknowledge the complaint of R. M. Hughes that "there are too many old men."[52] The
Survey's position accords with that of Hughes on the importance of
carefully dilineating the role of governing boards, however; but the
Hughes statement has more precision: "One of the first things that should
be impressed on a new trustee is that he is a trustee and not an executive. The operation of the institution, and the selection of the staff is
the function of the president and faculty. . . . If the president fails to
direct the institution in an effective and satisfactory manner, by all
means replace him as soon as possible. But do not assume any personal
part in the immediate direction of the college."[53]

The Survey combines praise of governing boards with implied criticism.[54] For land-grant institutions as a whole, "a great majority of the
presidents have held their positions for periods less than 10 years. Re-

sponsibility for this situation may be due to the fact that the institutions are public, but frequent changes in the chief executive officer tend to retard the orderly and progressive advancement of the institutions. The office of president of a State higher educational institution should not be a political position and should not be subject to the uncertainties of elective public service."

As public institutions, the land-grant colleges are subject to formal political control from sources other than their governing boards. In 1930 governors were members or presidents of college boards in a score of states, appointed all board members in nineteen states, appointed all members with senatorial approval in twelve states, and appointed some of the members in five states. Governors also had other means of control, especially through the executive budget procedures which were introduced in the movement, beginning about 1910, to reorganize state governments. Some thirty-five land-grant institutions were subject to the jurisdiction of the state budget system; control was mitigated somewhat, however, in that thirty-one of the thirty-five had "the privilege of appearing both before the budget agency and the legislative committees."[55]

The Survey found no uniformity in state control: "In many instances the contacts between the officers of the State governments and the institutions are merely nominal and transitory. In others they represent the routine machinery set up by the State legislature for the expenditure of State appropriations made to the land-grant colleges. In still others, however, the State officials exercise actual control and supervision over certain affairs of the institution which transcend the authority of the institutional governing board."[56]

The Association of Land-Grant Colleges and Universities was conscious of the constraints arising from state administrative control in the 1920's. A. R. Mann, of Cornell, reported in 1923 on a survey of forty-one institutions. Eleven of them enjoyed mill taxes, and twenty-five had lump-sum appropriations. Yet Mann was critical of legislative control. He argued that estimates should be itemized and that the itemization should be used as general guides. But the "injury and hardship arises when the Legislature fails to distinguish between an itemized budget of requests, and the appropriation act."[57] Mann found that the governors or state boards of administration often exercised detailed control over college expenditures.[58]

General interpretations respecting the role of land-grant colleges and universities in intrastate politics will be reserved until the conclusion of chapter ix. Foregoing pages show, however, that these institutions have been often, deeply, and intricately involved in politics since the beginning. Political storms that have beaten around these schools have frequently been brewed by farm spokesmen and fed by rural discontent.

VIII / The Recent Impact of Intrastate Politics
upon Colleges of Agriculture

What kind of intrastate political pressures confront colleges of
agriculture?[1] How strong are these pressures? Who exercises them?
How? And with what effect? What, if anything, can or should be done
about them? These difficult questions demand careful, continuous research into the political facts, state by state. No one can substitute
for responsible college officials and other state leaders in these tasks.
Rather (and ambitiously enough!), this chapter seeks generally to
illuminate the situation in which agricultural research and Extension
operate.

Colleges of agriculture are subjected to influences which are contemporary, pervasive, exacting, and often proximate. The issues to be
described are not remembered and then dismissed in charitable nostalgia;
many of them are still smoldering. They are not the monopoly of any
geographical section. They are reflected in the vigorous demands of
robust group leaders who contribute mightily to the vitality of politics.
And they are immediate, close at hand; sometimes they operate from
offices "just downtown" or even on the campus itself. A regent declared:
"The board is prepared to defend the president and the university from
the winds that blow. But none of the winds come from Washington. They
come from the state house, organized pressure groups, and other local
sources."

The task of describing and appraising political pressures is formidable. The process of politics has been called a "seamless web," stretch-
ing from the citizen in his primary groups to the presidents, judges, and
legislators in their offices. A given example of pressure upon an
agricultural college dean may express the demands of a very small
group or, perhaps, of only one person. At the other extreme, pressures
and counterpressures may include formal organizations (like the Farm
Bureau), members of the governing board, legislators, editors, heads
and members of the colleges' own departments, and larger groups
(usually unorganized and inarticulate) in the general public. This rami-

77

fying, interlocking, continuous human flow and interchange is reproduced more or less faithfully in the observer's mind; but how to record it "as it really is"? In what follows, some violence will be done to the interrelatedness of political reality by focusing upon pressures on the colleges, first from partisan sources, then from statehouse and boardroom, then from within the walls themselves, and finally from various groups.

But politics facilitates as well as inhibits—the land-grant-college system itself is a testament. The founders organized the power and resources of government, state and federal, to establish these institutions. Their inheritors have cultivated the same sources to expand and maintain the land-grant system far beyond anything that private efforts would have produced. Determined and skilful men have even turned political attacks into sources of support. Consequently, the following chapter shifts the focus to the colleges of agriculture as active political forces.

It is even more important to reiterate that political analysis has meaning only in relationship to political philosophy. The risks and possibilities of politics are significant only in terms of human purposes. What philosophical light upon the individual and the community illuminates the role of the college and that of those who operate it? Even more than the final description of their own political situation, this philosophical inquiry is peculiarly the task of the presidents, deans, directors, and professors of the institutions concerned. But no book like this can fail to acknowledge its primacy.

1. Partisan Politics

Partisan politics refers to the political parties—Democratic and Republican in some states; in the other states, factions of the party that enjoys a virtual monopoly or, at least, a clear dominance. Partisan influence upon the colleges is essentially of the state and local variety because political parties in the United States are loose federations of state and local machines.[2]

Partisan politics has influenced many land-grant institutions. Its characteristic southern form has been factional politics within the Democratic party. V. O. Key, Jr., remarked of Alabama:[3] "The State Agricultural Extension Service has a reputation for a more continuous activity in campaigns for Federal and state offices than any other agency." The board of trustees of Alabama Polytechnic Institute (Auburn) laid down a policy proscribing such political activity in 1947; in 1949 Auburn's President Ralph B. Draughon issued a strong statement to all personnel:[4]

"Political activity in the form of support of the candidacy of any individual, or of any partisan issue, by the Alabama Polytechnic Institute or by any of its divisions, schools, or departments is contrary to the express prohibition of such activity by the Board of Trustees in Resolution adopted on November 21, 1947, and duly recorded in the minutes of the Board.

"Further, such political activity by the institution, or any division, school, or department thereof, is deemed harmful to the best interests of the Alabama Polytechnic Institute and harmful to the general educational development of the state.

"Each employee of the Alabama Polytechnic Institute is hereby specifically exempted from any obligation or compulsion to support any candidate or cause when the support of such candidate or cause may be urged or suggested by any other employee of the institution, or division, school, or department thereof."

In another southern state the Democratic party has long been divided into two nearly equal factions. The land-grant college had a governing board which reflected the split in the party. For years the president of the college was supported by a majority of one on the board; when the balance tipped against him, he was summarily discharged. In a third southern state the land-grant college president was said to have two teams, one to support each of the leading rivals in the Democratic gubernatorial primary. The team supporting the winner would then figure in political negotiations during his term, while the losing team retired into relative obscurity. In three other southern states factional politics has sometimes borne down heavily on land-grant institutions.

Outside the South, some predominantly Republican states have occasionally produced factional politics that have caused college officials to walk gingerly. In one, a successful factional leader instituted a sweeping purge of the land-grant college in the 1930's; he was frustrated to a degree by the refusal of the USDA to approve some of his appointments (again, federal grants-in-aid may reinforce educational freedom from political control). In a neighboring state a recent fight between the president and ranking personnel in the college of agriculture eventually cost the president his position; reportedly, the struggle was rooted in factional partisan politics. Wherever partisan politics unsettles land-grant institutions, divisions of the university are strongly motivated to improve their own security by interlocking with their clientele groups. Colleges of agriculture and departments or divisons within them are especially prone to develop their own alliances, largely because of their excellent opportunities to do so.

The introduction of "constitutional boards" has probably helped to free a number of land-grant institutions from factional partisan attacks. Such boards are removed from raids by incoming governors. In Mississippi, for example, a constitutional amendment provided for a board of sixteen members (later reduced to thirteen) appointed by the governor; but the terms are staggered, and each governor can fill only those positions which become vacant during his incumbency.[5] In consequence of the creation of such constitutional boards, factional partisan influence upon certain institutions is said to have vanished. "Our present situation is so happy that I am afraid to pinch myself," said one ranking college official. On the other hand, an equally well-situated observer was less sanguine: "To be sure, the governor's direct partisan control has been legally eliminated. But notice that when Governor ―― was elected, the chairman of the board and enough other members resigned so that the governor could appoint a controlling majority. Furthermore, removal of the governor from direct control may stimulate him to give preference in the budget to other than the state institutions of higher education. In short, there are different ways to skin a cat." The "constitutional board" seems to have improved these situations; but even this institutional arrangement does not obviate the need for statesmen in high positions.

In states where two fairly equal parties confront each other, what is the effect of partisan politics upon land-grant institutions and agricultural colleges? The major problem, involvement in partisan politics through administration of agricultural adjustment programs, has already been interpreted as productive of profound, if indirect, effects upon agricultural research and Extension.[6] Speaking generally, political rivalry between state Democratic and Republican parties does not appear to have posed a serious threat to land-grant institutions; indeed, one is tempted to conclude that the parties have effectively policed each other on this matter. But there are some foreboding signs. In appraising the state of the party battle in December, 1953, Walter Lippmann wrote: "Men do not, men cannot, and men will not collaborate when the political contest of the parties is envenomed to the point where it becomes a war

of political extermination."[7] If the line between the parties becomes an
armed frontier, no public institution can escape the brutal effects. At
the profoundest level of its meaning, the dismissal of President Stoddard
of the University of Illinois was interpreted as a victory for the ultra-
conservative, isolationist, and irreconcilable wing of the Republican party
in Illinois. If this interpretation is correct, its seriousness should be
obvious.[8]

2. Influence of the Statehouse and the Boardroom

Governors can play havoc with educational institutions, or they can
add strength and clarity of purpose to them. The raids by Bilbo in
Mississippi and by Eugene Talmadge in Georgia are well known. It is
important to recognize that subsequent governors in both states led the
effort to establish higher education in greatly increased independence.
Sometimes governors will attempt to use university or college positions
(usually not academic ones) for patronage purposes. Even the presidency
of a state college may become merely a means to pay political debts.
Rarely, a governor may try to dictate the choice of a dean of the college
of agriculture. Recently a governor and a land-grant institution's
president reportedly came to the verge of fisticuffs over this issue.
But, again, governors may strongly support their educational institutions
and may help press them into more vigorous roles, as Governor Greg
Cherry did in the development of an agricultural program for North
Carolina.[9]

Governmental budgets are always significant manifestations of
political influences, representing the decisions of how much the governmental unit will spend and how it will be divided in the next fiscal period.
In one state the governor, an extraordinarily powerful political figure,
strongly preferred welfare, highway, public parks, and other programs over
education. Therefore, educational institutions generally organized drives
to increase state appropriations. A ranking agricultural college official
described the systematic process of recruiting support from all groups
interested in phases of the college's program. Leaders were made
intimately acquainted with the college's contributions and needs in order
to be able to document their demands to the legislature. Charts were
prepared to show that educational employees' salaries ranked well below
those of other states, with roughly comparable economic resources,

including similar per capita incomes. Finally, an executive committee of the agricultural college's clientele groups successfully pressed the financial program on the legislature.

In another state the governor recently won some national acclaim by embarking on an economy program. The legislature, however, granted state institutions of higher education budget increases, partly designed to offset the inflation in living costs, partly to bring up salaries which are widely reported to be "desperately low" in comparison to salaries in states with similar per capita incomes. The governor proposed to veto the budget bill and to call a special session to provide the educational needs.

The institutions were left without funds after July 1, but the governor presumed that they needed no money until school opened in late September! Eventually permitting the budget to pass without his signature, he immediately issued a "request" (really an order) that a certain sum should be saved out of the appropriation. For the agricultural experiment station this meant a cut in the appropriated funds of nearly 23 per cent.

A third state has a "governor's budget," which reflects both the influence that a succession of able governors has established in the legislative process and the effectiveness of a well-organized, ably staffed state budget director's office. An informed university staff member traced the budgeting process, necessarily complicated by the number of claimant groups whose requests had to be reconciled at various stages. Asked whether the land-grant institution ever attempted to appeal from the governor's budget to the legislature, he said, "No; it would hardly be worth while." But it developed that the college of agriculture had a special spokesman in the form of a sort of holding company of the state's farm organizations. This medium has been rather freely used, it is reported, to bypass the governor's budget and appeal directly to the legislature.

What political influence do state legislatures exercise upon public education as manifested by agricultural colleges?[10] Frequently, the term "legislature" refers to a handful of the legislature's controlling officers or to a committee or even to a strategically located individual. President Jesse of the University of Missouri (it will be recalled) acknowledged the necessity of nursing the legislature.[11] Sometimes presidents can be too attentive:

"Furious delegates shouted the president of the University of Mary-

land off the House floor early today, then swiftly killed his last-minute
move for more building funds.

"Bitter resentment over the eleventh-hour lobbying tactics of Dr.
H. C. Byrd welled up into an angry chorus of 'Get out! Get out!' that
forced the official to scamper from the chamber."[12]

On the other hand, college presidents may cultivate such excellent
relationships with legislatures over the years that friction becomes
unknown; but the era of good feeling may have been won at the expense
of the president's failure to fight for funds for an expanding institution.[13]

One of the most prevalent problems of colleges of agriculture is the
legislative earmarking of appropriations. Michigan State College, whose
governing board receives lump-sum appropriations over which it exercises full discretion, is regarded wistfully by many of its sister-institu-
tions. When earmarking is formally eliminated, it may reappear in the
form of "gentlemen's agreements" about the detailed expenditure of
funds.[14] Formal earmarking may be illustrated in a state where the
legislature has minutely itemized its grants, provided that they shall be
divided into quarterly instalments (the unexpended part of which returns
to the treasury instead of continuing to be available), and has created a
special board to approve all expenditures in excess of $1,000 and all
transfers among quarters and items. One year a vital piece of machinery
in the agricultural experiment station broke down. Since there was no
lump sum to draw upon to replace it, college officials had to spend a
great deal of time piecing together a sufficient number of small transfers from various items to make up the money and then get the special
board to approve them all. Ex officio members of this special board,
including the chairmen of the finance committees in each house of the
legislature, find in it a valuable dividend of extra political power. In
another state occurs an example of the tortuous administrative-political
processes that sometimes inhibit officials in land-grant institutions.
Thus a state experiment station director declared that he had virtually
no discretionary authority. On even the most minor personnel appointments, he had to clear through the director of nonacademic personnel
for the university, the university personnel board, the president, and
the board of control. To go through these channels and back required
six weeks. By the time the appointment had been cleared, the prospective employee often had another job. Similar red tape was involved on
any purchase over $100. Research funds were actually (though not

theoretically) earmarked. In addition, quarterly budgeting was required; the station director was forced to itemize on a quarterly basis. He was handicapped in dealing with the USDA respecting federal grants for research which have to be matched at a precise time if annoying technical difficulties are to be avoided. The upshot was that the director was immersed in details and frustrated in his efforts to review his program generally. Furthermore, he was held responsible for prompt action (that "energy" which Hamilton found the most important characteristic of the executive in the Federalist, No. 70) in the event of an outbreak of plant or animal disease; yet he was so hemmed in that he had no free funds to meet such emergencies.

These last remarks fairly point up the significance of strategic individuals, and especially state legislators, in the political situation affecting the college. In political science, one stresses "the presidency," "the governorship," "the legislative process," or "the judicial function"; but one's interviews on political matters are substantially devoted to individuals and their personalities. A college president deplored his personal relationships with the legislature: he wanted them to think of his budget as a financial reflection of the college's institutional function; but they persisted in asking him, "How much do you need?" and saying, "We will give you this much." Many legislatures, of course, have been generous to state institutions of higher education. A rather typical attitude was expressed by a conservative, "self-made" lawyer and veteran chairman of the Ways and Means Committee: "When I was in the House, we built the university and supported President ——, who staffed it; and the young people in this state now have opportunities that I didn't have."

On the other hand, the restrictive influence of individual legislators can be very great. In one state the chairman of a legislative finance committee threatened to cut the entire agricultural college budget unless certain research was dropped; the research was postponed and was later begun again in a modified form. In a second state the chairman of a similar committee brought pressure upon the Extension Service to hire his nephew, who was unqualified for the position in question; the director refused. In a third state a member of the college board of regents occupied a strategic legislative post respecting appropriations and used it to harass the experiment station respecting its research, which, he thought, adversely affected his interests. In a fourth state the chairman-

ship of the legislative subcommittee dealing with appropriations for
education was filled by an enemy of the farm organization with which
the college of agriculture was closely identified—the circumspection
with which college officials moved during the session may easily be
imagined! In a fifth state a college administrator remarked: "One
influential man can get hold of a powerful state legislator and literally
scare hell out of the president."

Like legislatures, governing boards (regents, trustees, state boards
of education) vary significantly from state to state and from time to time
in the same state in the degree of influence they exercise upon the land-
grant institutions and the agricultural colleges. Through their common
oversight of the budget and personnel actions, most boards have potential control of decisions vital to the freedom of the institutions—the
selection, retention, and dismissal of institutional presidents and the
effective scrutiny of the presidents' executive functions. As R. M. Hughes
has stressed, the president-board relationship is crucial.[15] Sometimes
presidents reportedly dominate boards, even to the extent of controlling
their membership (through suggesting nominations). On the other hand,
presidents have occasionally failed so utterly to fulfil their executive
roles that boards have had to administer the institutions in detail. When
a president acts his part, however, the governing board may be developed
into an effective shield behind which the institution can fully realize its
heavy responsibilities. The word may is underlined advisedly; some
boards have listless members; others are precariously divided between
two irreconcilable political factions, so that the best that can be hoped
is that they will neutralize each other; and, finally, one or two members
who are intellectually incapable of understanding the role of modern
state universities can corrupt the function of the board.

Incidents of pressure from an individual board member upon agricultural research or Extension occur less frequently than pressure from
legislators but are not entirely absent: "What worries me about the introduction of an agricultural Extension program in public policy is not the
legislature but the reaction of an extremely conservative member of our
board," said a college official. Most reports are that boards
virtually always accept the president's personnel recommendations.
One board of a famous land-grant institution, however, has inquired into
two prospective appointments and forced the cancellation of one of them
because the candidate was "too New Dealish," it is reported. On the other
hand, a recent attack upon a professor of agricultural economics at the

University of Nebraska was strongly rebuffed: the administration stood staunchly behind the professor, and the board not only dismissed the charges but indorsed a ringing declaration of principle on the subject of academic freedom. [16]

3. Group Political Pressures upon Agricultural Colleges

Many kinds of groups figure in politics. Here the focus is essentially upon formal, organized groups like the state Farm Bureaus, Granges, or Farmers Unions; associations like the Wisconsin Council of Agriculture or the Grange-League-Federation; commodity organizations like the Dairymen's League, the Land-O-Lakes Cooperative, the California Fruit Growers Exchange, the Sugar Cane League, state livestock associations, and a host of others; and organizations stimulated by a common interest in conservation, credit, rural electrification, or farm labor. Business groups are included—fertilizer, feed, seed, and petroleum companies; cattle dealers and dairy handlers; and proprietary interests which may feel threatened by farm co-operatives to which agricultural colleges may be giving aid and comfort. One must avoid overly superficial analyses, of course. The fact that a group's spokesman attempts to influence a college official does not necessarily mean that the members of his organization support him in this particular action; on the other hand, he may speak for allied interests outside his own organization. Most of the time it is probably true that only a handful of insiders will be aware of efforts to bring pressure upon agricultural research or Extension. But whenever there is pressure on a public institution like the college of agriculture, a public explosion may occur. Other organizations may declare themselves in, and large groups of commonly unorganized people may become activated politically. [17] The protean forms of group political action should be kept in mind to place the ensuing discussion in perspective.

The writer knows of no college of agriculture in which some professor has not been subjected to pressure—attempts to get him fired, to silence him on an issue, to force retraction of a publication, to require that a controversial manuscript be reviewed by representatives of an affected interest, or simply to protest enough so that he will think twice before he repeats the "offense." Occasionally, a college official has maintained that such things are unknown to his institution; unfailingly, his statement has been challenged with illustrations by another informed

person. A college dean said (in effect), "Anyone in a position like mine
who tells you that he does not have to deal seriously and often with group
political influence is either very new and inexperienced or is dissembling."

The ubiquity, persistence, and volume of these pressures will be
illustrated, beginning with certain commodities. Information was obtained
in interviews which were held with the understanding that no one would
be quoted in writing or identified without specific permission.[18] Hence
commodities will not be named, even at the cost of a certain air of
unreality in the account. The list does not include tobacco (see chap. vi),
margarine (chap. x), or fluid milk. Nine different states have provided
illustrations of agricultural college involvement in the politics of processing, distributing, and pricing milk or in the tangential politics of
dairy opposition to state laws requiring the enrichment of flour; but no
way has been discovered to use these examples without risking disclosure
of the source.

Commodity A is highly favored by federal legislation. Its spokesmen
have figured in the following situations, according to the writer's information. In one state the group concerned approved the experiment station
bulletins before publication. Some individual researchers who had departed from this procedure lost their jobs. In a second state a similar group
forced a change in an experiment station bulletin touching the commodity.
In two other states relevant organized groups vigorously protested college
research purporting to show that competing commodities had comparative
advantages under current conditions. In one of these an agricultural
economics department which had proudly declared that it would hold to
its course, come what may, was forced to backwater.

In one state, informants said, representatives of commodity B
secured the discharge of two ranking officials of the college and held up
the contract of a third for some time. In a second state the same commodity group was said to dominate the college of agriculture. When the
writer asked for evidence, the reply was: "Look at the background,
training, and careers of every member of the central administration,
and judge for yourself!" In two other states, representatives of the
same group were criticized for the pressure they put on the college
budget: "It has simply meant that other, relatively more important things
in the light of the patterns and trends of farming in this state have had
to be neglected." In another state, like forces prevented a college
inquiry into the operations and effects of public agricultural programs.

In still another state a researcher declared: "I know their power; I do nothing to antagonize them."

Producers of commodity C have been well-known advocates of high price supports. In an earlier frame of mind they wanted guaranties of cost of production. College economists were bitterly attacked for making analyses showing the impracticability of such guaranties. National price policy for this crop is made in the light of its main production in high-risk areas. In another area of low-risk production, however, concentration on this commodity is thought to impede an economically desirable agricultural adjustment. But no research or Extension work has been done on the problem; the colleges are reluctant to move in the face of the anticipated bitter reaction from the organized interest concerned.[19]

Many more commodities are the centers of organized interests which generate political pressure upon agricultural research or Extension from time to time; but other areas of influence need mentioning. Farm co-operatives have long been favored by federal and state laws and assisted by agricultural colleges. A number of state farm bureaus, to whose rise and rapid growth agricultural colleges have notably contributed, have undertaken to establish farm co-operatives. Unlike other general farm organizations, the Farm Bureau begins a venture with one hand and stretches out the other for help from the agricultural college. When the colleges sought to respond, however, with assistance to farm co-operatives created with Farm Bureau sponsorship or otherwise, they frequently incurred the wrath of proprietary businesses. The latter protested sufficiently that Extension Services were officially directed to abstain from assisting established farm co-operatives. If the colleges followed the directive too literally, however, they were sometimes attacked for refusing aid to co-operatives! Knowing the unhappy historical position of many colleges as brokers between these conflicting interests, the writer had still supposed that the growing conservatism of numerous farm co-operative leaders had laid this problem to rest. Interviews in eight states in 1950-51 showed that it is still alive. One Extension director reported his shocking experience in a businessmen's meeting of being accused of aiding and comforting Communists—it finally developed that the complainant had in mind a purchasing and marketing co-operative.

Farm labor problems, especially those concerning migratory labor, are apparently too hot politically for agricultural colleges to handle.

One college official declared that his institution did not feel like risking conflict with the powerful groups involved. In another state a researcher was discharged, reportedly for participating in a minor way in a study of migratory labor.[20] In a number of states farm tenure has been a dangerous subject for college study or Extension work. In the case of one state the writer was told flatly that inquiry into farm tenure or even into the size of farms was impossible. In recent years a courageous and imaginative Extension program to improve tenurial relationships has been conducted in one state; even though it has been considerably facilitated by the improved alternatives for tenants and sharecroppers and the desire in some sections to hold good tenants, the program is still a ticklish one.[21] Some colleges of agriculture in areas for which valley authorities, modeled on the TVA, have been suggested have found the air charged with as much electricity as the dams will ever produce. In several states the firm determination was expressed to refrain from any Extension activity which might conceivably cause identification with the "valley authority crowd."[22]

Finally, consider taxation. As proof that experiment stations can examine controversial issues freely, a college official cited bulletins published in the early 1930's which reported research into the nature and incidence of taxes in his state. Many states published bulletins on these matters during the depression. At the time, the farmer constituency of the agricultural colleges was suffering keenly from inflexible real property taxes; far from being risky, such studies presumably were very popular. But the story is different concerning state sales taxes. In two widely separated states the writer was told of efforts by proponents of state sales taxes to recruit college support in the form of favorable economic analyses. Both overtures were rebuffed—but in ways which cannot be described without risk of disclosing the source.

So much for the kind of issues that become the subject of state and local political influence upon agricultural research and Extension. As has already been suggested, these intrastate political pressures may stem from business interests.[23] One person remarked: "I should like to see you inquire into pressure by fertilizer companies which is bad in some places and often employed so cleverly that some of the college people involved fail to see that they are the victims of propaganda. The final result is bad for the sciences involved, for agriculture, and, most interestingly of all, for the fertilizer industry itself." On numerous campuses the writer raised questions about the influence of fertilizer manufacturers or distributors. In two or three states college officials said that, once significant, it had now disappeared—but that it was still vigorous in other states. In these "other states," however, similar questions brought vehement denials. Fertilizer politics might well be ripe for a searching inquiry if the political temper were different.

Other examples of business pressures upon colleges of agriculture, as drawn from recent interviews, follow. In one state methods have been developed to get supplies of certain experimentally developed seeds into the hands of farmers. The result has been to bypass "normal channels of trade" for perhaps 15 per cent of the supply of this particular seed. Several years' experience suggests that the fraction will not increase substantially, but the college has been attacked as sponsoring "socialism." In another state a similar interest was said to have successfully opposed appointment of a candidate for dean of the college of agriculture because of his reputation as a vigorous enforcement officer of seed laws. In another state, real estate groups strongly objected to college land-classification studies. In another state an analysis of engineering aspects of the road-construction program brought a prompt request from private contractors that the researcher be silenced. The university's retort was that the contractors were welcome to answer the paper in question, if they could. In another state a powerful politician wanted a state marketing facility located in his home town; research indicated that a different location was economically preferable. In spite of the risk inherent in the situation, the researcher was sufficiently strong (and courageous) to release the analysis. In still another state a power company is said to have tried to force changes in a research document which had been completed and scheduled for publication; strong "representations" were made to ranking college officials on the matter, but the researcher stood his ground, and the bulletin was published. In another state the processors of a commodity were so powerful politically that research workers had to retreat from efforts to study processing of the commodity and concentrate on studying its production.

In another state, a corporation approached the experiment station thus: "Here is $_____ for research. All we ask is that you release your findings to us several months before general publication." The station promptly refused, but the writer's informant declared that the corporation soon negotiated successfully with another station.

Certain other characteristics of group pressure upon agricultural colleges are noteworthy. Often intrastate influences upon the college are local. In numerous states some, at least, of the substations of the experiment station are monuments to the effectiveness of county politicians rather than examples of the most economic use of scarce resources. Again, local appropriations for the Extension office and local approval of county Extension personnel provide a fulcrum for control. Some states cope with the situation effectively: Oregon by requiring county moneys to be paid to the college, which expends them; New York by balancing an extremely decentralized Extension system with an alliance at the state level with the New York Conference Board of Farm Organizations; and there are other examples. But in one state the legislature appropriates money for local Extension work while starving the state Extension Service so that it is unable effectively to service the local programs. In another state, until the mid-1930's, when availability of increased federal grants empowered the state Extension Service to deal with the situation, county Extension personnel came very close to being part of the patronage of county political organizations. In another state the Extension director stressed the influence of certain business groups upon the county government, including the county agent's office— "But don't quote me; I have to live with these people."

If pressures come from many sources, they can be directed at physical and biological scientists as well as at economists. Illustrations are at hand of the involvement of soil science, plant and animal pathology, genetics, animal husbandry, agronomy, and engineering in politics. It is useless, however, to try to accumulate evidence enough to convince physical and biological scientists that <u>self-interest</u> urges them to cast their lot with social scientists—as well urge someone who takes an occasional swim in the pool that he runs as much danger from drowning as a coastguardman. There remains the moral appeal to all scientists to stand together in defense of academic freedom, an appeal made gracefully and forcefully by many writers[24] but expressed most eloquently by a city named Hiroshima.

"Pressure groups," "pressures on agricultural colleges"—such usages are anathema to some social scientists, who consider them incitements to prejudice.[25] In politics, as elsewhere, carelessly made moral judgments are often deplorable. A vigorous, driving group political life is a necessary sign of democracy's existence. Nevertheless, the accurate description and analysis of political things is the task of political science; and the term "pressure group" may be more scientific than some more neutral term if it is more descriptive.

Frequently, it is more descriptive: "We've got the Secretary of Agriculture by the short hairs of his chest, and we can move him this way, or we can move him that way!" So shouts a national farm leader in a crowded hotel lobby in Washington, D.C. "We own you, body and soul," says a state farm leader to an agricultural college dean, "and you've got to do what we say." Insisting that a farm product be shown to be superior to its rival, a group leader thunders at a college researcher: "Your job is to prove that butter is better than margarine." In the presence of his administrative superiors, the researcher quietly replies: "My job, sir, is not to prove anything." A paid officer of a farm organization swaggers into an agricultural dean's office, shakes his finger under the dean's nose, and tells him what's what. A harassed official's telephone rings all night during a heated agricultural college controversy; the regular intervals between calls suggest a concerted plan to wear the official down physically.

On the other hand, pressures can be most subtle. People who can bestow social recognition command social power—even more if they can also facilitate professional recognition. An impressive compliment to a man's scholarship may be to offer him funds for a research assistant or two, or it may be enough to help him attend a professional meeting, in the interests of science, of course. A little entertainment on a scale somewhat more lavish than his own budget affords may be most welcome. The writer has been told of photostatic copies of a list of agricultural colleges with tidy sums posted for each. The document represented part of the "public relations" budget of a certain business organization.

4. Conclusions

In many colleges of agriculture officials are rather continuously aware of the scrutiny of various interests. Skirmishes recur, their prevalence depending somewhat on the presence in the staff of an enfant terrible. But major attacks are usually sporadic and often quite infrequent. Meanwhile, most of the college personnel most of the time are probably unaware of the little, continuing frictions and the intermittent skirmishes; many of them hardly consider the possibility of a major engagement, let alone the fact that they themselves may become involved. An agricultural college is something like a political community —with its recognized leaders and some supporters who are continuously alert but also with an internal opposition (real or potential) and a populace the bulk of which is usually indifferent to political issues.[26]

Nevertheless, intrastate politics provide by far the most significant influences upon agricultural research and Extension in the colleges. Group pressures may be obvious, direct, and even brutal—or they may be most subtle and hardly perceptible. Their ubiquity, persistence, and volume have been discussed to stress the fact that they are neither monopolies of any state or region nor matters of only antiquarian interest nor merely negligible.

What are the significant characteristics of interest groups which attempt to influence colleges of agriculture? Groups may have large memberships (several farm bureaus have over one hundred thousand members, and many general state farm organizations have memberships in the scores of thousands). Or they may be small yet effective; on occasion, one large producer who has the ear of a strategic legislator constitutes a formidable influence.[27] Large groups may have many members who are uninformed about stands the organization takes or are indifferent or even antagonistic toward them. Leaders may cynically appear in support of positions that have little discernible relationship to their members' interests, and they may make only feeble efforts to get their members' views. On the other hand, leaders may work vigorously to establish two-way flows of communication in their organization, and they may modify and moderate the demands which many of their members would make if they could. Again, leaders may plead in vain for support of their members, or the latter may rally solidly when the issue is joined. Sometimes the membership will repudiate its leaders on one issue and support them on another;[28] the uncertainty involved lends politics much of its fascination. Nevertheless, two things may be said with some assurance. Through alliances, these interests can add considerably to their pressure potential. And the effectiveness of their demands depends upon their having support of the appropriate persons in government. At the very least, they must present a convincing show to college leaders of having such support—assuming that the latter really want to resist and are not themselves thoroughly identified with the group.[29]

If a genuine disposition to resist political pressure upon research and Extension exists in the college of agriculture, certain institutional devices may be helpful. Constitutional governing boards are noteworthy examples, if they are supplemented by appropriate delineations of functions between the board and the president.[30] Research foundations may be created both to increase finances and to protect research from undue influence from donors,[31] and research policy may be expressly safeguarded in the terms of contracts with donors.[32] The organization of advisory councils and the definition of their role in the budgetary process may improve the college of agriculture in its political position.

Institutional devices like these, however, are not substitutes for human ability and integrity. If they are essential to facilitate statesmanship, they cannot replace it. Furthermore, they are created and maintained by negotiation among the interests concerned in order to bring about certain results from human relationships. Thus a political attack upon one state university prompted a bipartisan meeting which underwrote an agreement to protect the governing board from the kind of political influence that stems directly from electoral changes in the governing party. No doubt research would disclose a similar pattern in many states where such changes have occurred: the concurrence of powerful political interests in reform. The land-grant institution itself, of course, is one of these interests. Behind any major policy the college or university lays down and any relationships it helps to formalize and establish lies negotiation—and, if the negotiators need wisdom and prudence, they must also be backed by power. The stakes may be considerable; and virtually any institutional arrangement is a two-edged sword.[33]

What, then, is the political strength of the land-grant institution and especially of its college of agriculture?

University presidencies and professorships may be springboards to the
highest political appointive offices, to the United States Senate, and even
to the Presidency. The importance of institutions of higher education in
the organized political life of this country is apparent. As members of
land-grant institutions, colleges of agriculture play active political roles
which have their own significant characteristics. Agricultural college
leaders—deans, directors, and department heads—commonly stay long in
their positions of power and influence. "When you call on Dean ———,
remember that you are talking to the real president of this university."
The writer's informant might have added: "And to one of the state's most
influential politicians."

This chapter offers a composite picture of colleges of agriculture
as active political forces. But, if the focus shifts from defense to offense,
the effort is still to help the actors to define their political situation and
to know and appraise their alternatives. A vital part of the political
situation is the college of agriculture itself and the political drive it has.
Surely no other educational institution is interlocked at so many points
with active groups; its departments, its Extension Service, and its sub-
experiment stations often are integrated in the living political process.
The considerable collective political strength of a given agricultural
college is often the sum of the rather independent influence its units possess.
One of the constant dilemmas of free political societies is how to reconcile
the driving interests of individuals and groups with the purposes of the
whole. As a microcosm, the college of agriculture often repeats this
dilemma. Within the land-grant institution and its society, the college
of agriculture has a role of its own to play. If its vigorous subleaders did
not nurse their constituencies, the colleges would be flabby politically
and probably intellectually. As it is, the colleges contain heady mixtures
of capabilities and internal challenges.

1. Educational Politics—Intramural and Interinstitutional

a) The Politics of Appointment

Power politics frequently influences appointments to ranking positions Examples come to mind in private universities, governmental agencies (often including civil service), proprietary businesses, trade associations, professional societies, labor unions, farm organizations, and co-operatives. In the maneuvers to control influential positions only a few "insiders" may be concerned; but often outside interests are involved, especially if the institution is a public one. When a state university president is appointe or dismissed, newspaper and radio comment, letters to the editor, and other signs of widespread interest appear. Agricultural college deanships or Extension directorships are often filled in situations of intense group political activity but with very little public notice.

Discussions of personnel actions affecting high positions in a score of agricultural colleges produced some information about the procedures and politics involved. Particularly on such matters one is painfully conscious of the inadequacies of his information. Here, especially, reticenc is likely to conceal the facts, or bias (perhaps unconscious) to distort them. Nevertheless, politics finds its essence in human interrelationships. Major appointments sometimes show what their makers believe about the balance of power in intrastate farm politics or about trends in the distribution of power. And the same appointments may affect the orientation, the tone, the morale, the emphasis, and the scholarship of the institution for years to come.

In summarizing his impressions on this subject, one must be extraordinarily careful to say neither too much nor too litte. Many top-level vacancies have reportedly been filled by careful canvassing of available persons according to their competence and personal qualities. Often Extension and experiment station directors are advanced from below in the same institution.[1] Consequently, political influences must be searched for early in their careers—and what omniscience would be required to generalize about the multitude of personnel actions, say, at the associate professorial level in agricultural colleges! One may say, of course, that in the sellers' market for agricultural professionals since World War II, competently trained men have been choosing jobs instead of vice versa; and, with due regard to their ability, the speed of the escalators they have found themselves on has been determined probably to an extraordinary degree by chance.

On the other hand, personnel actions involving deans of agricultural colleges, directors of research or Extension and their assistants, and professors often involve politics. Organized groups have been strong enough at times to dictate choices, to prevent removals from office, or even to force dismissals. An organized interest may be unable to dictate a choice but still be strong enough to veto an unacceptable candidate—in one recent example, a numerically small business group was reportedly able to veto the choice of a dean in one of the country's most famous agricultural colleges. Sometimes the ghost of an ancient controversy will rise up to prevent an appointment from being consummated. In situations like these, anyone interested in attaining and retaining a high position is prompted to get solid with the proper influences. Often aspirants and incumbents have built and maintained organizations, including college personnel and outside groups. The result has sometimes been creation of semi-independent fiefs within the college of agriculture or the emergence of the college itself as a fief in the land-grant institution. In consequence, college officials may be closely bound to the interests of their supporting groups; the relationship may be seen in assistance for the college or division or department in its appropriation requests; the reciprocal may be college support of outside group drives for tax concessions, helpful legislation, or administrative favors.

b)   Departmental Autonomy

Closely related to the politics of appointment and similarly significant in explaining the power base of the colleges of agriculture as active political forces is the phenomenon of departmental or divisional autonomy. Earle D. Ross wrote of pressures upon Iowa State College in the 1870's: "These interest groups were most menacing in their combination with factious elements within the institutions. This was more likely in a technical institution, where applied and general subjects were brought together, where traditions were unformed, where a considerable proportion of the staff had backgrounds of practical men of affairs and kept a connection with such groups and interests outside the institutions than in the traditional, like-minded college."[2] Even in Iowa the "combination with factious elements within the institution" recurs (see chap. x below). The practice in several states of Extension personnel serving as secretaries to various commodity organizations probably contributes to the autonomy of departments. So does the approach to appropriations in a number of agricultural colleges. One department

head who wanted more funds for research was told by his experiment
station director to "get himself a pressure group and go to work on the
legislature." In another state the Extension director remarked: "The
temptation is strong to use the commodity groups to press for appropriations even at the expense of earmarking the budget and committing
personnel." In a third state a widely experienced college official said:
"If a college of agriculture has difficulty over a controversial issue, the
source will often be one or more autonomous divisions of the college
which are systematically stirring up trouble with affiliated groups."
He considered this problem to be the most serious one confronting college administrators who are attempting to maintain an operating policy
of free inquiry into controversial matters.

c) Extension-Research Relationships: Co-operation Tempered by Frict

The Smith-Lever Act of 1914, except for a free grant of $10,000 to
each state, required dollar-for-dollar matching of federal funds. Experiment station grants did not have to be matched, and state legislatures were tempted to shift their appropriations to Extension. Total
annual state appropriations for the stations immediately dropped by
$445,000—a decline approximately equal to the sum required for states
to match federal Extension grants. State funds for experiment stations
did not regain their 1914 level until 1918; meanwhile, appropriations
for Extension had markedly increased.[3] There was an 80 per cent turn-
over of the technical personnel of experiment stations in 1914-19.[4]
Experiment station directors testified to the unsatisfactory state of
station affairs. Of the twenty or more directors assuming positions
in 1920-22: "Far too few found records to contain definite programs of
work to give them intelligent grasp of present scope and policies."[5]

In 1926 H. W. Mumford advocated closer Extension-station relationships but noted that "extension specialists have been known to carry on
their work so independently that they were unaware of the investigations
in their own institutions which threw light on the questions asked by
farmers." He cited an Illinois county agent who replied, to a query
about what the station was doing, that it "had nothing important to
contribute to the subject" and that it was "asleep at the switch." Yet
the station had been working on the subject in question for five years,
with useful results. In consequence, conferences were held between
the station and the Extension Service, and the experiment station project
book for Illinois was developed.[6]

In 1941 T. W. Schultz and L. W. Witt reported that only twenty-four of forty-eight institutions had integrated agricultural economic research and Extension. In nineteen institutions, resident teaching and research were combined, but Extension economics remained separate. This was a "major weakness." Where the work was separated, Extension economists failed to keep up with their professional field; experiment station workers, to keep abreast of developments in the state. Where integration had been achieved, joint appointments mitigated these faults; elsewhere, Extension economics was "distinctly inferior in its design and scope"; it was "frequently promotional and occasionally propagandistic in character."[7]

Rivalry between Extension and research still manifested itself in recent years. Many land-grant institutions have made their agricultural college deans also directors of Extension and the experiment station; associate directors are then appointed for each of the latter. Extension directors often are critical of this development: "The job is too big for one man to handle, and the man in charge of Extension needs the authority which only a full directorship can give." Occasionally, an Extension director criticizes the theoretical (therefore, impractical) nature of experiment station work. Experiment station personnel sometimes retort that Extension is not sufficiently scientific. The tendency of many Extension Services to promote from the ranks is deplored. Conceding that Extension's morale may gain thereby, the critics argue that the costs are still too great—costs in the relative downgrading of Extension worker's educational attainments and the provincialism and clannishness that this induces.[8] It may, of course, be argued that high morale and even a certain amount of clannishness and provincialism are valuable qualities in an agency upon which the whole institution may have to rely for its legislative appropriation. On the other hand, it must be stressed that an increasing number of land-grant institutions are working toward a more effective integration of Extension and research through joint appointments in the several departments, rotating assignments, and conferences.[9]

Behind the occasional failure effectively to integrate Extension into colleges of agriculture is Extension's power, often reinforced by the Farm Bureau. If a group is organized, it has power in proportion to the members' willingness to stick together and to support each other—as well, of course, as to the skill with which this willingness is trained,

marshaled, deployed, and led. In their state, district, and county staff,
Extension Services have the nuclei of power organizations which, in turn,
are usually reinforced by the groups and associations that Extension serv
In most relationships between Extension directors and county agents,
"superordination and subordination" do not exist; but a healthy reciproca.
understanding obtains of the good or ill each can do the other. Strong
systems of personal loyalty and of informal communication characterize
Extension Services. The writer knows of only one experiment station
official (not a director) who challenged the college leadership in recent
years, and he was promptly dismissed. In at least half-a-dozen states,
on the other hand, Extension has been able to win or (more frequently) to
prevent showdowns with the central administration. Sometimes, of course
college deans, rather than Extension directors, are the effective leaders
of Extension Services as power organizations.

d)   The Politics of Publicly Supported Higher Education

The primary questions included under this subheading concern the
most fundamental characteristics of universities and colleges which are
supported by taxes. Are their presidents, deans, and major professors gr
educators? Are they, indeed, prototypes of the "American character" at i
best? Or do they reflect merely a desire for efficient administrators and
an insistence upon men whose main qualities in the field of ideas is that
they have never harbored any unusual ones? What is the orientation—and
reputation—of the institution on such matters as scholarship, service to
the commonwealth, and academic freedom? These are the highest politica.
questions touching universities and colleges; but at present we are seekir
to understand the power politics involved—especially who gets how much
of the appropriations.

In the power politics of higher education in many states, agricultural
colleges play significant roles. Again, the occasional autonomy and even
intransigence of the colleges as political entities need stressing. One doe
not summon a power organization to straighten out the legislature as he
calls in a plumber to fix a leak. In one state the writer heard a detailed
description of the major campaign of the Extension Service to remove the
institution's president by packing the governing board against him (as it
turned out, the presidency became vacant, so that the maneuver was not
a decisive test of Extension's power). In a second state a major reorgani
zation of the governance of higher education was described as an effort

to limit the power of the college of agriculture to write its own appropriations ticket, an effort which had clearly failed in the light of subsequent distribution of funds to agriculture. In a third state, with a population one-fifth "rural farm" in 1950, three-fourths of that year's appropriation for the state university went to the college of agriculture. In a trial of strength between the dean of agriculture and the president, the latter lost. In a fourth state an effort by the president of the institution to discharge the heads of agricultural research and Extension failed so completely that the president himself felt obliged to resign. In a fifth state a ranking official of the land-grant college bitterly complained that elements in the college of agriculture at the behest of a powerful commodity group had quietly supported appropriations for an elaborate building on the state fairgrounds; in view of his institution's acute need for funds, he considered this expenditure unconscionable. In a sixth state the complex process of consolidating and reviewing the budget for all state-financed higher education was described; but the special institutional means enjoyed by the college of agriculture of appealing over the boards and commissions to the appropriating committees in the legislature was also confirmed in several interviews.

Apparently some agricultural colleges help the financial quest of the land-grant institution as a whole. In one state an informant remarked: "If the administration believes that a new stadium is needed, word goes out to the county agents, who get to work through their numerous county and local groups to stir up favorable sentiment." And in another state new buildings named "Agricultural Chemistry" and "4-H Club and Student Activities" were pointed out: the former did have a few agricultural chemistry offices on one floor, and the latter was primarily a field house; but the names of both buildings were symbolically useful in getting the money. In nineteen states the physical separation of land-grant institutions from state universities places the two in competition for legislative favors.[10] The state university often reaps an advantage from its law-school graduates, who typically make up powerful blocs in the legislature. Consequently, the Extension Service (sometimes reinforced by the outlying substations of the experiment station) may support appropriations not only for the college of agriculture but also for the entire agricultural and mechanical school.[11]

The upshot is that a premium is placed upon the colleges of agriculture as political organizations—as centers of systems of influence, at least, for purposes of obtaining appropriations. The systems of influence include especially the state farm bureaus but also other organizations, particularly commodity groups, in varying patterns in different states. More recently, however, a movement has developed to institutionalize the advisory—and supportive—relationship of organized agriculture to the college, especially respecting the budget.

2. The Advisory Council Movement

The Office of Experiment Stations (OES) reported in 1952 that three-fourths of the states have standing committees representing producer groups and commodity and consumer interests meeting regularly to advise with station officials on research. Over half the states had "an over-all advisory council" tending to co-ordinate the advisory committees and to help general program formulation. At least five other states were creating similar councils.[12] The writer doubts that "consumer interests" are effectively represented in advisory committees to agricultural experiment stations, as the OES implied. But the movement has mushroomed recently.

It began much earlier, however. In 1901 Dean Eugene C. Davenport of the Illinois college of agriculture obtained the first sizable state legislative appropriation for agricultural research by systematically mobilizing commodity group support.[13] In New York the milk strike of 1919 prompted editor Eastman of American Agriculture to propose an organization to defend farm interests. The state Grange, the farm bureau, the horticultural society, and the Dairymen's League (the country's larges fluid-milk co-operative) and others created the New York Conference Board of Farm Organizations, a powerful body in the Empire State (when it can achieve the unanimity which its charter requires). The Conference Board is especially helpful in the cause of appropriations for the college of agriculture. The secretary of the New York Farm Bureau is also secretary of the Conference Board. California developed an agricultural council in 1921, probably suggested by the New York Conference Board. It includes general farm organizations (especially the Farm Bureau) but is largely organized by commodity interests. Apparently, the council minutely scrutinized budget proposals in the 1920's but has played a general advisory role in recent years.[14]

The present movement apparently began in 1944-45 with action by

Florida, Montana, North Carolina, and Oregon, followed by Idaho, Kansas, Michigan, and Missouri[15] in 1947-48 and by Ohio and Minnesota in 1949-50. Washington's Institute of Agricultural Sciences was also created during these years. Thus in some fifteen states, to the writer's knowledge, some kind of systematic advisory relationship existed in 1952, usually respecting the experiment station's program and budget, sometimes with broader responsibilities. In five other states spokesmen were rather strongly opposed to establishing similar councils.

Experience of states with advisory councils is difficult to appraise. Among the earlier ones, Dean Davenport's system of commodity groups was invaluable in establishing appropriations for agricultural research in Illinois; in New York the Conference Board has apparently strengthened other considerable advantages of the college of agriculture in the legislature (an informed observer believes that 90 per cent of the Conference Board's legislative requests have been granted).[16] Respecting the more recent batch of councils, in some states increased appropriations have been attributed in considerable part to them; they are sometimes credited with inducing the research staff to think more systematically about research programs; and occasionally they are said to have caused special group demands to be weighed against the needs of each other, so that a more programmatic review of research emerges. Many are hopeful that the councils will spread group support more evenly, so that departments like those of economics and rural sociology will not continue at great disadvantage compared to those of dairy industry, agronomy, and animal husbandry and others with heavy clientele support. On the other hand, some critics believe that the councils simply institutionalize log-rolling, so that groups are facilitated in piling demand upon demand until the legislature rebels. Critics also object that the creation of formal advisory councils will prompt the inference that advice will be rigorously followed; or they argue that, since it is impossible to include all groups, those included will presume that they have a special entree and those left out will be disaffected.[17]

Along with the numerous committees that have been created to advise the administration of the Research and Marketing Act, the state advisory councils sharpen the issue over the proper relationship of lay groups to research. W. C. Coffey (then dean of Minnesota's college of agriculture) remarked: "In these four splendid and historic addresses delivered by

the grand old stalwarts, Kerr, Davenport, Bryan, and Thompson, in
our meeting two years ago, we caught their conviction that a great
achievement of the experiment station, and perhaps the greatest, has
been to bring farmers and scientists together to make the farmers
science-minded and the scientists farmer-minded."[18] Many would
agree in general terms. One group says, however, that, while lay control
is essential, it should be institutionalized in ordinary political channels
and reduced to deciding how much to invest in research and to holding
researchers responsible for results. This group opposes the use of
advisory committees, either by the RMA or by state colleges of
agriculture. Its spokesman says: "They can't grasp the importance
of determining what goes on in a cow's stomach or of the effect of
minute differences in feeding upon the livers of several generations of
mice. Had such a committee watched the experiments that led to hybrid
seed corn and noticed the kernels getting smaller year by year, they
would have urged that the research be stopped."

Opinion on the other side holds that lay advice is probably inevitable,
that it is better to institutionalize it than to let it emerge spontaneously
(to require it to accept some responsibility along with power), and that
it can have a healthful effect upon research programs. There is, of
course, a large body of opinion which is not violently pro or con. One
says: "The RMA committees and the state agricultural councils are
exasperating, but they are learning. One beneficial effect is to teach
politically influential people that research cannot be ordered like a
ham sandwich."

Weighing these arguments, the writer tentatively favors broadly representative, advisory councils. They are in keeping with the secular rise
in the intermingling of governmental functions in economic and social
life, the increasing ramification of communication systems and ease of
movement, the continued organization of group interests, and emergent
theories of the role of public opinion.

At the same time, research and education (whether publicly or
privately financed) stand above all other temporal social functions in
their need to be free and untrammeled. Consequently, the warnings of
the critics of advisory councils should be carefully heeded. Councils
should be advisory—not minatory—to the research and educational function
Details and refinements of experiments should be made known not in an

atmosphere of "Should we do this?" but as part of an enunciated intention
to afford the council at least a glimpse into the depths of modern scientific methods. And what is the advisory function? It is to suggest where
the shoe pinches, what problems need exploring, and, possibly, an order
of priority. But, in the age that has witnessed nuclear fission and its
first fruits, surely the advisory function should rise to the exploration of
philosophical problems. What obligations are imposed upon science by
human nature in its potentialities for good and evil? Rather than in some
phrase embodying their beloved "enlightened self-interest," the councils
might find a motto in Edmund Burke's words: "Society is, indeed, a
contract . . . but the state ought not to be considered as nothing better
than a partnership agreement in a trade of pepper and coffee, calico or
tobacco . . . to be taken up for a little temporary interest, and to be
dissolved by the fancy of the parties. It is to be looked on with other
reverence; because it is not a partnership in things subservient only
to the gross animal existence of a temporary and perishable nature. It
is a partnership in all science, a partnership in all art, a partnership in
every virtue and in all perfection. As the ends of such a partnership cannot
be obtained in many generations, it becomes a partnership not only between
those who are living, but between those who are living, those who are dead,
and those who are to be born."[19]

The questions whether to have advisory councils, what relationships
to establish with them, and what orientations to give them are political.
That is, they are made by human beings as conscious adjustments among
the goals they seek, the means they command, and the constraints they
feel. The fact that the choices are political is congenial to the conciliar
movement, both in its origins and in the organizational form it takes.

Dean Davenport's original operation in Illinois was a frank recruitment of group influence in the legislature. The New York Conference
Board was formed explicitly to safeguard farm political interests. These
are the prototypes. In more recent years the formation of a council in
one state was attributed to commodity groups which had failed by themselves to secure legislative grants; therefore, they banded together to
make a stronger organization. In another state, a serious laggard in
appropriations for agriculture according to its per capita income, the
Farm Bureau and the college combine to create a council. In a third
state the council was formed when agricultural groups became conscious
of growing competition for the legislative dollar. In a fourth state the

council can be explained in part as a considered attempt to balance
three or four somewhat antagonistic political groups.

In the manner of organization of state councils, political power is
recognized. In several states presidents and secretaries of commodity
and general farm organizations are members (in law or in fact). In
others, the councils are set up by commodity areas rather than by
organizations (so they say), but the rosters of council members corre-
spond to lists of the most influential men in agriculture in these states.
Frequently, influential legislators are also on the agricultural councils.
Beyond these observations, the form and organization of the councils
vary considerably. Idaho has twelve members; but Washington has
eighty farm organizations represented (though an executive committee
of nine members exists). North Dakota has a state executive committee
which co-opts council members from nominees made by the county
agricultural councils (the result is said to balance the two general farm
organizations and the two wings of the Republican party). In Kansas
the council does not include representatives of general farm organizations as such; but this appears exceptional. Except in Montana, to the
writer's knowledge, no state council which formally includes general
farm organization representatives has a member of the Farmers Union.

Both in origin and development, the recent councils reflect the
reaction to the sharpened competition for legislative favors incident to
the rapid growth of political organization and the rising demands for,
and cost of, governmental services. This means that the analysis can
break out of educational politics and follow the activities of agricultural
colleges into the more general issues and alignments in the several
states.

3.   The Politics of Issues, Alignments, and Relationships

This section will show the involvement of colleges of agriculture
in the political affairs of their states—not just as interest groups in the
competition for appropriations but as participants in the most obvious[20]
political actions, like the passage of legislation or the building of
political organizations. The central focus of this book remains, of
course, upon agricultural research and education as they deal with controversial issues. This is still assumed to be the colleges' most significant political activity; but further appraisal of it must wait upon a fuller

portrayal of the colleges as participants in politics.

a) Specific Issues

The farmer constituencies of colleges of agriculture have taken sides in a wide range of issues. As sellers, farmers have been interested in market regulation. Milk provides the most common example, with some sixteen state milk control laws in 1951, in addition to federal milk-marketing orders under the Agricultural Marketing Agreements Act of 1937. Controversial issues in milk marketing include classification of milk according to its uses, price levels for different uses, differentials for different forms of delivery of milk to consumers (if retail prices are fixed), alternative plans for organizing particular milk markets, provision of premiums for evening up production throughout the year, representation of interests on the control board, the inspection and qualification of farms as producers for the fluid-milk market, and so on. Other dairy issues involve the regulation of the production and sale of margarine and of filled milk and legal requirement of the enrichment of flour according to certain standards. The marketing of some other commodities, especially fruits and vegetables, has created issues in state politics. As producers, farmers have been interested in the cost of the factors of production and in the quality of the factors. States have passed laws regulating the sale of fertilizers and seeds and providing for the incorporation of farmers' purchasing and marketing co-operatives. Other issues include public policy respecting migratory labor; flood control, reclamation, and the regulation of the development and use of water resources generally; and taxes, schools, and roads.

Agricultural colleges have been involved in all the kinds of issues mentioned. True, involvement has sometimes meant only that a member of the college faculty has helped analyze issues and draft proposals for legislation; but such actions often carry over into negotiation and other aspects of agreement and enactment. Even if the faculty member is on leave for this work, he remains identified with the college. Again, contro-versy has arisen over college administration of research in hybrid seed corn and the development of improved pasture seeds, including provision for testing under farm conditions and some distribution of the product; and land-classifying projects of agricultural colleges have been vehement-ly opposed because of their effect upon assessment of farm real estate for tax purposes.

When controversies of interest to their clientele have arisen, many college officials have answered calls for help as a matter of course. In subsequent interviews, a few have been frankly partisan, as in the case of one professor who said: "Sure, you can process any old fat into some kind of a spread for bread. But God made butter yellow!" Most interviews on the subject, however, have recorded a painful consciousness of the difficulties and dilemmas of college workers in such situations. They have felt an obligation to serve; they have tried to be scrupulously honest, as scientists and according to their lights; often, however, they have not been able to avoid censure as partisans. And the censure is frequently projected from the individual involved to the institution he serves.

Sometimes the censure is deserved;[21] often it is not. But the point is that colleges of agriculture become involved, probably to unusual degrees, in a wide range of controversial public issues. Some of these are essentially between specialized, but politically powerful, interests, such as proprietary handlers, dealers, manufacturers, or distributors, on the one hand, and co-operatives on the other. But some issues, e.g., those arising around milk or margarine, potentially involve very large parts of the public.

<u>b</u>)   Relationships and Alignments: The Farm Bureau and Others

Among alliances between public agencies and private groups, the farm bureau-Extension relationship is of great interest. In 1953 it continued to rest in part on statute laws in a few states (especially in Illinois, Iowa, and New York); but it finds sufficient basis in formal or informal understanding in more than a score of other states as well. Economically, socially, and politically, the arrangement is mutually felt to be too advantageous to be lightly thrust aside. True enough, farm bureaus have generated great pressures upon agricultural research and Extension in many states; but they have also provided valuable political support to colleges of agriculture, in Washington as well as in state capitals. Numerous state agricultural Extension Services continue to show a deep concern for the success of the farm bureaus in recruiting members. College leaders often diverge, more or less vehemently, from farm bureau leaders on important issues; but very often the two agree—and it must not be forgotten that the political interests of the college often coincide closely with those of the farm bureau. As in family relationships generally, members feel free to criticize one another; but they bristle when an "outsider" joins in. A shared feeling exists among what Gabriel Almond calls the "attentive public" that state agricultural Extension Services and farm bureaus are intimately associated; the belief is fairly borne out by the facts.

A similar intimacy between colleges of agriculture and other general farm organizations is highly exceptional. State farm bureaus seek college services promptly, vigorously, often, and as matters of course and of right; on the contrary, state Granges exhibit attitudes toward agricultural colleges that range from mildly co-operative to indifferent; and state Farmers Unions, from indifferent to antagonistic.[22]

On the other hand, commodity groups in sugar cane, sugar beets, livestock, cotton, potatoes, tobacco, fruits and vegetables, and so on, are characteristically close in their association with agricultural colleges; their intricate research problems involve them with the experiment station; their marketing problems, with the Extension Service. Prominent college officials have at times been closely identified with such commodity interests, helping them to organize, to draft programs, and to formulate legislative proposals.

In the early 1920's the late H. E. Babcock, one of modern agriculture's most celebrated figures, was able to marshal the resources of the New York agricultural Extension Service, of which he had been county agent leader, in support of the fledgling Grange-League-Federation. The latter organization made its mark under Babcock's general managership, and it has never lost its close association with Cornell. In a number of other states, councils of agricultural co-operatives trace their origins, in part, to agricultural college leaders.

So agricultural colleges have contributed to the political organization of society, for both the farm bureaus and the commodity groups are active political interests. Their positions on numerous controversial questions form important parts of the political calculus in state after state. And, in stressing the close association of the college with such groups, another of its aspects as a positive force in state politics has been underlined.

c) General Issues of Major Public Importance

Attention now centers upon certain foremost political problems: decentralization of governmental functions to the states; the underrepresentation of urban areas in legislatures; and (what the writer believes to be) the growing antagonism between organized agriculture and organized labor. Profound challenges to the American constitutional system and its democratic political processes flow from such issues. Presumably, American educational institutions, including agricultural colleges, share heavily in the obligation to assist in their peaceful resolution or amelioration.

Political decentralization is a classic American political ideal which the Eisenhower administration has made a major theme. The proposal falls happily upon the ears of most farm leaders and their allies. The Farm Bureau, after having (perhaps in a "fit of absent-mindedness") contributed heavily to the centralization of government as exemplified in the economic control and support of agriculture, now calls for decentralization. As state institutions, agricultural colleges have long advocated the transfer of federal agricultural "educational" activities to themselves. Presumably, not all federal functions even in agriculture are to be decentralized—one can hardly conceive of forty-eight Commodity Credit Corporations. We cannot debate the substantive issues here; but the possibility should be noticed that farm interests, including agricultural colleges, in their anxiety to wrest certain functions from the USDA will become allied with other interests bent on decentralizing other governmental functions. Offshore oil has already been given to the coastal states. Other issues are ownership of public lands, including national forests; the regulation of natural resources, including grazing, timber-cutting, and the exploration for and exploitation of minerals; development of natural resources, including water power (specifically, governmental rate and distribution policy); federal financial assistance to local governmental, co-operative, or private enterprises in housing, hospitals, and other fields; social security; the regulation of business practices, labor-union activities, and labor-management relationships; and the ratification of foreign policy. Aside from analysis of each of these as substantive issues, absorbing questions emerge for the college as a political interest. Is it appropriate for agricultural colleges to roll logs with other interests to get what they want decentralized? If appropriate, is it expedient? If it is neither, can agricultural colleges escape identification with the allied decentralizing interests, which include many of the closely associated farm organizations?

Political decentralization is frequently advertised as "giving government back to the people"; but what people? The combination of controlling interests and the institutional devices by which they achieve and employ

power varies, of course, from state to state.[23] But a prime and persistent element in the intrastate division of political power is the underrepresentation of the larger urban areas in state legislatures. In California,
Los Angeles, with 2,780,000 people in the 1940 census, had one state
senator; so did Inyo and Mono counties, which had a total population of
9,900. Hartford, Connecticut, with 116,000, had the same number of
state representatives as Colebrook, with 547. Portland, Oregon, gained
230 per cent in population in 1910-50 but received no increased apportion-
ment in the legislature; one state senator from Portland represented
81,000 people; at a near-by desk sat a senator representing 7,200. Other
underrepresented cities include New York, Chicago, St. Louis, Detroit,
Birmingham, Tulsa, New Orleans, Minneapolis, St. Paul, and Baltimore.[24]

There is nothing funny about this situation. Since Aristotle examined
the causes of revolution in governments in the fifth book of the Politics,
analysts have stressed the dangers inherent in constitutions which fail
to adjust to sharp shifts in social power. For us, these dangers may be
compounded if governmental functions and decisions are freely transferred
to the states regardless of the states' ability to handle them to the satisfaction of the great potential political interests largely in metropolitan
centers. Agricultural statesmen, including college leaders, should note
that spokesmen of these emergent interests vehemently complain of the
rural domination of state legislatures. The United States Conference of
Mayors, representing cities with populations of fifty thousand and over, has
estimated that "in the nation as a whole 75 per cent of the state legislative seats are allocated to the 41 per cent of the population which is
rural."[25] Standard textbooks in political science maintain this theme:
"As matters stand, nearly all legislatures are rurally-controlled";[26]
"The rural control of our legislatures has given rise to what has often
been called the American rotten-borough system."[27] Rather than to use
the term "rural control," it would be more accurate to describe state
legislatures as dominated by antimetropolitan complexes; but the general
indictment must stand.

Among the metropolitan interests underrepresented in state legislatures is organized labor. V. O. Key, Jr., has written: "The remarkable
uniformity with which the Farm Bureau has taken an early and aggressive
position on antilabor measures in the states of the South suggests the

desirability of a full-dress inquiry, empowered to compel testimony and subpoena documents, to determine the nature of the nexus between the Farm Bureau hierarchy and those interested in such legislation."[28] This statement of a foremost authority on politics deserves the respectful attention of agricultural college leaders.

The phenomenon is not confined to the South. In 1920 the Massachusetts state Farm Bureau agreed to support a bill, wanted by the Federated Industries of Massachusetts, for a state police "to put down strikers." In return, the industries agreed "not to push Daylight Saving."[29] More recently, in two other northern states, campaigns have reportedly rebuffed efforts by union labor to organize dairy farmers; the campaigns were led by farm organizations, which are closely associated with colleges of agriculture.

Observations have been made to the writer that farm organization drives to enrol the "marginal" member often play upon farmers' fear and distrust of labor unions. On the other hand, many agricultural colleges are becoming sensitive to another aspect of farmer-labor union relationships. "Fringe" developments around factory cities and towns find union members moving out to small farms, from which they commute to work—and call for help from the county agent. If enough of them move out, they may upset the balance in some state legislatures! And certainly they represent a serious challenge to Extension and to the college of agriculture, which are obligated to assist all rural people but are commonly neither organized nor oriented to serve the kind of operations represented in fringe developments. This is not the place for a systematic examination of farm-labor political relationships, however; the concern here is only to point to the prima facie evidence of growing friction between organized labor and those farm groups with which the agricultural college is closely identified in the public mind.

Again the introductory note of this book has been sounded: a study of the influence of politics upon agricultural research and Extension must begin by recognizing that the colleges of agriculture are political interests. They have their own heavy commitments, and they take on additional political coloration from the interests of their allies among farm groups—and sometimes from other interests with which their allies are associated. The more one ponders this political involvement the more significant it becomes in evaluating the present and potential roles of agricultural colleges in illuminating controversial issues.

4. Conclusions

No ivory towers exist for agricultural researchers and Extension
workers on the public payroll. For them, academic freedom is not a
moat but a shield and buckler which they themselves must largely fashion
and keep in repair. As with the ancient Spartans, their walls are in their
own wills and abilities to resist and, indeed, to turn resistance into
attack. To write less symbolically: the immersion of agricultural colleges
in politics notably affects their orientation toward controversial matters,
the strength they have in attacking them, and the restraints they may feel
in the face of them.

Beyond academic curiosity, agricultural college workers are
prompted to examine some controversial issues by the pricks of interest,
their own and their constituents'. Let farm prices or the farmer's share
of the consumer's dollar fall rapidly, and the commodity interests
concerned will demand an explanation, at least, and perhaps a program to
counter the trend. College interests are prods to the same activities, from
the obvious ones arising from the fact that many college professors
grow the same commodities on their own farms to the more subtle interests
arising from the integration of the college into its constituency; the expectations funnel in upon the college with an almost physical impact. As they
are fulfilled, individual and institutional prestige rise. And few induce-
ments exist stronger than the glittering promise of "reputation." On the
other hand, the network of continuous interaction between the colleges and
their clientele may dampen the researchers' ardor. Some farm interests
are always hanging "no trespassing" signs on certain problems; and their
proximity to the college facilitates their discerning the approach of an
unwary researcher to the posted area.

Other interests, however, impinge upon the college. Few will expect
tax-supported agricultural researchers to trample on their clients' toes—
for example, by criticizing a market-control law which their own faculty
colleagues have helped commodity groups to draft. Some frontal attacks
are made on just such problems by agricultural colleges (see chap. x);
more frequently, and perhaps more judiciously, college workers manage
to tack against the winds of opposition. But the price of intimacy is identification, and the college cannot escape it. If tensions rise between the

cities, on the one hand, and the small-town, rural complex, on the other, or if friction increases between organized agriculture and organized labor—then the difficulty of the college of agriculture in confronting controversial issues will grow, for its obligation to deal with such issues presumably varies in direct proportion to their seriousness, and so does its tendency to identify (and to be identified) with one party to the controversy.

Potentially, the strength of the agricultural colleges and the land-grant institutions is very great, though seldom fully realized. Their inherent power has been recently demonstrated in the quick, thorough, and profitable establishment of agricultural advisory councils in certain states. Consider the following ideal or model.

Suppose that the land-grant institution and the college of agriculture lay down clear policies (1) to maintain academic freedom, liberally and broadly defined, and (2) to fulfil the obligation of the college to illuminate controversial issues (see chap. xi). Suppose, further, that these policies are communicated clearly to all departments, including sub-experiment stations and Extension field offices of the agricultural college—are communicated in an informal system which is strengthened, first, by a reciprocal confidence that each point in it is being kept fully informed by every other point and, second, by a common understanding of the same things by the same terms. Grant, further (and the foregoing would be impossible without it), that the entire college is ably led and staffed, so that in every department and activity its members are very highly regarded by their clientele. Then imagine that a controversial issue breaks out, and one or more college personnel speak or write about it (and not necessarily in agreement with one another) in a way that calls down political wrath. Formidable powers of resistance now come into play. Led by the president and supported by the entire institution, its own morale heightened, its thousand lines of communication crackling, the college is able to promote and defend its right to study, report, publish, and teach on any controversial subject.

Total mobilization in such ideal terms is doubtless out of reach. The perception of the goal may be clear and the purpose firm; yet achievement will be blunted somewhat by the inevitable indifference among the faculty and staff. "Let me alone!"—all politicans must become inured to that heartfelt cry, and educational politicians have a little extra burden in

the self-righteous smugness that seems to go with the political indifference
of Ph.D's. Furthermore, colleges of agriculture are commonly hampered
in achieving their political potentials by Trojan horses, perhaps in
several departments, for the colleges tend to splinter into commodity
interests, many of them rooted in powerful constituencies.

Absolute achievement of the ideal, however, is not essential. Indifference, apathy, and the tendency for dissident minorities to develop—all these
also plague the interests which bring pressure on the college. The question
is, then: Given the resolution to deal freely and vigorously with controversial issues, can the college develop power sufficient to repel attacks on
its research and teaching?

A combination of institutional moves may help the land-grant colleges
and universities in this endeavor. They center in the governing board
and its relationship to the president. The board should number enough
persons to provide the values of deliberation and of the sense of collegial
responsibility but not so many that the sense of personal obligation is
lost. Boards of seven to fifteen would seem desirable. Members should be
appointed by the governor for long, staggered terms and should be fairly
equally divided between the major political parties or factions. The
board should be the recipient and dispenser of legislative and other funds;
otherwise, the state government should keep its hands off the university.
At the same time, the board and the president should lay down and rigorously follow a definition of their own functions which endows the president with responsiblity to hire his staff and to operate his institution.
It should never be forgotten that the highest purpose of the board is to
come to the aid of the university promptly and decisively whenever it is
attacked—"to protect the university from the winds that blow."[30]

Clearly, the essence of this kind of board is the men who make it
up. Psychologists may suggest appropriate personality and character
types; the writer will merely list humanistic knowledge, a capability for
strong sentimental attachments, and a profound sense of duty. Board
members should have a grasp of the fundamentals of our constitutional
theory and practice, particularly as expressed in the First Amendment
of the Bill of Rights of the federal Constitution and its counterpart in
most of the state charters. Unafraid of controversy, even a little contemptuous of the violent storms that occasionally rise, the board should
insist upon the representation of arguable[31] points of view in the faculty.

When the issue is drawn, the board should stand up and be counted on the side of academic freedom. If these ideals are exacting, some boards have lived up to them rather well; but some serious failures have also been made.

As with boards, so with presidents, deans and directors, and professors. Institutional safeguards are essential, but they can do no more than create the conditions for the realization of human abilities and the fulfilment of human obligations. The single most important condition if a university is to work freely on controversial matters is a qualified president. What kind of qualities? Abilities to thrive on controversy; to meet challenges easily; to occupy the pontiff's seat without losing his sense of proportion—and of humor; to have untold reservoirs of physical endurance; to be capable of righteous indignation yet cheerfully to argue even with the devil and not to consider himself fully clothed unless he has an invisible chip on his shoulder representing academic freedom. Yes, and to recognize that a university is not like a business, that one is picking neither sales managers nor foremen nor vice-presidents in charge of production (to all of whom, no disparagement). One is choosing scholars and teachers whose particular gifts are fruitful in direct proportion to their freedom from the restraints of the "Thou shalt not" variety—men and women who will take a reasonable amount of risk but who generally do not aspire to martyrdom. Finally, presidents often have to combine a dedication to the university with a knowledge that they are expendable. Security of tenure cannot be guaranteed them. They must be subject, as it were, to a daily vote of confidence of the governing board— and, at worst, they cannot escape the possibility of attack by political mountebanks. They must find the inner resources to work under these conditions.

There are presidents who approximate these qualities and others who fall miserably short. In several states the writer was told that current or recent presidents of the institution had "abdicated." In other states: "He runs to the board on the most trivial matters" or "There is plenty of courage in the field, in the laboratories, and in the classrooms, but the closer one gets to the president's office the less there is of it." (In one state, on the other hand: "The president will stand like Gibraltar, but the dean is less of a rock, and the further down you go the more timidity you'll find"; this statement occurred, however, during a transition from a weak president to a strong one.) Time after time, speculation about how much academic freedom really exists terminates in the question, "What will Prexy do if the chips are down?"

The president needs help. Winston Churchill's general theory of leadership is applicable: "At the top there are great simplifications. An accepted leader has only to be sure of what it is best to do, or at least to have made up his mind about it. The loyalties which centre upon number one are enormous. If he trips he must be sustained. If he makes mistakes they must be covered. If he sleeps he must not be wantonly disturbed. If he is no good he must be pole-axed."[32] The university president is the closing link in a chain—not of command but of communication and support. The central staff should support the president, and so should the deans and the heads of departments, and, not least, so should the professors and, in agriculture, the county agents.

Let us be perfectly clear on the problem: backing for what? Back the president in his support of free inquiry. It takes a staunch man to define the line and stand by it, even with support. It is so much easier to hedge a little. The writer has listened to many of the hedging propositions from men experienced as presidents or as ranking administrators in agricultural colleges. One hedge is, "I've got to look out for the university; if I hire that fellow who is supposed to be a radical, the legislature might cut a million dollars off my building fund." Probably every first-class teacher since Socrates has been considered a dangerous radical or (like Socrates himself) a subversive reactionary by some group. "Yes, Sir!" runs another hedge. "Every professor has the right to write and speak freely so long as he confines himself to the truth and operates only in the area of his competence." This statement is dangerous in its sweetly reasonable sound. On numerous controversial matters that divide society, the facts themselves are in dispute, and the faculty will be gagged if they can speak only "the truth."[33]

Consider also the proposition that a man should speak only on matters that fall within his own "competence." In this age of specialization, nothing would more effectively silence researchers and educators. A local government professor should be free to criticize Congress for encroaching on the Presidency; a professor of constitutional law, to criticize the administration of the national parks—or a professor of agronomy to blast the state highway program or the way Shakespeare is taught in high schools. Anyone is free to answer a professor, and certainly many do answer them (sometimes even a little before the professor has spoken or beside the point of his remarks). In a free society with a large complement of active scholars, competence gets its due—and so does chicanery.

Perhaps the most common hedge, freely employed by many of us professors as well as by administrators, is expressed by the prayer: "Oh, God, keep me from making a fool of myself!" And keep anyone else from making a fool of my institution!

1. Events in 1943

During 1942-43 the department of economics and sociology of Iowa
State College undertook a series of "Wartime Farm and Food Policy
Pamphlets," designed as brief, semipopular brochures on such controversial issues as price controls, rationing and manpower problems,
the production of food, and nutrition. The project was supported by a
Rockefeller Foundation grant, and pamphlets were published by the
Iowa State Press, but they also carried the notation that research was
carried on as part of project 818 of the Iowa Agricultural Experiment
Station. Pamphlets were conceived in considerable consultation, circulated
in preliminary form, and finally adapted for publication. A special review
committee of four members of the department of economics and sociology
gave editorial approval; this meant a departure from normal experiment
station editorial procedure, but the departure was accepted because of
the nature, objectives, and manner of financing of the series.

On March 19, 1943, O. H. Brownlee's pamphlet Putting Dairying on a
War Footing was published as No. 5 in the series. It argued for dairy
policy which would encourage the human consumption of fluid milk, an
objective which would involve decreasing the amount of butter manufactured.
The pamphlet acknowledged the substitution of margarine for butter then
in progress but noted that the increase of margarine consumption was
impeded by restrictive legislation, both federal and state. It commented
that properly fortified margarine "compared favorably" with butter in
nutrition and palatability.

The pamphlet was vigorously attacked by representatives of organized
dairy groups and the Iowa Farm Bureau. A protest meeting was held at
Ames. Demands were made that several professors be fired. C. E. Friley,
then president of Iowa State College, made a strong statement of principle
in favor of freedom of research to discover and report the facts; but he
also said that, if facts were found to be wrong, errors should be acknowledged and corrected. President Friley appointed a joint committee, six
representing the dairy interests of Iowa and six members from Iowa State

College, to review the pamphlet. This committee unanimously (according, at least, to public statements) agreed that many statements in the pamphlet were either incorrect or susceptible to misinterpretation or inadequately documented. The committee recommended that Pamphlet No. 5 be retracted—and that the best form of retraction would be the "preparation of a complete revision" which would consider all criticisms and recommendations made concerning Pamphlet No. 5; moreover, the revision should be "worked out with a committee representing the dairy and farm interests of the state." President Friley, in a statement to all recipients of the earlier pamphlet, approved the committee's report, retracted the pamphlet, and announced a revision "with the proviso that the recommended revision be in the form of a new study of the dairy situation, undertaken cooperatively, and including the wartime problems and those likely to be of interest and concern in the postwar period."

Whereas three of the six Iowa State College members of the review committee were agricultural economists (Professors T. W. Schultz, G. S. Shepherd, and W. G. Murray), President Friley had also appointed an internal review committee, composed of the director of agricultural relations and professors of dairy husbandry, animal husbandry, dairy industry, and home economics. No one from the faculty of the department of economics and sociology was included. This committee brought in a most unfavorable report, which may have considerably influenced the president.

Brownlee took steps to revise the pamphlet; but, to some, at least, the revision procedure appeared to be operating very slowly (the new edition was published in 1944). On September 15, 1943, Professor T. W. Schultz, head of the department of economics and sociology, wrote a long letter to the president which (a) examined very critically the official actions of the college with reference to a number of matters other than the dairy pamphlet; (b) laid out an advised program of action on these matters; and (c) announced his intention to resign. The letter was duplicated and given some distribution among Schultz's professional colleagues the author did not intend it to be published, but it was probably inevitable that it should find its way to the press. Part of it, at least, was published.

On September 24, 1943, the Des Moines Register published a long article by T. W. Schultz entitled "Iowa State College and Social Science Research." The Iowa state board of education examined the issues raised by Schultz and unanimously reported to the governor on

November 5, 1943: "After a thorough and intensive consideration of the
whole situation, it is our mature judgment that the charge of the violation
of the fundamentals of academic freedom in all particulars is without
foundation in fact." Meanwhile, there had been considerable editorial notice of the issues in Iowa and elsewhere; much of it was unfavorable to the
administration at Iowa State College.[1]

2.   Interpretations and Inferences

The Iowa margarine incident of 1943 is by no means unique. In
another state, for example, favorable remarks of a college researcher
about the nutritional qualities of margarine brought such prompt, vigorous,
and persistent protests to the president of the university that the latter
became physically ill. Some of the rich significance of the Iowa incident
appears in subsequent repercussions. In one state it was immediately
declared: "Had we attempted to go so far as they did in Ames, we would
have been blown out of the water." (Some of those who left the Ames
faculty at this time for other positions faced searching questions about
their stand on margarine.) In another state an agricultural Extension
director reported attending a meeting of a farm organization in which
the tendency was to be a little smug about "how the boys in Iowa were
taught the score." The director said that he protested this attitude vigorously and with some effect. In still another state a college official reported
an agricultural group leader's remark that "we might have to clean house
here the way they did in Iowa." "You probably have the power," the official
conceded, "but if you succeed, how long will you retain confidence in the
research work of this college?" In other widely scattered states, interviews have suggested that the Iowa incident has been firmly in the minds
of many college administrators.

Recently a number of state excise taxes on colored margarine have
been repealed, to the accompaniment of bitter political fights. In none
of them, to the writer's knowledge, has the college of agriculture engaged
in an educational program on the issue in an effort to lay the facts and
probabilities before the public, with interpretations. A fairly general
policy has been to affirm that the issue was too hot to handle and that
the college had better keep hands off. But, again, in spite of this general
policy, some reports from certain states indicate that elements in the
college lined up with the dairy interests or (much more rarely) with the

margarine interests. It would be interesting to know to what extent colleges of agriculture in states where margarine excise repeal has been an issue have become identified with the dairy interests in the minds of various groups.

Again—though it does not appear in section 1 above—the Iowa affair pointed up a split between physical and biological scientists versus social scientists. Having become conscious of this split during a visit in Ames in 1943, the writer discussed the matter in a number of other states. Many respondents were alarmed then at the mutual distrust between the two great branches of science (but especially at the suspicion in which social scientists were frequently held by the other branch). In spite of the subsequent awakening of atomic scientists to the importance of politics, much suspicion remains, at least in the agricultural field. Here is one of the major obstacles to the fulfilment by publicly supported research institutions of their obligation freely and effectively to examine controversial issues.[2]

In the light of these comments, we turn to a further examination of the Iowa margarine affair of 1943. Immediately, this experience suggests that, if a massive, open attack upon the freedom of publicly supported research and education occurs, a large part of the public will rally to support freedom of inquiry. A number of interviews testify to this conclusion. During the incident the influential Des Moines Register and Tribune sought, apparently with some success, to rally the public in this fashion. Furthermore, the marked change in the leadership of the Iowa Farm Bureau, with Allan Kline replacing Francis Johnson as president, seems to suggest considerable dissension within the ranks. The writer has seen or heard reports of other evidence to suggest that the 1943 incident continued to weigh heavily on many Iowa consciences. It seems, then, that a college administration, faced with an open, severe, frontal attack, can expect at times a rallying of public support—although the rally may be somewhat belated. In order to take advantage of this kind of situation, the administration needs the courage to stand its ground while its support is rallying (perhaps somewhat tardily). The administration also needs to have considerable political skill.[3]

Many other accumulated grievances added to the force of the explosion of which Pamphlet No. 5 was merely the detonator. It would take a literary master to record the situation, if the examination were to probe deeply below the surface manifestations. The mixture of ambition, jealousy, and other motives, and of actions, movements, clashes, rallies, and alliances was too complex to be understood scientifically. But in this involved political situation as in others, the inability fully to comprehend the problem did not absolve the leading figures from their responsibility to make wise and prudent decisions. To fulfil this obligation, the leaders needed to state the central issue properly. In the writer's judgment, the central issue was falsely stated by asking whether the "facts" and the inferences of the researchers were right, important though these questions always are. The central issue was whether to maintain a vigorous established team of social scientists whose general competence was widely accepted and who were strongly oriented in their research toward controversial issues of public policy. Let us examine this proposition.

We take as "given" the political society as we know it: a system of organized political power but one so organized that power controls power—"ambition is made to counteract ambition." A fundamental assumption is that the drive for power is widely observable, that it provides an indispensable dynamic in a free society, but that it must itself be somewhat checked and controlled. The problem of maintaining a free political system, we further assert, is increasingly aggravated by the expansion of governmental activity and the consequent emergence of more and more controversial issues.

Again, while we reject scientific "solutions" to political issues, we assert the need to handle them in a prudent and knowledgeable fashion. In part, prudence and knowledge are gained from appeals to reason made on the basis of research and education which is carried on as objectively as possible. The "Wartime Farm and Food Policy Pamphlets" of Iowa State College were distinguished examples of this kind of research and education. Moreover, the series was only one manifestation in a remarkable history of forthright inquiries into controversial issues on the part of an extraordinarily able department.[4]

The writer would conclude that it is sound public policy—no more and no less—to sustain the kind of attack upon social problems which was being made by this department of Iowa State College.

This analysis has been advanced in order to get away from the usual confinement of the argument in such situations to whether the "facts"

found by the researcher were "right." This question deserves some
attention, however. The difficulty with it has to do with the nature of
facts, particularly of social facts. One of the two most controversial
statements in the original Pamphlet No. 5 was to the effect that restrictive margarine laws had been enacted under political pressure of
organized dairy interests. This is one social fact that can hardly be
controverted, although it would, of course, be hard to "prove." (It
was implicitly acknowledged by the United States Supreme Court in
Magnano v. Hamilton, 292 U.S. 40 [1934].)

More generally, agricultural policy (like other policy) is full of
controversial issues in which the facts are often disputed. The writer
has listened to fierce arguments over the production and consumption
functions in agriculture, the terms of trade between the agricultural
and other sectors, farmers' response to price changes, the feasibility
of land reform, the proper allocation of costs in multiple-use develop-
mental projects, the effects of grain-storage programs, the workability
of farm and home planning programs, the relative effects of economics
and engineering in improving soil conservation, the practicability of
various marketing-control schemes, and so on, ad infinitum. In all these
battles, the significance for public policy of the controversial facts was
apparent to everyone; indeed, it was the chief source of conflict. In all
such inquiries, of course, a healthy regard for the facts is indispensable.
At the same time, a disposition to choke off research because researchers
have made (or are alleged to have made) a few factual mistakes is deadly.
This by no means advocates irresponsibility. The social scientist expects
to be judged professionally by his peers and pragmatically by his
community; but he ought to be able to expect that the community's judgment will be made on a fairly large part of his record.

Thus an examination of the correctness of particular facts in a
particular controversy leads back to the more general issue: whether
it is sound public policy to maintain vigorous social science research.
If the decision is in the affirmative, the community must be prepared
for controversy and for mistakes of the researchers at times. It must
further be prepared to overlook annoyances, to acknowledge that uncomfortable proddings may have their value, and to permit attacks even on
firmly held shibboleths. In short, institutionalized social science research
needs to be appraised over its entire record—as, in a marriage, occasional

nagging, some prodding to do a little better financially, and a few pieces of burnt toast ought not to constitute grounds for divorce.

A major test of our constitutional democracy is the freedom of its
educational and research institutions to examine controversial issues.
Such issues multiply in modern societies; and they have continuously
to be "settled," compromised, or postponed in the political process.
"Politics ain't beanbag," said Mr. Dooley. Without intense emotional
loyalties, democratic politics would be unthinkable. It presumes the
constant interplay of contending groups which are willing to use almost
any means to advance their separate causes and undo their opponents.
It even grants some value to partisan commitments so extreme that
their owner is virtually blind to the interests of others. Conflict is not
only inevitable in democracies; it is essential. A kept opposition in a
free society is a contradiction in terms.[1] Liberty was built into our
constitution by counterposing power to power. "Our strongest Presidents," writes Sidney Hyman,[2] "have made ample use of the Constitution's open-end invitation to hard in-fighting; and by their wrangling with
the Congress . . . they have produced the material means for the survival
of constitutional government itself."

And yet—"if all are partisans, who is to umpire?"[3] Reasoned analysis must enter the political fray to confront and chasten the thrusts
of organized group interests and the drives for individual and group
power. Now "reason" is implanted in the individual; in order to develop
it, however, he must have training, tools, libraries, students, and colleagues. Reason needs the discipline of professions and the support of
institutions. But the latter—the colleges and universities, especially—
are more and more maintained by public funds. So the argument makes
its full circle: can publicly supported educational institutions freely
examine issues which are publicly controversial?

Let us apply this question in another way to agricultural research
and Extension. Previous chapters have examined colleges of agriculture:
first, as targets of political influence; later, as emergent and often very
significant political interests in their own right. To the furtherance of

what public purposes has this strength been developed?[4] What kind of
attack have agricultural research and Extension made on public policy
issues? Chapter x afforded a glimpse into the role of Iowa State College
and its accompanying tribulations. This chapter will glance more generally
at the performance of individual agricultural colleges in policy-oriented
or "programmatic" research.[5] Chapter xii will press essentially the same
question regarding the Association of Land-Grant Colleges and Universities; chapters xiii-xv, regarding the USDA, using the late Bureau of
Agricultural Economics as an example. Beyond programmatic research
lies another kind of "appeal to reason," for in democracies public opinion
approaches imperium. What steps can be taken to enlighten it? A systematic Extension program to that end will be studied in chapter xvi.

1. Self-criticism

Few public institutions have been so vigorously criticized by their
own leaders as have agricultural colleges for their shortcomings in
public policy research. Dean C. E. Ladd of Cornell's college of agriculture declared in 1929: "Our land-grant college organization . . . makes
for provincialism. . . . The organization . . . by states brings many
wonderful advantages, but it also brings just one small disadvantage
that we all develop with more or less of the provincial mind. . . . We
have not made very much progress in the development of a national
viewpoint toward agricultural policy."[6] Nearly a quarter-century later,
Secretary Ezra Taft Benson told the same forum: "Traditionally, the
land-grant colleges have been reluctant to enter the area of public policy.
You have not felt a direct responsibility in this sphere, and you have
realized the dangers of getting involved in an area so controversial. But
can any of us continue to disown responsibility in this critical age?"[7]
The intervening years produced many similar statements.

President Alfred Atkinson of the University of Arizona said in his
presidential address to the Association of Land-Grant Colleges and
Universities in 1937: "Land-Grant Colleges and other agencies must dig
deeper into social and economic fields, just as they learned to go fundamentally into chemical and biological fields. This need will call for
men and women with training in fields now generally undeveloped in
Land-Grant College offerings."[8] In his presidential address to the same
body four years later, Dean F. B. Mumford of Missouri's college of

agriculture praised the experiment stations for their scientific work and spoke of the change of farmers' attitudes from incredulity and ridicule to belief as "one of the most significant phenomena in our educational history." He added: "It seems entirely logical that the Agricultural Experiment Station should now more specifically undertake the very important task of determining how its vast store of knowledge gained by painstaking research can be so utilized as to insure social progress and to prevent, cure or ameliorate social disorders."[9]

Other presidential addresses before the Association of Land-Grant Colleges and Universities convey the same theme.[10] In 1948 President J. L. Morrill of the University of Minnesota referred to the address of Cornell's President Edmund E. Day in 1943. President Day had "called upon our institutions to remobilize and reinforce what he called the 'lost battalion of the Land-Grant movement.' He urged them to provide, even if belatedly, the desperately needed common meeting ground for agriculture and industry, the two most important branches of the American economy." Neither Day nor Morrill were advocating a combination of agriculture and industry against labor, an idea with an unfortunate appeal for some agricultural leaders.[11] Thus Day had declared that the land-grant institutions "were established to promote the practical and liberal education of the 'industrial classes.' The 'industrial classes,' of the 1860's were really the common people. The Land-Grant College is really democracy's college. It is the common possession of all America. May it never fail to represent education of the people, by the people, and for the people."

In 1944 the association's committee on postwar agricultural policy reported.[12] The following year, its chairman, Noble Clark (director of the agricultural experiment station in Wisconsin) told the National Association of County Agents: "Most Land-Grant Institutions are today in an exceedingly vulnerable position as regards this matter of research and extension in the field of public policy." In 1947 the same committee conducted a thoughtful symposium on the problem.[13] H. R. Wellman, then head of the Giannini Foundation of the University of California, analyzed the nature of the required research. Wise public policy, he concluded, requires knowledge of the pertinent facts and their interrelationships, which "in this complex field are not self-evident, but must be discovered." O. B. Jesness, head of the department of agricultural economics of the University of Minnesota, said that "if we are to deserve to be called educators, we must earn that right by demonstrating true educational statesmanship." G. H. Aull, of Clemson College, reported that only 60 per cent of the colleges had courses in agricultural policy (though another 25 per cent "touched upon" it) but that policy courses were postponed until the Junior or Senior year and were elective rather than required. Aull observed:

"This nation is faced with public policy questions, the answers to which may lead to peace and plenty or to war and starvation. The Land-Grant College's contribution regarding such practices as raising sheep and increasing the yield of wheat has been great. Is the Land-Grant College prepared to make an equal contribution to an understanding of the problems and implications involved in tariff 'protection' for wool and price supports for wheat? In other words, where, if not to the Land-Grant College, can farmers turn for guidance in separating fact from fiction in public policies affecting agriculture?

"A committee of Congress is touring the United States to get 'grass roots' public opinion on agricultural policy. If by chance the people interviewed have received a one-sided and distorted view of the question, the damage which could result from their answers may be irreparable. In my state a man must have training in veterinary medicine and be licensed in order to vaccinate a hog. Yet all the hogs in the country cannot compensate for one big blunder in agricultural policy. The Land-Grant College has a responsibility to see that farmers have a sufficiently comprehensive understanding of policy questions to forestall such a blunder.

"Too many people are inclined to measure the significance of a science by the number of requests which come in for information concerning it. This is fallacious. Those who are unfamiliar with the science of nutrition ask for candy more frequently than for vitamins.

"Obviously it requires knowledge, tact, patience, and perseverance to teach a course in agricultural policy, but a first-class instructor should not have any more difficulty in laying open and exposing to his students the intricate 'insides' of his subject than his associate in the zoology laboratory. Don't, however, expect them to exchange jobs! Instruction in agricultural policy cannot be done by men whose background and training have fitted them for other work."

The volume and persistence of these strictures are as impressive

as the eminence of their authors. True, some of the statements reveal
an extremely stark faith in science. But the idea is familiar that physical
and biological sciences have outstripped social science, which must,
perforce, "catch up"; and some speakers may be merely following the
fashion. Other critics may subconsciously be provoked by feeling that
the agricultural colleges have been squeezed out of the crucial national
policy councils, and they may tacitly suppose that research and the
enlightenment it creates will return power "where it belongs." Some
may reflect a puritan tendency toward self-recrimination.[14] And some
may arise from the absence of enough strong, well-financed colleges
of agriculture to cope with the social problems associated with the
scarcity and uncertainty of water in the seventeen western states and
especially in the Great Plains (agricultural colleges from Fargo, North
Dakota, to Stillwater, Oklahoma, are located on what Elmer Starch calls
the "college meridian" and have tended to be oriented toward the humid
corn belt rather than toward the subhumid to arid plains). Qualify as
one may, what emerges is still a massive complaint from the colleges
themselves about their own performance.

2.   Appraisal

Even in the light of this criticism, the writer is unable satisfactorily
to appraise the positive role of individual colleges of agriculture in
policy-oriented research. To be sure, since the early 1920's many colleges
have participated in comprehensive analyses of their states' agricultural
and related problems. Paul V. Maris, the prime mover in Oregon's plan,
described it in 1924. Farmers, businessmen, bankers, and editors were
invited to Corvallis; over five-hundred came, the majority being farmers.
Divided into subject-matter sections, each with technical advisers, this
conference underwrote a plan which probably contributed to considerable
adjustment of Oregon agriculture. A continuing tradition was initiated.[15]
Led by M. L. Wilson, Montana prepared an analysis of its agricultural
problems which set the tone for the systematic approach that the state
college has generally maintained since; a 1949 bulletin, for example,
brought the original analysis up to date.[16]

North Carolina provides an excellent recent example of comprehensive
state agricultural planning. Prospective declines in tobacco income, which
comprised 57 per cent of North Carolina's cash farm income in 1946,

stimulated Governor Gregg Cherry to call a meeting to study the tobacco export problem. A committee of specialists, chaired by Dean J. H. Hilton of North Carolina's school of agriculture, produced a comprehensive analysis and recommendations which were adopted by the original group.[17] This program became the basis of a more elaborate approach by the North Carolina Board of Farm Organizations and Agencies in 1951.[18]

Widely varying, according to land-grant college estimates,[19] in their significance and success, state plans inevitably have centered upon problems in their intrastate and local impact. Appropriate in its setting, this focus contributes little to the development of Dean Ladd's desideratum, "a national viewpoint toward agricultural policy." In the light of the spate of national agricultural policy and programs since 1929, the most systematic intrastate analysis is clearly insufficient and needs to be expanded to regional and national levels. It is largely in pressing this expansion that the self-critics believe the colleges have failed. The evidence, however, is difficult to appraise; valuable as they are, state plans, other bulletins and circulars, and annual reports of experiment stations are to the public policy contributions of agricultural colleges as the visible spur is to the rest of the iceberg.

For the political process is intensely interpersonal. A number of years ago, a distinguished scholar-administrator was actively engaged in a great many "top-level" actions of which his formal job description in the USDA gave no inkling. "There are two kinds of people around here," he said. "Most of them are like red blood corpuscles which do extremely important work but stay locked in accustomed and assigned channels. A few, however, are more like white corpuscles which combine and recombine and seem to move in defiance of habit or regulation. I am one of the latter." The same phenomenon occurs on the highest governmental levels. One hesitates to mention Harry Hopkins because the conservative press may have succeeded in making him an evil symbol of the New Deal for many readers. Nevertheless, the greatest conservative of modern times has written: "Roosevelt, Hull, Stimson, Knox, General Marshall, Admiral Stark, and, as a link between them all, Harry Hopkins, had but one mind. Future generations of Americans and free men in every land will thank God for their vision."[20] Vice-President Richard Nixon seems to have assumed much the same role in the Eisenhower administration.

In many states the colleges of agriculture have contributed significantly to the small but vital number of these organizational catalysts and repositories of political intelligence. In 1951 two nationally known agricultural college economists in states three thousand miles apart detailed to the writer their rich experience in policy formation. These interviews recalled a score of similar ones in as many states, often with administrators and economists, occasionally with a natural scientist (the memory of one field-crop specialist is most vivid). What emerges from such experiences is a strong impression that one has broken the surface and had a glance at "the real thing." It is difficult to exaggerate its importance. Thus the Illinois Agricultural Association, which has always been a key power bloc in the American Farm Bureau Federation, instituted a searching inquiry into public policy matters soon after Charles B. Shuman succeeded Earl C. Smith as president. Although the report was never released (in mimeographed form, it approximated one hundred pages), the experience appears to have been profoundly influential upon Illinois farm leaders and, through them, upon the thought-processes of larger, widely distributed groups. Professor L. J. Norton, of the agricultural economics department of the University of Illinois, was one of the foremost, if not the chief, prompter of this inquiry. Or consider Oscar Heline, Iowa farmer, president of the Farmers Grain Dealers Association of Iowa, member of the National Planning Association's agricultural committee, and a vitally useful person in farm-policy circles. Heline "got that way" in no small part as a result of his twenty-year informal seminar with Professor Frank Robotka and others of Iowa State College.

3. Conclusions

Agricultural colleges contribute to public policy development by undertaking policy-oriented research and by participating in the process of formulating policy in other ways—for example, as critics and as catalytic agents. Although the distinction cannot be pressed too far, it is useful to separate policy-oriented research and discussion which is centered at the points of policy formation (the subject of this chapter) from research and education dealing with the agricultural citizenry as they relate themselves to the governmental process (the subject of chap. xvi).

Three kinds of activity stand out in an appraisal of the contributions of agricultural colleges to policy formulation: programmatic research, systematically carried on by college departments; the same kind of research pursued essentially by individuals; and the participation by college members in the political process as critics, organizers, and catalytic agents.

The first of these, the writer believes, has been quite rare. Few colleges, primarily.in their departments of agricultural economics and rural sociology, have maintained a systematic attack upon a set of interrelated public policy issues (not many have had the resources to mount such consistent attacks, of course). Cornell's agricultural economics department has long been deeply involved in policy-oriented analysis. From time to time and on particular subjects Connecticut, Wisconsin, Minnesota, Illinois, and California have been among those making notable contributions. The most striking, consistent, systematic attack by a team of social scientists seems to have been made by Iowa State College, especially during the decade which opened with The Agricultural Emergency in Iowa (1933) and closed with the "Wartime Farm and Food Policy Pamphlets" (1942-44).

Individual research on current policy questions has naturally been much more widespread. Any informed person can roll off a score of names of agricultural college professors who have made significant contributions since 1920. Beyond these are the significant but elusive activities of politically alert persons in agricultural colleges who have worked informally with interest groups, politicians, or members of the "attentive public."

In spite of this listing, however, the vigorous, persistent self-criticism by college spokesmen for lack of sufficient attention to policy questions has been noted. While this self-castigation probably under-estimates the informal contributions made by college personnel to public policy, the appraisal seems to be fairly just respecting the lack of systematic, policy-oriented research, especially on the pattern set at Ames in the New Deal decade.

The Association of Land-Grant Colleges and Universities has been
a factor in the politics both of higher education and of agriculture. What
has it done to protect its members from political influence and to encourage them as educational institutions to attack controversial issues?
The association has been a significant forum for the annual ventilation
of many problems touching the member institutions and the national
welfare; par excellence, it has been a means of defending its members'
political interests in Washington. Subsequent analysis (which, in keeping
with this book, centers upon the agricultural experience) shows, however, that the association has largely been neutral either as a protection
of research and educational freedom or as a promoter of a vigorous
intellectual assault upon public problems.

1.   Organization, Scope, and Manner of Operation

The association was formed in 1887 after the passage of the Hatch
Act.[1] Its members include the forty-eight land-grant colleges and
universities.[2] Its object is to assist its members in effectively fulfilling
their assigned functions, especially through maintaining "proper legal
relationships between Land-Grant Institutions and the Federal government" and through taking "appropriate action" on federal legislation,
present or proposed, which affects its members.

These purposes were declared in the revised constitution of 1945,
which also restated the traditional limitation on the association, namely,
that its members act together in free co-operation. The executive committee clearly described the relationship in 1936, when it stated that
"there is an immemorial policy in this Association to take no action which
can be construed as coercive or as an attempt to contravene the independent individual responsibilities of the members. . . . That principle . .
is not . . . to be violated even under conditions of emergency and pressure.

From 1921 to 1945 the legislative organ of the association, composed
of presidents of member institutions, was called the "executive body."

The early association had its cleavages, especially the controversy between the presidents and the experiment station directors: "The lobbies
of the 1902 Convention seethed. There was much talk of cleavage into
two associations, one . . . of presidents, . . . which should deal with official
matters, and one . . . of station directors and staff members . . . to deal
primarily with subject matter and incidentally with station administration.
The published proceedings give no picture of the upheaval. The issue
was determined in the hotel lobbies."[4] This internal difference apparently
arose because, on the one hand, the presidents were responsible for the
entire institutions, which were essentially state institutions, while, on
the other hand, the station directors, though subordinate officers in the
state colleges or universities, were also administrators of programs
partly financed by federal grants. In 1902 the constitution was amended
to create sections on college work and on experiment station work; but
no action could be taken by the latter without approval of the college
section and the executive committee.

In 1921 the executive body was created. Dean Mumford of the Illinois
college of agriculture pointed out that the presidents, having responsibility
for the entire universities, were the natural constituents of the association's
legislative body, whereas it was anomalous for agriculturalists to vote
on matters that concerned engineers and vice versa. President W. O.
Thompson of Ohio State declared that the amendment simply clarified
the intention of the change of 1902. He stressed the growing complexity
of affairs involving the members, saying that "there is no group of
institutions in this country that possesses as large and as varied a program
or touches so many vital interests of the community as that represented
by the Association."[5] Thus college presidents have, quite naturally,
dominated the formal organization of the association.[6]

The presidents—or, more precisely, a handful of them—exercised
control essentially through the executive committee until recently.[7]
The chairman of this committee was the association's most powerful
figure.[8] The executive committee was composed of five members (plus
the annually elected president, ex officio, after 1923) until 1938, when
the number was raised to eight. The executive committee determined the
time and place of annual conventions, had charge of arrangements and
conduct of meetings, controlled the order of business (subject to special
action by the association), and reported at any time. The annual reports

of the executive committee provided the most important key to the association's actions, as distinguished from its gestures. Between annual conventions, the executive committee acted for the association.[9]

President Thompson of Ohio State chaired the executive committee from 1909 to 1919; R. A. Pearson, from 1919 to 1935. President T. O. Walton of the Agricultural and Mechanical College of Texas served through 1943.[10] If we omit the association presidents, who serve ex officio, the eighty places on the executive committee during 1921-36 were held by twelve men; the forty places during 1938-42, by twelve men. The four-year term partly accounts for the small number of men in the large number of places; but re-election has been frequent, and men like R. D. Hetzel (New Hampshire and Pennsylvania State), C. A. Lory (Colorado State), and A. R. Mann (Cornell) were on, off, and on again.

The 1945 amendments, which were in the making for several years, leave little of the old constitution untouched. The executive body was replaced by the senate as the "principal deliberative, policy-making and legislative body of the Association." The senate includes all presidents of member institutions but also three representatives of each division. Divisions include agriculture, home economics, engineering, and arts and sciences and may organize their own sections and subsections. Each division elects three representatives to the senate and designates one of them as a member of the association's executive committee. Thus the executive committee is enlarged to twelve members; but it now has a rotating membership and chairman. The retiring association president becomes chairman for one year. Elections are for three-year terms, with the proviso that individuals become ineligible for re-election until one year has elapsed. Finally, the representatives of each division to the senate also compose an executive committee for that division, and the divisions can report directly to the senate instead of through the executive committee.

What is the significance of the changes? Conflicting general interpretations have been offered. One college official told the writer that the senate was created to curb the influence of the presidents, who were becoming increasingly subservient to Washington; another declared that the senate would establish more co-operative relationships with Washington. Thomas P. Cooper dwelt upon the continuity with the past in 1946; Lyman Jackson stressed the degree of change from the old constitution.[11] In any event, the new organization appears to establish the agricultural college deans and directors in a more independent position and to give them a more direct collective relationship to Washington Agencies.[12] At the same time, the 1945 reorganization acknowledged the growing importance to members of the association of nonagricultural relationships with Washington.

Certainly the required rotation in office of the chief positions of the association seems significant. Further, the division of labor which the new constitution emphasizes is probably helpful in a period of pyramiding demands upon the association. Milton Eisenhower's report as chairman of the executive committee in 1946 declared: "In the course of a single year, the Executive Committee handles literally hundreds of problems affecting the welfare of the Association and all constituent members. Many of these problems involve relationships with federal administrative agencies or with the Congress. Working alone, the . . . committee would soon become bogged down. . . . But with the aid of numerous . . . committees . . . the total job gets done with amazing effectiveness."[13] The association has improved its financial position. Until 1936 it operated on less than $6,000 annually; in 1940 dues were fixed to yield $16,000, and this amount was doubled in 1946. The association provided for a Washington secretary in 1940 and changed the job to secretary-treasurer in 1945.[14]

2. A Political Interest

As the presidents of tax-supported colleges and universities must be adept in intrastate politics (J. L. Hills once praised President Atwater's "success in drawing legislative milk from Connecticut nutmegs"),[15] so the land-grant institutions have interests to look after in Washington. By 1890 the association's leaders were scolded on the floor of Congress for "buzzing" in the ears of Solons.[16] Since then, many measures have been supported successfully, and a few failures have been recorded.[17] The Purnell Act of 1925 provides a useful illustration. It not only shows political acumen but also reveals the association's interest in policy-oriented research.

Purnell funds were provided chiefly to stimulate work in agricultural economics, demand for which had increased sharply after the 1920 break in farm prices. Passage of the act consummated a long drive by the association.[18] In 1921 E. C. Johnson, of Wisconsin, canvassed methods of recruiting political influence, including the support of county and state committeemen of both political parties.[19] The executive committee advised marking time that year; in 1923, however (while noting that some colleges were pushing other praiseworthy measures), it advocated unanimous support of the Purnell Bill.[20] Congressman F. S. Purnell (Republican, Indiana) said that "until my good friend George Christie . . . educated me I had no conception of the value . . . of the experiment station." He said that the bill had been reported favorably but that the steering committees would not permit it to come to the floor.[21] Would the association help? It would! The executive committee had secured the support of the American Bankers Association. It intended to approach the resolution committee of the American Farm Bureau Federation (AFBF), "trusting that it will adopt the measure as part of its congressional program." Every member of the association was urged to familiarize himself with the measure and see his congressman personally. So ended the conference on political strategy. The next speaker's subject was "The Content of a Liberal Education."

The association has also looked after its members' administrative interests. It successfully opposed congressional action which would have vested authority in the Secretary of Agriculture to co-ordinate experiment station work,[22] and it established satisfactory relationships with Washington agencies charged with administering federal grants.[23] When the Assistant Secretary of Agriculture, who then supervised scientific work, died, the association presented President Theodore Roosevelt with suggestions for his successor. Professor W. M. Hays, of the Minnesota experiment station, was selected.[24] The association pressed for a director of scientific work in the department at least nine years before the office was established in 1921. E. D. Ball was the first incumbent; he was followed in 1924 by the conservative A. F. Woods, former president of the University of Maryland as well as of the association.[25] In 1919 a bill before Congress to create a federal department of education was vigorously criticized by President Lory of Colorado State; such concentration of educational activities might initiate federal encroachments upon the states. The executive committee was authorized "in its judgment to oppose all movements that would tend to sever" the existing connections between "this body" and the USDA.[26] It should not be forgotten that the "divide-and-rule" principle works both ways.

3. Reluctance To Face General Policy Issues: Pre-New Deal

If the association has assiduously looked after the Washington financial and administrative interests of its members, it has been reluctant to address itself to major policy issues. To be sure, it was active in obtaining uniform fertilizer and feeding-stuff legislation from several states.[27] In 1908 Congress was memorialized to restore basic slag to the free list, removing the tariff of $1.00 a ton.[28] In 1912 the association adopted a resolution offered by the executive committee to recommend that the USDA send experts abroad to study foreign agriculture.[29] In 1923 Dr. Alonzo E. Taylor's recommendation that the association approve the current proposal for a five-year agricultural census was accepted; the executive committee was authorized to present the proposition to Congress.[30]

But the association was chary of major issues in this period. In 1902 the National Arbitration Congress was scheduled to meet in Charleston, South Carolina. A suggestion that the association participate was countered by the executive committee: such action, "entirely outside the province of the Association," would be inexpedient.[31] The same year a report by the association's committee on pure food legislation offered a resolution favoring enactment by Congress of a national pure-food law; the resolution was passed, but the executive committee offered a cautious statement of principle: "In the judgment of the committee it is not advisable for this association to give expression to an opinion on any question of pending legislation except in cases where it has had opportunity to consider and discuss the provisions of a separate bill."[32]

Elsewhere the writer has shown how little attention the association paid to the Roosevelt-Pinchot conservation movement.[33] It is enough to say here that the association depreciated the conservationists' cries of alarm when it was not ignoring them. Of policital economic issues, beginning with those raised by the Populists in the 1890's, the story is similar. Indeed, the perennial agricultural policy issues, manifested in forestry reserves, reclamation, pure food and drug controversies, federal farm loan institutions, the tariff, cotton futures and grain standards regulation, the policing of packers and stockyards, the provision of intermediate credit, the exemption of agricultural co-operatives from the direct impact of antitrust laws and the initial proposals for "fair exchange value for agriculture"—all evolved as issues, became crystallized into proposals, consummated themselves as policy, or missed their mark with, at most, slight attention from the association qua association.

Agitation for farm relief in the 1920's provides the most telling illustration.

In 1919 Dean Russell Davenport of the Illinois college of agriculture delivered his presidential address to the association. He called for a permanent agricultural commission, like the Country Life Commission of Theodore Roosevelt in purpose and like the National Advisory Committee created by the War Food Administration and the USDA in form. The commission should report on the state of the nation, improve public relations, and "be influential in maintaining sound national policies for agriculture."[34] The same year the association's committee on experiment station organization and policy concluded that agriculture was no longer a private business but a public concern.[35] Individual institutions should work on the problems in their states; but "the situation is largely a national one," and the association should at once appoint a study committee. Agriculture needed economic stability, some diminution of risk, and a "fair return"; but it should beware of "professional agitators, reformers, and those seeking remedies from high prices of food without consideration for the producers."

After the price break in 1920 initiated a rather dismal decade for agriculture and presented the country with the "farm problem," however, the association as an association[36] ignored the issues until it was jarred into action by the National Chamber of Commerce's report on the agricultural situation. In 1927 the executive committee offered the association's own report on the subject "to our many friends who are trying hard to find the solution." It added a disclaimer: "This problem . . . comes exceedingly near to the field of politics. Neither this Association nor our Committee has made any effort to get into that field or to direct thought in that field."[37]

The AFBF sent copies of the report to all members of Congress.[38] Professor John D. Black compared the association's report to that of the Chamber of Commerce; the latter had the better statement on both the tariff and the surplus questions, but the association's analysis of agricultural adjustment was preferable.[39] Chester C. Davis wrote: "The report of the land-grant college special committee, like so many reports of the period, was strong on analysis and weak on remedy. It was important chiefly as a belated recognition by the agricultural colleges that a national agricultural program did exist, and that they should be concerned with the development of a national agricultural policy to meet it. The discussion of the agricultural situation was revealing; of the tariff, straddling; and of the surplus problem, vague. 'The movement toward stabilization and control,' it concluded, 'may be hastened by favorable and sound types of legislation.' "[40]

A second study of the agricultural situation was made in 1931, but again the report was merely released for the edification of the country. Meanwhile, the association was held aloof from the numerous congressional hearings of the "McNary-Haugen" decade.[41] In 1929 occurred the first (and apparently the only) exchange between the association's representatives and congressmen on pending farm relief legislation during this period. Dr. Anson Marston, dean of engineering at Iowa State College, was then president of the association; with President Hetzel of Pennsylvania State College, who was chairman of the executive committee, Marston appeared before the House Committee on Agriculture in support of certain of the association's perennial projects. These were federal grants for engineering experiment stations and increased federal aid for agricultural Extension.

When Marston confined his remarks to these subjects, congressmen became irritated. They plied him with questions about the proposed federal farm board, the McNary-Haugen bills, and the co-operative movement. Despite their insistence, Marston's answers, which, he stressed, were merely those of an Iowa farmer, were guarded and qualified. Representative Ketcham complained that the association's spokesmen were not looking at the farm relief issue as a social problem.[42]

Representative Victor Christgau (Republican, Minnesota) declared to the association's convention in 1931: "A criticism has frequently been made, and probably with some justification, that the net result of all extension work, excellent though it has been, has been to increase the volume of production, and that little or no information has been fed into the extension channels, which has had as its object the adjustments in production."[43] In the light of these strictures, one is appalled at the usually statesman-like Pearson, chairman of the executive committee, telling the House Committee on Agriculture in 1930: "The Land Grant Colleges and Universities Association, Mr. Chairman, looks upon this engineering experiment station bill as the most important measure in Congress at this time in the interest of farm relief. I would not belittle the importance of any other measure, but our association puts this one at the head of the list."[44]

The experience of the association with the Agricultural Marketing Act of 1929 is also illustrative. This Republican answer to the farm problem was to provide for orderly marketing of agricultural commodities through co-operatives or governmental corporations. It was administered by the Federal Farm Board, whose persuasive first chairman, Alexander Legge, fired the imagination of the association. R. A. Pearson, of the executive committee, declared that the association would "go the limit . . . to assist you." The Farm Board requested the association to appoint a committee "to advise and assist the . . . Board in . . . developing a wise national agricultural policy and . . . devising and administering effective agencies for supporting and administering an American agriculture based on Ameri standards of life." The executive committee, plus five members co-opted by it, became the committee.[45]

That was in 1929. In 1930 Chairman Legge reported that the associati had given "sincere, cordial cooperation" but that a series of crises had prevented full use of its advisory committee. He praised the Extension program but argued for "more frequent meetings with groups of farmers . an intimate, personal discussion of . . . the outlook . . . on any particular commodity."[46]

Some friction developed between the Farm Board and agencies of the land-grant colleges.[47] The Farm Board felt constrained to enter the Exte sion field[48] and, in so doing, to criticize existing Extension programs. As events proceeded, the Federal Farm Board acquired vociferous political enemies,[49] with whom the association undoubtedly did not want to become embroiled. When the Senate Agricultural Committee conducted its Agricul Conference and Federal Farm Board inquiry in 1931, the association did appear. The final appearance of a chairman of the Farm Board before the association in 1932 went unreported.[50]

Nevertheless, the Federal Farm Board probably stimulated the forma of the National Land-Use Planning Committee in 1931.[51] In 1923 the asso tion made a gesture toward establishing such a committee,[52] but its form awaited the call of Secretary Hyde for a conference in Chicago.[53] This co ference, including land-grant college presidents and others, set up a temp committee. The latter brought in recommendations respecting land policy credit, tenure, reclamation, and so forth; suggested formation of a Nation Land-Use Planning Committee, to be composed of five each from the coll and the USDA, three from the Department of the Interior, and one each fr the Federal Farm Board and the Federal Farm Loan Board; and proposed also a national advisory and legislative committee, with representatives of farm organizations, the farm press, and others. The recommendations were all adopted.[54] The following year members of the National Land-Use Planning Committee and others discussed land policy in the association's convention.[55] The joint committee on projects and correlation of research of the association recommended establishment of a national, co-operative land-use research and planning project, to be jointly financed by $100 contributions from each station. The executive body accepted the recommendation.[56]

In 1933 the National Land-Use Planning Committee made its first—and last—report. It had stimulated analyses of various land-use problems and had taken a position on proposed regulation of public grazing lands. Meanwhile, the New Deal was here and had created a National Planning Committee,[57] which appeared to pre-empt the place of the National Land-Use Planning Committee. Chairman Delano of the National Planning Committee requested that the association form a committee to represent state and local interests in consultation with his own group. The association acquiesced; its committee, renamed the "committee on land problems," reported in 1935 and 1936, largely on matters affecting the co-ordination of federal and state agencies. In 1937 it was discharged.

4. Policy Contributions in and after the New Deal

Throughout the New Deal and the early part of World War II, the association continued its unwritten policy of nonparticipation in major agricultural legislative decisions. This conclusion rests upon an examination of the public record of the passage of the Agricultural Adjustment Acts of 1933 and 1938, the amendments to them in 1935, the Agricultural Marketing Agreements Act of 1937, and the amendments to the charter of the Commodity Credit Corporation in 1941. Twice during the second World War the Extension committee on organization and policy requested the association to take a hand in important agricultural policy developments, but each time to no avail.[58] With the brief but important exception of the activities of its Committee on Agricultural Policy (see next section), the association kept aloof from the process which culminated in passage of the Agricultural acts of 1948, 1949, and 1952 and of the Commodity Credit Corporation Charter Act of 1948.

The association's most absorbing concern in its relationships with the agricultural New Deal stemmed from its role as protector of its members administrative interests. It appointed a committee to confer with President F. D. Roosevelt on the reorganization of the USDA and listened to friendly overtures from Secretary H. A. Wallace and his aides.[59] In 1935 the association and the USDA each appointed a committee on relationships with the other. Sometimes the committees worked together; sometimes they worked separately. The association's committee noted the exacerbation of relationships in 1937, rising out of "new and extraordinary federal enactments." Some delicate situations had been handled satisfactorily, it said. It discussed, but not for the record, returns from a questionnaire in which state college officials had reported their degree of satisfaction with relationships. In 1938 the two committees helped bring forth the Mt. Weather Agreement, which provided the basis for the co-operative state and local land-use planning program—a major, if short-lived, accomplishment.[60] Ironically, it came on the threshold of a period of increasing friction between the major action agencies of the USDA and the colleges of agriculture.[61] The association's committee on relationships, understandably, had nothing further to report; and it was discontinued in 1944.[62]

But the mutual problem of accommodation between the colleges and the USDA continued; and important achievements have continually emerged as the result of hard work and good will on both sides. The joint committee on Extension programs, policies, and goals brought in a thoughtful report.[63] The "grasslands program" was also developed successfully in co-operation with the USDA.[64] Representatives of the association's agricultural division helped secure congressional appropriation of the sums authorized by the Bankhead-Flannagan Act and assisted in writing bills to consolidate the numerous grant-in-aid statutes for agricultural Extension and research. The executive committee of the association began to meet with Secretary Charles F. Brannan annually for an extended session and at other times for briefer meetings. Indeed, Milton S. Eisenhower, president of Pennsylvania State College, president of the association, and member of its executive committee, declared in 1951: "Relationships between the U.S. Department of Agriculture and the Land-Grant Colleges are better now than at any time since 1933."[65] In the same meeting, however, the division of agriculture adopted a resolution of the National Association of County Agents protesting "encroachments" by the USDA in the field of Extension.[66] On the basis of interviews, the writer's judgment is that USDA-college of agriculture relationships were adversely affected by the postwar activities of both the Production and Marketing Administration and the Soil Conservation Service, by the Brannan Plan in 1949, and by the Family Farm Policy Review and the reorganization of soil conservation agencies in 1951.[67] (This does not mean that if the USDA had only behaved properly all would have been smooth.) On the other hand, some relationships—and especially those with the Agricultural Research Administration during P. V. Cardon's directorship—were probably never better.[68]

Finally, even if the association kept out of most major agricultural policy developments, it could enter them when the interests of its members were involved. An interesting illustration is the recommendation to divorce Extension from the Farm Bureau (Dean H. P. Rusk, of Illinois, dissenting) in the Report of the Joint Committee on Extension Programs, Policies, and Goals.[69] Perhaps the major example of an important contribution to policy which stemmed from the organizational interests of its members is the report of the association's special committee on the preservation of phosphate deposits and their natural use[70]—an important document in the history of soil conservation.[71] Reviewing deficiencies in available phosphates in the nation's soils, the committee declared that three times the current inputs of phosphatic fertilizer could be economically used, in combination with agricultural limestone, in the humid areas of the United States. The committee believed it to be "high time that the Association . . . took an active part in the development and execution of a comprehensive plan to assure agriculture an abundant supply of phosphatic fertilizer in the all-out effort which must now be made . . . and to assure . . . in post-war years . . . a supply adequate to maintain soil fertility." The federal government should develop the western potash and phosphate reserves, thought the committee![72]

5. The Committee on Agricultural Policy

Probably the most significant contribution of the association to public discussions of agricultural and related policy occurred in the report of its committee of eighteen on "Postwar Agricultural Policy" in 1944.[73] Beginning with an examination of agriculture and the national welfare, the report discussed agricultural production adjustment, prices, land tenure, conservation, and rural living and considered the role of farm people in policy-making. The committee managed to be brief, clear, forceful, and forthright on a wide range of subjects. For example, it opposed governmental price supports at high levels but recommended three measures in depressions: subsidized food-consumption programs; certain deferments of farm mortgage payments; and (in long and severe depressions) certain income payments to farmers and other groups. Especially respecting wheat and cotton, the report bore down on the need for designing governmental programs to assist adjustment. For example: "Such aid should be positive in character, temporary in nature, and directed toward the partial replacement of cotton production by other types of activity including the production of food for consumption by the farm family." Instead of using public funds to support cotton prices, the purpose should be to encourage "the development of alternative enterprises."

The association received, commended, and released the report for the nation's edification. A considerable wave of activity was thereby initiated. By 1945 nearly 120,000 copies of the original report had been distributed. Many farm organizations and land-grant colleges had used it. The California legislature urged that the report's objectives be translated into public policy.

Moreover, the association continued the committee—its name was changed in 1945 to the "Committee on Agricultural Policy"—and granted it $1,000 annually for expenses. Several other reports followed;[74] what is more, Chairman Noble Clark and others of the committee amplified and discussed their analyses before numerous audiences and organizations[75]—including congressional committees. The departure in association policy seemed very great. Its two previous reports (1927 and 1931) had been merely received and released; now, however, the committee was actively entering into the policy-forming—i.e., the political—process. Indeed, testimony by the committee on agricultural policy began to take on an official ring as being representative of the association. When Chairman Clifford Hope (Republican, Kansas) of the House Committee on Agriculture asked the executive committee of the association for testimony on the long-range farm program, Noble Clark appeared (May 3, 1947). Later, the committee supplied Chairman Hope with a comprehensive written statement on a number of questions.[76]

In the light of the association's previous history, the activities of its
committee on agricultural policy posed a problem. The committee was
composed of agricultural economists; the association has been primarily
the forum of college administrators. Noting this, the committee asked in
1946 whether the association was ready "to provide technical counsel,
publications, regional conferences and other services required if the
Land-Grant institutions are to give coordinated and effective educational
leadership as regards public policies which affect agriculture?" If the
answer were affirmative, the committee needed more money.[77] In 1948
Chairman O. B. Jesness thoughtfully analyzed the committee's role and
urged that it be reconstituted as a "standing committee of the Senate
whose function will be to deal with problems of public policy, including,
but not limited to, agricultural policy." The division of agriculture discharged the extant committee and proposed creation of a senate committee,
as suggested. But the association concluded that through either existing
or ad hoc committees, it could meet its obligations to analyze public policy
issues.[78] Moreover, the senate of the association laid it down[79] "that
no position should be taken at this time with reference to long-range
agricultural policy legislation. There are certain basic positions that
this Association has consistently supported and repeatedly stated before
the Congress. Any new position or attitutde should be arrived at only
after a careful poll of the desires of all member institutions, and then
such recommendations would be made to the Executive Committee
before any representations are made to the Congress."

The wording of the resolution suggests that university presidents
had become alarmed because testimony of the committee on agricultural
policy was being (or might be) taken as an official commitment of the
association. Understandably, institutional presidents want to avoid easy
identification with positions on nationally controversial issues unless
they have had the opportunity to study them; such men have a full ration
of trouble in their own states. Even with constant disclaimers, moreover,
statements of the committee on agricultural policy inevitably sounded
ex cathedra. Nevertheless, as the writer has tried to show, the land-grant
institutions have special obligations in policy fields, especially—through
their colleges of agriculture—in agricultural policy. Agricultural colleges
cannot be political interest groups, representative institutions, and major

arsenals of experimentation and educational work without acquiring a duty to help meet the public policy problems generated by agriculture. Inevitably, their obligation carries through to their mother-institutions and to the association. Dr. Jesness is right: a need clearly exists for national forums—other than those provided by formal government, on the one hand, or organized groups, on the other—in which national issues may be sytematically, thoroughly, and repeatedly examined. Risks would be entailed, of course; but experience should make them bearable.

6. Policy-oriented Research

The underlying assumption of this section is the desirability of policy-oriented research. Not that the "scientific method" holds the key to a millennium. The fervent belief of an earlier generation in "increased knowledge and good works" has proved "no inconsiderable faith," as Harvard President Nathan M. Pusey has written. And yet "by itself, this faith will no longer do."[80] For the moment, however, this formidable insufficiency can be set aside. Policy-oriented research here simply deals with studies of comparative advantage, interregional competition, mobility of the factors of production within agriculture and between it and other sectors, and similar subjects, particularly with emphasis upon the inferences for policy and administration. These economic and politico-administrative formulations are not meant to disparage the great and often crucial significance of physical and biological research to the resolution of public policy issues.[81] We have heard Dean Ladd's complaint of the "provincialism" generated in state institutions and the failure to develop "a national viewpoint toward agricultural policy."[82] What has the association done in protecting and promoting such research in its member institutions?

a) Protection of Member Institutions from Political Influence

The association has ably protected members' administrative interests and "job rights" in dealing with Washington. No doubt it would help repel overt federal political attacks upon research and education; but, in agriculture, at least, the federal influence has been much more subtle and indirect (chap. v above). The association does not protect member institutions from intrastate political encroachment, however. When investigations in animal nutrition at Pennsylvania State College were threatened by the college board in 1907, the association investigated and made recommendations; but the official position was as follows:[83] "It is not quite clear how the interests of this important enterprise may be advanced by this association, excepting through cordial approval and moral support."

In 1919 K. L. Butterfield reported a resolution of the college organization and policy committee to the general session "that the Executive Committee take steps to secure the coordination of the authority and activities of the various National and State Departments, Bureaus and Boards that deal financially with the Land-Grant Colleges." But W. O. Thompson, president of Ohio State University and long-time chairman of the executive committee of the association, queried "what business it is of the Executive Committee to secure such coordination. That is a matter of law within the purview of the several state legislatures and of Congress."[84] Thompson's position was borne out by the experience of the 1920's. The executive committee inquired into "encroachment by governmental agencies on the freedom of administrative officials and governing boards of land-grant colleges . . . in the use of state appropriations." A. R. Mann suggested that a uniform classification system to harmonize federal and state requirements might be urged upon the states for adoption. Discussion held his suggestions "more or less visionary." Yet a committee on state fiscal policy was created. In part, the Office of Education's Survey of Land-Grant Colleges and Universities (1930) was a product of antagonism between the colleges and the reformed state governments of the 1920's. The association's state fiscal policy committee was somewhat more forthright than the Survey, naming institutions and states in which encroachment was held to be severe. Yet the association could offer only moral support to any of its beleaguered members.[85]

Nonintervention by the association in intrastate affairs is strongly supported by precedents, and these are buttressed by two leading characteristics of the association itself. First, its operating purpose is essentially confined to promoting and defending its members' interests vis-à-vis Washington; additional functions are hard to acquire and easy to discard. Second, the leading figures of the association are presidents and ranking officials of member institutions. They are the natural centers of controversies over research and education in their own states—"And these are not in plight to bear, if they would, another's care. They have enough as 'tis. . . ."[86]

b)   Promotion of Policy-oriented Research

During the 1920's, committees of the association repeatedly urged systematic research upon agricultural problems that crossed state lines. In 1919 the joint committee on projects and correlation of research (henceforth referred to as the "joint committee") recommended the organization of a national agricultural research council. The executive committee indorsed the principle but considered its immediate application impracticable.[87] In 1922 the experiment station committee on organization and policy stressed that no single station could "hope adequately to attack all the many and difficult problems with which the agriculture of a region is confronted."[88]

The Purnell Act (1925) provided federal grants especially for research in economics and rural sociology. Testifying for the bill, the president of the association declared that the colleges had stimulated production during the war—"we have helped to get the farmers into their present situation; we were the agency of the government, the chief agency. They are coming to us now for help to get out, and we are not able to give it to them."[89] When the act was passed, the joint committee called a meeting at St. Louis to discuss its administration. Six special committees were created to help co-ordinate Purnell research on a number of national projects.[90] In 1928 the joint committee reported a gain in co-operative projects, especially where the USDA was a partner, and opined that adequate machinery for the effective co-ordination of research existed for the first time.[91] Nevertheless: "Relatively few stations have embraced the national projects, especially in some of the newer lines. In the large majority of cases investigators have set up projects of their own on independent and unrelated bases. In other cases the so-called cooperation is to a considerable extent a paper affair, with little coherence and with an indefinite conformity to a working plan."

The following year the joint committee continued its strictures: "Consciousness of membership in a common cause has not been a conspicuous product of operations under the national projects set up [pursuant to the Purnell Act] nearly five years ago."[92] Dean C. E. Ladd of Cornell was more biting in his criticism: "The research programs of the agricultural experiment stations in the United States today are wholly inadequate to meet the needs of extension and of practical

agriculture. Research programs are still giving entirely too much
weight to the problems of production and an entirely inadequate amount
of time and effort to the problems of economics in spite of the fact that
all agriculture has been crying for more economic work for a generation.
In all friendliness but still in all frankness, to one who is on the firing
line it looks as if the guiding of research programs is entirely too
conservative, entirely too far removed from the needs of agriculture,
and entirely too little responsible to the aims and intentions of our
legislators at the time they passed the Purnell Bill. We need an accounting on this point."[93] Thus committees of the association as well as some
distinguished land-grant college officials rather consistently criticized
the failure of agricultural research to organize itself for an effective
attack upon emergent problems.[94]

But rather suddenly a new attack upon the colleges drew the association's attention from self-criticism to self-protection. President Hoover,
acting through Interior Secretary Wilbur, created the National Advisory
Committee on Education in 1929. Two years later it recommended an
end of federal grants-in-aid for education.[95] At once the association
appointed a committee which brought in a contradictory report.[96]

The attack was renewed by Lewis Douglas, first director of the Bureau
of the Budget under the New Deal. President Glenn Frank of the University
of Wisconsin charged that Douglas, little familiar with what the agricultural
experiment stations were doing, had advised President Roosevelt to
withdraw federal funds from them. He linked the attack with that of
interests traditionally opposed to the agricultural Extension Service as
part of the "advance guard of the cooperative movement."[97] Only by
close maneuvering did the association forestall a 25 per cent cut in grants-
in-aid for agricultural research in 1934, when state appropriations for
this work were still falling.

In consequence, the association largely ceased to be self-critical
and became self-laudatory. College leaders were sensitive to the ill-
founded attacks that agricultural research and education had stimulated
farmers to produce themselves into bankruptcy. They would have
been less than human had they not resented the slurs that their lifetimes
of service to agriculture had been misdirected. So they turned to the
defensive. Then the New Deal came, and they had continuously to seek
satisfactory arrangements with the agricultural action agencies; and

this, too, diverted the colleges and their association from critical self-examination.

Thus the association appointed a committee on federal-state relationships in research in 1931.[98] Reporting on a canvass of the states, the committee found, as usual, that relationships with the USDA were "mutually cordial and helpful" but that there was a "lack of harmony in certain important respects." The committee said: "The state experiment station has gained the moral and political support of the state by its service to local interests. It now stands in a supreme position of local leadership. But if local control of its functions were to be divided by any sort of partnership, or its prestige lessened by any competitive influence, the experiment station would rapidly lose its leadership and the confidence of the people. A disastrous reduction of financial aid from the state would follow."

This revealing statement strongly implied that the state stations have no real responsibility on the national level. It based the station's strength on its "service to local interests." The report continued by pointing to the "most embarrassing feature" of federal-state relations, namely, the existence of fifty-one USDA field experiment stations in twenty-four states. It further complained that co-operative research with the department "has meant the complete subordination of the stations"—but it gave no examples.

The joint committee on projects and correlation of research, which had often critically examined co-operation in research during the 1920's, was reportorial rather than critical in the 1930's. It brought forth imaginative suggestions,[99] but its temper had changed: it was no longer the vigorous and consistent advocate of programmatic research in agriculture that it had been in the 1920's. Likewise, the Office of Experiment Stations, which has been characterized as an "adjunct of the Association,"[100] departed from its brief fling at critical evaluation of experiment station research in the 1920's[101] and reported, year after year, that "distinct progress" had been made in co-ordination, that there had been "notable progress," and that the stations "continued to co-operate."[102]

In subsequent years the association carried through one major operation in furtherance of policy-oriented research, the work of the committee on agricultural policy, which has been discussed. It shared

in the passage of the Research and Marketing Act of 1946, section 9(b)
(3) of which provides funds for regional research.[103] With the USDA,
the association created a joint committee on extension programs, policies,
and goals which brought forth an excellent (and apparently an influential)
report.[104] It pressed important inquiries respecting phosphatic fertilizers
and irrigated agriculture and water resources.[105]

Nevertheless, the committees of the association never returned
to the critical self-appraisal of the orientation of experiment station
research that characterized the 1920's.[106] One cannot explain this
failure on the grounds that the critical temper of the earlier decade
merely reflected the attitude of a few individuals who have since passed
on; as has been abundantly shown, outstanding individuals have continued
their strictures on this score. Again in 1950 Director H. C. Sanders of
the Louisiana Extension Service called for a "clear-cut policy statement
by the Land-Grant College Association on work relating to public policies";[107]
but none, apparently, has been forthcoming.

7. Conclusions

In terms of this study the major role of the association has been
effectively to represent its members' legislative interests before Congress.
It has also made impressive contributions in furthering co-operation and
accommodation between its members and Washington agencies and in
resolving many of the minor conflicts between them. What has it done
to protect its members from political influence and to encourage them
in an active, vigorous attack as educational institutions upon controversial
issues? The agricultural experience has been drawn upon to answer this
question.

As a buckler against efforts by Washington to control educational
policies of its members, the association has presumably been a second
line of defense; the few overt attempts disclosed by an examination of the
agricultural experience have been effectively rebuffed by other means.
On the other hand, the association has rigorously followed a policy of
noninterference in state affairs; the obvious prudence of this policy
should not obscure the fact that the association has therefore provided
no safeguard at all against the prime source of overt political attacks
upon public educational institutions, intrastate politics.

As a promoter of policy-oriented research and Extension work in

agriculture, the association has provided a significant forum for prominent individuals to air their criticisms. Since the 1920's, however,
as an association it has provided only sporadic critical examination of
the work of its member institutions upon controversial issues. Its
committee on agricultural policy was a national agency of considerable
importance and influence during the mid-forties; but the association
has ordinarily avoided major policy issues, unless propelled into them
by their obvious bearing upon the organizational interests of its members.
Meanwhile, activities of the association have grown enormously, and
most of the increase has been outside agriculture—as one can readily
discover by comparing the business of the old executive body in 1939.
It is doubtful, therefore, that the association will provide the services
required to assume a position of educational leadership on agricultural
policy issues; it is even more questionable that the association will
endeavor to expand such leadership in order to deal with public policy
generally.[108]

XIII / The Bureau of Agricultural Economics

General Characteristics and the
Fate of Land-Use Planning[1]

The major question of this book is whether a constitutional democracy
(the United States) can maintain publicly supported research and educational agencies which are fairly free to probe controversial issues,
especially those incident to public policy. The field of inquiry is agriculture. Generally the focus has been upon the agricultural work of the
land-grant colleges. But it is appropriate to examine the USDA as well;
and, within the USDA, the history of the Bureau of Agricultural Economics
(BAE) provides the best example.[2]

1. Organization and Activities

In 1922 the Bureau of Markets and Crop Estimates was consolidated
with the Office of Farm Management and Farm Economics to form the
BAE. In 1952 the BAE had some 1,300 employees, quite evenly divided
between Washington and the field—the field meaning almost universally
campuses of agricultural colleges. The BAE's subappropriations were
economic investigations and crop and livestock estimates. The former
were more controversial; but the BAE's error in cotton-crop estimates
in 1951 showed that the latter was also subject to dispute.[3] As Table 2
shows, economic investigations were reduced by 30 per cent from 1942
to 1952; meanwhile, crop and livestock funds rose 240 per cent.

Table 2 sharply contrasts the fall in funds for economic investigations with the rise in money for crop and livestock estimates. It also
shows that the attrition of economic investigations did not stop in
1946, when H. R. Tolley was replaced by O. V. Wells as chief of the
BAE and the controversial "planning" activities of the bureau were
de-emphasized. Funds for economic investigations continued to fall into
1948, rose as the result of transfers from the Research and Marketing
Act (and other sources) in 1949,[4] then declined again (in spite of continuing sums from the Research and Marketing Administration).
To anticipate a conclusion: the considered policy of neutrality repeatedly

155

TABLE 2

BAE APPROPRIATIONS, 1941-52*

(In Millions of Dollars)

Fiscal Year	Economic Investigations	Crop and Livestock Estimates	Fiscal Year	Economic Investigations	Crop and Livestock Estimates
1941...	3.9	1.1	1947...	2.5	2.5
1942...	3.3	1.4	1948...	2.3	2.5
1943...	2.4	1.2	1949...	2.7	2.7
1944...	2.5	1.6	1950...	2.6	2.9
1945...	2.4	1.7	1951...	2.5	2.9
1946...	2.4	1.7	1952...	2.3	3.1

* Source: Senate Hearings, Agricultural Appropriations, fiscal 1945, p. 126; House Hearings, Agricultural Appropriations, fiscal 1947, p. 92; and House Hearings, Agricultural Appropriations, fiscal 1953, Part 1, Table 5, p. 94.

propounded by Wells in and after 1946 did not protect "economic investigations" from continued attrition. Three things about economic investigations are not shown by the table, however: first, the extent of the real decline in funds for them; second, the degree of their emphasis upon record-keeping and service; but, third, the considerable breadth of what remains.

First, the real decline in manpower available for work in economic investigations was brought out by F. F. Hill, of Cornell, in 1951. He quoted the figures shown in Table 3 to show the man-years (professional and clerical) made possible by funds for economic investigations. Not only

TABLE 3

Fiscal Year	Man-Years	Fiscal Year	Man-Years
1943*.........	832	1949	453
1944	838	1950	512
1945	701	1951[†]........	500
1946	702	1952[‡]........	500
1947	602	1952[§]........	380
1948	411		

*Actual
[†] Estimated

[‡]Budget-estimated
[§]House bill-estimated

does this table bring out dramatically the extent of real decline in
resources for the BAE's economic investigations; it also demonstrates
again that reductions continued after 1946.[5]

Second, what was the nature of the economic investigations work of
the BAE? Wells has taken pains to emphasize its statistical and service
character: "Only about 50 per cent of the funds available under 'Economic
Investigations' . . . are used for what we would ordinarily think of as
research, and this includes a considerable amount of service research
in connection with our outlook and situation work as well as such
semiservice tasks as the production capacity project."[6] This and
similar statements of Wells appear to be efforts to identify economic
investigations with the crop and livestock estimates work of the BAE—
the latter being less controversial, more traditional (it began shortly
after the Civil War), and productive of results whose utility is more
easily understood by many congressmen.[7]

Third, it is necessary to note the breadth of the BAE's economic
investigations, many of which were carried on in co-operation with
agricultural economics departments of colleges of agriculture. Otherwise, it might be falsely inferred that economic research in the BAE
was ground to nothing between the upper millstone of congressional
"realism" and the nether millstone of statistical work. Such investigations can be discussed under the headings "economics of production";
"prices, income, and marketing"; and "farm population and manpower."[8]

Economics of production.—These investigations included[9] studies of
agricultural productive capacity in the aggregate and in terms of output
per man-hour; aggregate studies of the progressive mechanization of
agriculture and of changes in farm practices, as well as specific researches into the economic potentialities of recombination of enterprises
or the introduction of specific practices, etc.; and estimates of costs
and returns for sixteen types of farms in eight major farming regions.
Studies of low-income farms were made. The agricultural balance
sheet was kept up to date. The incidence of federal and state-local taxes
on farmers was examined. The debt structure and agricultural credit
were studied. Irrigation agriculture's economic problems were probed.
Some research was continued on tenure.

Prices, income, and marketing.—Researches here included farm
income analyses, appraisals of demand for farm produce, food consumption, commodity situation reports, the share of the consumers' dollar

which goes to the farmer, and studies of the economics of marketing.

Farm population and manpower.—This field included studíes of
trends in the farm population, the effect of defense mobilization upon
farm manpower, farm wage rates, migratory labor, and some work
on the distribution of incomes within agriculture.

Turn now briefly to crop and livestock estimates. Nineteen different
kinds of projects were maintained in 1951-52 to provide a continuous
statistical picture respecting farm crops. Eight projects similarly
dealt with farm prices; thirteen, with milk and dairy products; sixteen,
with livestock; eleven, with poultry; and eight, with miscellaneous items.
Wells said that the service currently "releases about two reports each
workday or over 500 a year."[10]

In his first appearance before the House subcommittee on agricultural appropriations as chief of the BAE, Wells laid down his concept
of the BAE's scope of activity. Rejecting policy-oriented research,
he proposed to "look across the agricultural field and try to find out
the items we need to cover in order to provide a good working knowledge of the entire field."[11] The foregoing recital suggests that the BAE
managed to maintain a considerable breadth of coverage, in terms
of the policy that Wells laid down in 1947,[12] in spite of shrinking appropriations.

2. Inherent Controversiality of the BAE

Wells said in 1947 that there had been "very little criticism of the
Bureau" as a statistical and research agency; but Secretary Henry A.
Wallace had "assigned . . . the responsibility for planning" to the BAE in
1938, and this "brought a good deal of grief and a great deal of criticism
to the Bureau." In 1945, Wells continued, "the planning function was
transferred back to the Office of the Secretary, where I think it belonged
all the time." Actually, he declared, "the Office of the Secretary never
abdicated as chief of the planning agency of the Department."[13]

Wells depreciated the inherent controversiality of the BAE. He had
then been its chief for a little more than a year, during which "all
remnants of [its] planning function as such" had been eliminated. He
knew of virtually no criticism of the BAE at the time, although he
conceded: "You cannot do a good job of research and you cannot even
publish straight statistics without running into some criticism, to be
perfectly honest."

The writer respectfully disagrees. The BAE was conceived in controversy. If it continues to exist (or, more accurately, is re-established), it must learn to live with controversy, even to thrive on it. If it is really the federal Bureau of Agricultural Economics, it cannot possibly escape controversy. Let us look at the record. The first chief of the BAE, Henry C. Taylor, became identified with the program of Henry C. Wallace, Secretary of Agriculture from March 4, 1921, until his death on October 25, 1924. Russell Lord[14] describes Taylor's conversion to Wallace's belief in the need for vigorous federal price policies for agriculture, the progressive worsening of the Wallace-Taylor relationships with President Coolidge (after President Harding's death), the pressure placed upon Taylor to resign after Wallace's death,[15] and Taylor's eventual "resignation" under the prodding of Secretary William Jardine.[16]

Other examples of controversy involved the outlook service, which was begun in 1923 as a major part of the program of "assisted laissez faire"—to give farmers better information to improve their individual adaptations to the market. In 1927 the outlook service accurately predicted a fall in cotton prices; immediately congress proscribed such predictions about cotton. In 1931 the outlook service contradicted President Hoover's opinion that the debt moratoria would be beneficial in its effect upon the wheat market; by presidential order, the BAE was prevented from further use of the future tense in such announcements.[17]

The restrictions upon the outlook service show that the policy of studied conservatism which the post-Taylor leadership of the BAE followed did not keep the BAE entirely free from major controversies. At the same time, some observers believe that BAE leaders bought a degree of safety at the price of a certain ineffectiveness. Thus, when the Federal Farm Board was created to administer the Agricultural Marketing Act of 1929, it reportedly pumped the BAE dry and had to assemble its own economic staff. The early Agricultural Adjustment Administration (AAA) repeated the experience with the BAE and established, as a mark of the concern of Henry A. Wallace and his associates over the possible misdirections of agricultural policy, a Land Policy Section.

3. Origin of State and Local Land-Use Planning

In addition to the AAA, the creation of other agricultural action agencies in the 1930's produced difficulties of relationships, among these

agencies and between them and the land-grant colleges. In 1938 at the
Mt. Weather (Virginia) conference, representatives of the land-grant
colleges and universities and of the Department of Agriculture agreed
to a method of co-operative policy considerations designed (a) to provide over-all program formulation with respect to operations of the
federal department and state agencies affecting land use; (b) to establish
a means for departmental collaboration with the land-grant colleges;
and (c) to bring to life the cherished "two-way" democratic concept of
M. L. Wilson and others by enlisting the active co-operation of farmers.
The BAE was made the federal partner in this effort. Howard R. Tolley,
who had administered the AAA after Chester C. Davis' retirement early
in 1936, became chief of the BAE.

The state and local planning program (later the agricultural planning
program) was initiated as a co-operative endeavor between the USDA
and the colleges of agriculture. The BAE signed memoranda of understanding with most of the colleges. Counties were selected, committees
of farmers and of agency representatives were created therein, problems
were assessed intensively, and a "unified" stage was projected in which
agency representatives would sign agreements respecting their performance in achieving the common program. In January, 1942, nearly 1,900
counties and some 8,000 communities were at one stage or another in the
planning process. Nearly 125,000 farm men and women served on county
and community committees, and another half-million attended meetings.
Some 18,000 federal, state, and local government employees participated.
The BAE had representatives in land-use planning in forty-seven states
(Pennsylvania was never in the program).[18]

4.   Attack on Land-Use Planning

The first public attack upon the planning program was made by
the American Farm Bureau Federation (AFBF) at its 1940 convention
in Baltimore. Alarmed at the prospect of new farm organizations
emerging from the county planning committees, the AAA committees,
soil conservation district supervisors, or other such groups, the Farm
Bureau proposed to formulate and administer national agricultural
policy through a five-man nonpartisan board, representative of the
nation's agriculture. On the state level, farm programs, so far as

practicable and including the "state-wide planning program of the Bureau of Agricultural Economics," were to be administered by state committees composed of men appointed by the five-man Washington board from nominees submitted annually by state Extension directors, who previously had consulted with "state-wide membership farm organizations."[19]

Congress refused to accept the entire Farm Bureau proposal, but it did cut the BAE by $500,000.[20] In reporting the bill to the House, Congressman Cannon said that the department should have discretion in applying the cut; Senator Bankhead remarked that the argument against the land-use planning activities had "influenced to a large extent the reduction."[21]

The Farm Bureau was probably aided in its attack upon the BAE by the Soil Conservation Service (SCS) and the AAA. The SCS may have felt that it would have a stake in the future of agricultural planning if soil conservation districts rather than counties could become the local instruments. In 1941 Congressmen Terry (Arkansas) and Collins (Mississippi), both members of the subcommittee for agricultural appropriations, were critical of the planning program as encroaching upon, or duplicating, or taking credit for, the work of the SCS. Terry asked Tolley: "Now you are claiming credit for the work that is being done by the Soil Conservation Service?"[22] Both these men were among the House managers on the conference committee, who prevailed upon Senate managers to accept the House cut.[23]

By 1941 the AAA was rapidly becoming, in effect, the Department of Agriculture. It had two-thirds of the USDA's appropriations and the custodianship of "the farm program." Under Tolley, the BAE criticized the AAA,[24] and this may have rankled. But the issue between the two involved a power struggle in the summer of 1941 respecting control of the defense (and later war) administration in agriculture. Secretary Wickard, who had come up the AAA career ladder, announced that the war boards would be built around the AAA committees. This move was interpreted by many agricultural college officials as a slap in the face. They were disposed to fight, but with what weapons and what allies? The land-use planning committees seemed to be an obvious alternative; but, at the critical juncture, the AAA appears to have communicated a story to the agricultural colleges that Tolley foresaw the land-use planning committees' replacing the Farm Bureau. This fabrication may have contributed to the colleges' failure to seize an opportunity.[25]

Nevertheless, the Extension directors tried to save the $500,000 cut in BAE appropriations. The most impressive demonstration in favor of the planning program was that of Cornell's Extension director, L. R. Simons, then chairman of the Extension committee on organization and policy of the Association of Land-Grant Colleges and Universities.[26]

5. Liquidation of Land-Use Planning

In 1942 the planning program was done away with. In the appropria-tion act for 1943 Congress provided "that no part of the funds herein appropriated or made available to the Bureau of Agricultural Economics shall be used for State and county land-use planning." This restrictive language marked the success of a continued attack by the AFBF. Presi-dent O'Neal's prepared statement on the appropriation bill commended Congress for "effecting a substantial saving in the administration of the land-use planning program" for fiscal 1942. He proposed complete elimination of the program, saying, "We have not had a single protest from any farmer with respect to the elimination of this appropriation." He praised research functions of the BAE, for which "here in the city of Washington" adequate funds should be provided.[27]

Nevertheless, the House Appropriations Committee did not recommend the death of the planning program. In reporting the bill for fiscal 1943, Congressman Tarver (Democrat, Georgia) said: "The committee is very favorably impressed with the prospect for beneficial results from the activities of this organization."[28]

Congressman Dirksen, from the heart of rural Illinois, the strongest Farm Bureau state, led the fight against the planning program. On March 3, 1942, he was eloquent in his praise of Tolley: "The Bureau of Agricultural Economics is a planning organization. They have one of the headiest, one of the finest, and one of the most able men in the United States in charge of its activities. That is Howard Tolley. He could make far more money in private business than he does working for the Govern-ment, but notwithstanding all that, I am inclined to believe that we are almost planning some of our farmers out of existence." He then pro-ceeded to detail the "seven broad phases" of BAE work, of each of which he gave a curious interpretation.[29]

Dirksen proposed an amendment in the committee of the whole to cut the BAE by $1,000,000, saying, in effect, that he was carrying out the wishes of the AFBF.[30] He charged that the BAE had "set up area offices in the country, they have set up regional offices, and they have made an attempt to set up county offices."[31]

Congressman Tarver, chairman of the subcommittee on agriculture of the House Committee on Appropriations, vigorously opposed Dirksen's amendment. No one should vote for this amendment, he warned, unless he had read pages 312-16 of the committee hearings.[32] The subcommittee had listened to the Farm Bureau's point of view for two days, he informed the House; the Farm Bureau had offered valuable suggestions which were adopted, but not all their points had carried: "I do not believe the Congress would be justified in writing an appropriation bill based solely on the opinions of representatives of the Farm Bureau Federation."[33] Recalling Dirksen's praise of Tolley, Tarver also commended the chief of the BAE.[34]

The planning program was allowed to die without objection. Energies of the land-grant colleges were directed in 1942 to fighting off a threatened reduction in appropriations for Extension work. With the exception of Extension Director H. J. Haselrud (North Dakota), no state college official testified one way or the other regarding the planning program.[35] Remember that the BAE had been cut for the fiscal year then current by $500,000, most of which had been used to contribute to the salaries of 308 employees in the Extension Services of co-operating states. Supposedly, the BAE could have reduced elsewhere and saved these co-operative employees.[36] To do so might have meant to recruit the aid of the land-grant colleges in 1942—but at the expense of relinquishing nearly the entire program to the states. For these "co-operative employees," although the BAE paid as much as three-fourths of their salaries, were responsible to state Extension directors.[37]

1.   An Ill-advised Reorganization

The reorganization of the USDA in 1938 made the BAE the "general
agricultural program planning and economic research service for the
secretary and for the Department as a whole."[1] Congress acquiesced;
the USDA's appropriation act for 1940 said: "Economic investigations
[of the BAE] : For acquiring and diffusing useful information among the
people of the United States, and for aiding in formulating programs for
authorized activities of the Department of Agriculture, relative to agricultural production, distribution, land utilization,and conservation in their
broadest aspects."[2]

In retrospect, the 1938 order seems ill advised. If the BAE is
staffed with persons of proper ability, its personnel will inevitably have a
staff or advisory function respecting policy. BAE personnel performed
this function after 1938—and after 1946, as will be shown later.[3] What
was unwise in the 1938 order was the identification and formalization of the
BAE's central role in policy-making. The BAE thus became the target
of powerful action agencies, with their millions of dollars to spend,
where the BAE has only its tens of thousands. The BAE also became
the target of the Farm Bureau or any other organization which disagreed
with the Secretary on policy. It became the whipping boy for certain congressmen. The attacks resulted in a reorganization which stripped the
BAE of its planning function and resulted in considerable reductions in
funds for the agency in 1946;[4] but the attrition has continued since.

A preview of future difficulties occurred in 1944. Secretary Wickard
said that farmers' incomes were higher than ever before. Yet, said
Judge Tarver, look at the plight of the dairy farmers! Auditors' exami-
nations of Georgia dairy farmers' books had proved that such farmers
had operating losses. The Secretary of Agriculture, Tarver continued,
drew upon Tolley and the BAE for advice upon which to base his statements. When Tolley offered to examine the records to which Tarver
referred, the latter said he would be glad to accord Tolley all the time

necessary, if the latter would go to the OPA or Marvin Jones or Fred Vinson,[5] tell them on the basis of Tarver's facts whether the dairy farmers were going broke, and "try to influence them to grant relief of a character that would enable these folks to stay in business."[6]

Tarver, like many congressmen, was a lawyer. Lawyers believe in advocacy. Everyone is entitled to his day in court and to the benefit of counsel. The common law is hammered out by judges case by case in adversary proceedings of "right and wrong, between whose endless jar justice resides." This belief in the way justice emerges in the legal field is projected to the political field, where the farmer, too, is seeking collective "justice." The value that a lawyer ought to be an advocate is in turn projected to the economist and others; the economists in the Department of Agriculture, "the farmer's department," ought to present "the farmer's side" of the "case."

In his oral report to the House on the committee bill, Tarver referred to a difference of opinion among committee members regarding the BAE. Admitting the vital need of its economic investigations "if properly conducted" and emphasizing that he spoke for himself alone, Tarver said that, "while the information it furnishes should, of course, be accurate," the BAE "is supposed primarily to be working for the benefit of agriculture and of the farmer and . . . too much of its effort has been devoted to an attempt to prove that the condition of the farmer is satisfactory, and that he is being accorded a fair deal in comparison with other classes." Tarver thought this wrong. If the farmer was disadvantaged, then the BAE should show it—"and I, therefore, feel that it has not been wholeheartedly the servant of agriculture it should have been." If the committee were sure that the BAE would mend its ways, he added, it might feel justified in asking for an increase in appropriations for economic investigations.[7]

In 1945 Tarver again was critical of the BAE's analytical work. Tarver pointed out that, although farmers' net income had risen in 1944 over 1943, their share of the national income had fallen from 9.2 to 8.5 per cent. He scored the BAE for having no better counsel to offer for the farmers' relief than subsidy payments.[8] Yet Tarver successfully opposed the efforts of Congressmen H. Carl Andersen (Republican, Minnesota) and Rich (Republican, Pennsylvania) to reduce by an additional $210,000 the appropriation for economic investigations. The result was a bill which cut economic investigations $100,000.[9]

2.   The Coahoma County (Mississippi) Report

A sharp issue arose over a sociological study allegedly raising the racial issue. Congressman Whitten (Mississippi) implied that the Coahoma report was the chief cause of a reduction of nearly $500,000 in funds for economic investigations in fiscal 1947.[10] But apparently the Department of Agriculture and certainly the Bureau of the Budget had already recommended a reduction in funds for the BAE that fully covered surveys of this kind.[11]

What happened was this.[12] In July, 1944, the BAE initiated a series of studies of seventy-one counties in the United States. The report of the chief of the BAE for fiscal 1945 states: "The regional field staffs have conducted studies on current and anticipated rural migration problems in 71 counties representative of the major type-of-farming regions of the country. These studies are being summarized into region-al and national reports. Studies of the economic and social problems of veterans returning to agriculture and changes in farm-family expendi-ture patterns are being carried on in this 71-county sample" (p. 12; cf. 1944 report, p. 6). The approximate total cost of the project was $17,795, according to a statement submitted by the BAE to the appro-priation subcommittee.[13]

Frank D. Alexander prepared a report entitled "Cultural Reconnais-sance of Coahoma County, Mississippi" (December, 1944). Thirty-five copies of the report were dittoed, of which sixteen were distributed: nine in the Department of Agriculture; three to Congressmen Abernethy, Whittington, and Winstead, of Mississippi, upon request; and four to persons outside the department for review and criticism.[14]

These facts are as stated; but the record is scanty, perhaps by intention. As Congressman Whitten, of Mississippi, said: "Again, I have not put these matters in the record because I did not want to spread an indictment of fine folks, regardless of the types and character of folks that may have made it, or the motives they may have behind them in this report." The "fine folks" were the people of Coahoma County, whom Whitten and Tarver thought slandered by the report. In addition to the alleged slander, the charge was raised that the report was published when Tolley denied this, the dittoed copy was waved in his face. When he sought to explain that the copies were for administrative use, Whitten termed the reports "secret documents" and suggested "ulterior motives" behind the collection of the material. Whitten asked: "Do you think that would be doing the American farmer any good if we were by legislation, if necessary, to put your Bureau back to gathering agricultural statistics and take you out of the socialization field and the accumulation of claimed data and the printing of such vicious attacks on the county and its people, as is done by your Bureau in the case before us."

When Tolley asserted that the BAE was a "public agency," Whitten agreed that it should be, but "I do not see how you can say you are, fairly and frankly." Whereupon Tolley stated: "I say we should be a public agency, we should conduct ourselves, and what we do and what we find out in such a way and in such a manner that it will be available to the public at all times, and we should at all times welcome the public to know what we are doing. We should be glad to tell them what we are doing, why we are doing it and how we are doing it, and what we have in mind. I think that this line of work is quite valuable in enabling the Bureau . . . to keep abreast of the agricultural situation and the status of the agricultural situation and its people in this country."

Now what was in this document? That we shall probably never know. Whitten and Tarver both were skeptical of its purposes or, rather, the purposes of the seventy-one-county study, as Tolley stated them.[15] Tolley himself repudiated the paragraphs "on the matter of the race question" which had been excerpted from the report by someone for circulation—"which I think personally were unfortunate, and no reason for them being in there." Tolley maintained that this part of the report comprised only 3-5 per cent. Tarver and Whitten thought it comprised 40-50 per cent. The only excerpts were read into the hearings by Tarver, as follows: "'At present the militant Negro leadership in urban centers of the North is making its opinions felt on the rural Negroes of Coahoma County, for a number of them subscribe to northern newspapers which do not hesitate to emphasize injustices done Negroes'";[16] and "'The city of Clarksdale has a highly rated white school system and a junior high school for Negroes. The municipal swimming pool for whites is located on the campus of the white high school. The school system maintains a free kindergarten for white children of preschool age. The superintendent of the white school is strongly opposed to employing Negro teachers who come from the North or who have been educated in northern schools.'"

Setting aside Tolley's repudiation of such paragraphs, both of those reproduced here seem to report observations "subject to empirical verification."[17] Prospective dwellers in Coahoma County, veterans looking for farms, for example, might want to know such "facts." Presumably, there are some Negro veterans.[18] Finally, the reader may judge the inflammatory quality of these paragraphs.

3. Disputes over Price Policies

It would be seriously wrong to construe the 1946 attacks upon the BAE as deriving essentially from the paragraphs in the Coahoma report touching the Negro problem. That perennial subject of controversy, agricultural price policy, was also under debate. Researchers in colleges of agriculture and private universities were criticizing it.[19]

These outside critics have been denounced by agricultural politicians; but when the BAE, as part of the "farmers' own Department," presumed to suggest a critical note, the politicians had a more effective weapon than denunciation: they could punish the agency through its annual appropriations.

Secretary Wickard proposed a plan for cotton in December, 1944. This was followed in April, 1945, by a mimeographed analysis of the BAE further exploring alternative approaches to the cotton program.[21] In both these statements, the alternative program given strongest support would have involved drastic redirection of existing policies. Not long after Secretary Anderson's incumbency, he was making speeches in the South which strongly suggested his acceptance of the more drastic alternative discussed by his predecessor, particularly for cotton.

Strategically placed congressmen became increasingly concerned about such official criticism of the farm program. In the Hearings upon the department appropriation bill for 1947 repeated efforts were made to pin the formulation of the new proposals for agriculture on the BAE, but Tolley steadfastly refused to admit a function larger than that of gathering facts, making analyses, reaching conclusions, and—if called upon—offering recommendations.[22] In short, Tolley said that any BAE recommendations on policy were made upon request and were freely accepted, rejected, or modified by the Secretary. In addition, Tolley insisted that recommendations were presented as alternatives, a practice which, of course, would strengthen the interpretation that the Secretary alone is responsible for choice of policy.

But the real question is whether this kind of analysis impresses congressmen. They granted the ability of members of the BAE; their very attack proves that intimidation is the severest form of flattery. The upshot is that Tolley might make all manner of denial without avail. The rumor was being spread that certain members of the BAE were "writing the secretary's speeches for him." Some congressmen were convinced that the BAE had sold Secretary Anderson the "let-prices-fall" policy. After three days of Tolley's testimony, Tarver said to Secretary Anderson that Tolley favored the "let-prices-fall" policy. "I do not know that he made any unequivocal admission of that type because the doctor does not make unequivocal admissions of any kind."[23] Tarver understood that speeches of the Secretary indicated his approval of the policy.

Secretary Anderson denied it. He was "not attracted in any way to the proposal that we allow prices to drop to the world level, whatever it may be, or whatever the domestic level may be, and then fill out the difference with a payment from the Treasury." He had so informed his staff. Parity had been "a fine thing for the farmer." The parity formula needed re-examination. But proposals to change it "would have to come from the farmers themselves and from the farm organizations."[24]

The Secretary's position was acceptable to congressmen. H. Carl Andersen stated on the floor of the House:

"Mr. Chairman, in fairness to the Secretary of Agriculture, I want to state that he personally has refuted any intention of foisting any such program upon the American farmer. I fear, however, that he may be overridden by certain men who have more authority in policy making than he has in this administration.

"We must have for agriculture, not a defeatist program as seriously studied by the Bureau of Agricultural Economics, but a constructive forward-looking program, which will hold up farm commodity prices, union labor wages, and give a decent scale of living for all of us here in America."[25]

Thus do congressmen reach over the heads of "responsible" secretaries to smite their wicked advisers. Note that the objection is even to giving "serious study" to any program that might be an alternative to that already become sacrosanct.

4. Controversial Cotton Ceilings

The BAE was also attacked because Chester Bowles, while administrator of the OPA, had announced raw-cotton ceiling prices. The press
stated that this was done with Secretary Anderson's approval, and Tarver
assumed that the Secretary acted upon the advice of the BAE. Tolley
and O. V. Wells, assistant chief, were queried on this point. Wells said
that, under the law, the Secretary of Agriculture was required to state
that price ceilings on agricultural commodities, as announced, would
return parity to the farmer. Wells described the calculation whereby
it was determined that the minimum announced ceiling would do so.[26]
The Secretary of Agriculture would have an opportunity later, according to Wells's statement, to decide on the advisability of promulgation
of ceilings. Tolley emphasized that the BAE had not been consulted on
the matter, although granting, of course, that BAE statistics had been
used. Wells's statement was in accord with Tolley's concept of a public
servant's functions: his analyses and conclusions are available to his
superiors. Many of them are available to the public; his recommendations,
however, are available only to the superiors and then only upon request.

Neither Tarver[27] nor Whitten[28] were satisfied. Tarver thought it
might be the BAE's duty, even if not specifically requested, to advise
the Secretary of Agriculture what price ceilings would mean to cotton
farmers. Tolley said that, not having been asked, he did not know what
statement he would make in this regard. Tarver thought this an "indefinite statement" from one in Tolley's position, "upon whom I think the
farmers . . . have a right to rely to exert his full influence and ability
in their behalf."

He would propound the question to Tolley; he, Tarver, was trying
to ascertain whether appropriations should be granted. Was Tolley
really fighting for the farmer, or had he the consumer's interests and
the high salary levels of his bureau in mind? Then: "Just what can you
say, or will you say, regarding this problem of the cotton farmer which
to him is a matter almost of life or death? Have you any opinion about
it? If so, will you express such opinion as you have? Just where do you
stand?"

This gave Tolley an opening that he exploited fully:

Mr. Tolley: "That is a different question. I am very glad to
talk. You have asked me how I feel toward the farmer and how
I feel about the welfare of the farmer."

Mr. Tarver: "We all feel kindly toward the farmer. I was more specific than that."

Mr. Tolley: "I have said this afternoon that I personally feel that the farmer should have an opportunity to have a level of living equal to other classes in the United States. . . . That is the basis of the analysis and the research done in the Bureau. . . . That is . . . my personal philosophy and the way that I try to run my job."

Mr. Tarver: "I am trying to find out—"

Mr. Tolley: "That is my philosophy."

Mr. Tarver: "I am trying to find out—"

Mr. Tolley: "Now, you asked me about cotton in the South."

Mr. Tarver: "No; I did not ask you that particularly. I asked you about this action of the Office of Price Administration. Have you any opinion about it? Is it fair to the cotton farmer? If not, why . . . not? . . . Do you have any opinion? Say so if you have."

Mr. Tolley: "I think that it is in line with the legislation that the Congress has enacted."

Mr. Tarver: "And you think that it is fair?"

Mr. Tolley: "I did not say that. First of all, I think it is in line with the legislation that Congress has enacted. Now, has Congress enacted legislation that is fair to cotton farmers? I think that Congress has enacted legislation that has helped cotton farmers."

Mr. Tarver: "I do not want your opinion of the legislation enacted by Congress. You have not been asked for that."

Digging further into the question of cotton prices, one finds that congressmen thought that, if industrial labor was to be guaranteed 75 cents an hour,[29] so should cotton farmers. Cotton, therefore, should sell for 75 cents a pound, since, it was argued, it took approximately an hour's labor to produce a pound of lint. Judge Tarver set out the one hour-one pound figure, and Sherman Johnson, assistant chief of the BAE, gave some appearance of approving Tarver's statement. Later, however, Johnson declared that the national average was half an hour's labor per pound of lint cotton. To this Tarver retorted: "I think it is a very generally accepted fact that the statement you made on yesterday [i.e., one hour-one pound] is more accurate."[30]

But Johnson could not agree. His previous estimate had been too high. Tables were printed showing hours of direct labor per pound of cotton and income from cotton on family-operated cotton farms in various regions. A glance at these tables will convince readers of the difficulty of the Piedmont, from which Tarver hailed, in the light of the comparative advantage of the Southwest. On Piedmont two-mule farms in 1940-44, over half an hour was required per pound of lint; in the southern plains (e.g., the Texas Panhandle) the figure was only a little more than seven minutes. Consequently, 1944 figures for return for an hour's labor show 28 cents on such Piedmont farms but 88 cents in the southern plains.[31]

But congressmen were dissatisfied with the BAE's method of calculation. What labor should be included? Should labor to produce feed for mules to work the cotton be shown as labor directly for cotton production, or separately? Tolley and staff desired to consider typical farms as units and to compare different combinations of enterprises on typical farms respecting the total costs involved, including labor, and total incomes received. Congressmen Whitten and Tarver apparently wanted to single out cotton specialty farms, show all labor on such farms as incident to cotton production, arrive at a figure for the time consumed in producing a pound of lint under such circumstances—and then take this figure as a general one for cotton's labor requirements, thus indicating what the price per pound should be for cotton. Both congressmen were lawyers; this approach appeared to make the best possible case for their client. The BAE, then, was requested to provide an economic rationale for cotton prices high enough to compensate farmers for labor, the necessary amount of which congressmen had predetermined. Any failure on the BAE's part so to perform brought the prompt charge of "consumer-mindedness," of OPA-mindedness, or of having "an innermost attitude of mind" that twisted the evidence against the farmer. No respect was shown for the integrity of Johnson, a man of high reputation in the profession. It is no wonder that Tolley felt compelled to defend the honesty of his staff.[32]

Later, Secretary Anderson told the subcommittee that he had refused to join in the press release with the OPA on cotton ceilings. Absent from the department when the request came from the OPA to agree to the legality of the announcement of the intention to place ceilings on raw cotton, Anderson himself had not signed the approval: "I certainly would not go back on that approval, because we cannot put ourselves in the position of saying we would not ever approve a ceiling on cotton if cotton got completely out of hand." He further assured congressmen that actual establishment of a ceiling "will require the approval of the Department of Agriculture." Congressman Tarver asserted that even the contemplation of ceilings was having unfavorable effects upon the price of cotton. He invited the Secretary to issue a statement in the immediate future as to whether he would accord approval to ceilings if they were finally proposed to become effective. When the Secretary wished to comment, Tarver informed him: "There was today a meeting of some 100 or more Representatives from the South to discuss this question and they appointed a committee to wait on you, on Mr. Bowles, and on the President to discuss this general subject. . . . So I do not want you at this time, unless you feel inclined to do, to give any positive expression of your views . . . until you have heard . . . the committee."

The Secretary obeyed this injunction.[33] On the floor of the House Tarver stated that the BAE was largely responsible for the "perfectly senseless and ridiculous proposal" of the OPA to place ceilings on raw cotton.[34]

5. Explosiveness of Income Investigations

The farm income and expenditure investigation called forth further attacks upon the bureau. To appraise this controversy, one must re- member that the idea of a governmentally planned agriculture appeared well accepted in the United States in 1946. Congressmen wanted it that way. Among farm groups, so did the AFBF.[35] Critics had noted the regressive income effects of the program as it has developed—the tendency to give "to him that hath" and take away from him that has little even that little which he has.[36] True, there had been some pallia- tive modification of the program. But the operative principle remained the historical base.[37] In the light of these remarks, consider the admis- sion of O. V. Wells: "We know very little about the distribution of . . . in- come between farm families."[38] In short, for nearly thirteen years we had been plunging ahead with regulatory programs which tended to freeze a pattern of income distribution among farmers without really knowing what the actual distribution of that income was. Wells also said: "There is at the present time, in the Department of Labor, a rather well conceived program of finding out as much as possible about the income and living conditions of laboring people. I believe the Congress of the United States . . . directed the Bureau of Labor Statistics to calculate a minimum cost budget for the American working family, for the average American workman in cities. Such a minimum cost budget will . . . be used to compare with the income of those laboring people.

"Now we have done a great deal of work in the Bureau of Agricultural Economics on agricultural income . . . (and) on parity prices. However, parity price and over-all income do not in my opinion adequately measure the living conditions that American farmers either now have or expect."

But, in addition, Wells had stated: "We also know very little about the total amount of income received by farmers and farm people from work off the farm, although of course we are well aware that it is rather substantial." And it was this and similar utterances upon which Tarver seized: "If I judge correctly . . . , one of the purposes is to show that the farmer has a better income than he has been supposed to have." And, brushing aside attempts at explanation, he continued: "The trouble about it in my mind is that I used to be a very strong advocate of the work of your Bureau. I resisted efforts to decrease an appropriation some years ago, and have always thought that sufficient funds ought to be provided for you; but during the last year or two a suspicion has grown up in my mind that you may not be working for the farmer; you may be working more for the consumer of agricultural products; and if I interpret part of your testimony correctly, one of your purposes here is to gather information which will show that the farmer's income is not so deplorably low as has been heretofore represented from the sale of agricultural commodities, but that in addition he has some kind of mythical income from work that he is supposed to do off the farm. I am just not convinced in my own mind that your purpose is to help the farmer."[39]

There is no question of Tarver's previous strategic support of the BAE. He was to come to its rescue again in 1946, when Congressman H. Carl Andersen attempted to slash the funds for economic investigations by another $300,000 on the floor of the committee of the whole.[40] But the appropriation for investigating income and expenditures was not granted. The USDA's production-control programs were to be continued without at the same time making the fullest possible effort through the BAE to ascertain their effect upon differently situated individuals.

1. The BAE's Role Redefined

In 1946 H. R. Tolley resigned and O. V. Wells became chief of the BAE. The bureau had been forbidden to spend money for state and county land-use planning (1942); the Secretary's order transferred the formal policy functions of the BAE to the Secretary's office (as of January 1, 1946); and the appropriation act for 1947 forbade the BAE to use its funds "for the maintenance of regional offices, or for conducting social surveys."[1]

Wells immediately complied by eliminating the regional offices and discontinuing the Program Study and Discussion Division and the Program Analysis and Development Division. The Program Surveys Division was renamed "Special Surveys." Some further reorganization was undertaken, and the bureau initiated conferences with representatives of farm organizations and colleges of agriculture to get advice about its program.[2]

In his first appropriation hearing Wells set forth his conception of the BAE's role:

"There have been from time to time two general philosophies as to how the Bureau . . . might organize its work. One . . . has held that we should endeavor to forecast the emerging problems—those things that are going to be most important—and center our work, especially our research or economic investigations, around these emerging problems.

"Another philosophy has been that we should realize that practically all discussions of the agricultural outlook and of agricultural programs, as well as of the actual administration of those programs . . . , rests on factual and statistical information; that we should look across the agricultural field and try to find out the items we need to cover in order to provide a good working knowledge of the entire field, reserving a relatively small portion of our time so that we can . . . move fairly fast into new fields that require special effort.

"Rightly or wrongly, as Chief of the Bureau . . . , I feel that our first function is to cover the entire agricultural field; secondly, to specialize on particular problems."

Wells attributed his decision partly to the difficulty in forecasting what "major or emerging problems" will be; partly to the influence of subjective value judgments upon what is important; and partly to the existence of special agencies to handle particular problems. He had always thought the BAE a general service agency working for agriculture. With the Bureau of Labor Statistics and the Bureau of the Census, the BAE should be responsible "for seeing that the administrative officials, the Congress, and the people are reasonably well informed across the entire economic field."[3] Wells reiterated this position several times, emphasizing that planning and policy decisions should be made elsewhere, that the BAE should remain a scientific agency, "so that in policy arguments you may start arguing from the facts about the policy issues rather than about the facts as such."[4]

There were scrupulous efforts to conform to this statement. Thus in 1950 the production adjustment project had been discontinued, since the emphasis had shifted from "How much can farmers produce?" to "How can supplies be kept in line with what appears to be the effective demand?"[5] By 1951 the growing emergency had thrust the BAE and the land-grant colleges into a reappraisal of the first question—the "farm capacity study."[6] Economic investigations have been sharply scrutinized. For example, the rural organization studies were reported in process of liquidation in 1950.[7] Wells attempted to perform the "Function of the Executive"[8] by setting forth the purposes of the BAE in a manner that makes sense to its personnel and to those who deal with it. An inherently controversial agency like the BAE may advisedly withdraw from formally sharing in policy-making. Careful reading of the preceding chapter will show, however, that the professions of Tolley and Wells are much alike respecting the BAE's role. There may be difference in "attitude, temper, or . . . approach";[9] there probably were differences in the "confidence" which some powerful men had in Wells and that which they had in Tolley just before his resignation. The question (as one observer privately said) may "resolve itself entirely in personality." If these are imponderables, they are the vital stuff of relationships in highly political situations.

2.   Controversy Continued

Still, the BAE could hope to achieve only some diminution of controversy, largely because of its inevitable involvement in the policy-making
process. When debate on agricultural policy became heated (as it did
following Secretary Brannan's release of "the plan" on April 7, 1949),
the bureau was almost sure to become identified with those for or against
a given position. It must be simultaneously condemned for sins of omission
and commission. Some illustrations of the BAE's post-1946 controversies
are in order.

Emphasis upon service and gathering of statistics has not eliminated
controversy. — Examples are the price-forecasting difficulties of the
outlook service in the 1920's; the issues respecting the makeup of the
parity index in the 1930's;[10] and the attacks in 1946 upon the BAE for
studies of distribution of farm income or of production costs in cotton.
In 1951 the BAE estimated the cotton crop at over 17,000,000 bales on
August 1; it increased this estimate slightly on September 1 but lowered
it a little on October 1 and, a month later, dropped it to 15,771,000 bales.
The earlier estimates were 12-13 per cent too high. The BAE was criticized for the error; the House Committee on Agriculture probed the
matter, which was also discussed in the appropriation hearings. Secretary
Brannan stoutly defended the methods and performance of crop reporting.[11]

More significant than these controversies, in the writer's judgment,
is the question: What is included in acquiring "a good working knowledge
of the entire agricultural field"? Tolley had defended the disputed
"social surveys" as part of a general effort to "keep a running picture
of the agricultural situation." The prime example since 1946 has involved
Wells's concern with the need for statistics and analyses in anticipation
of the reimposition of production controls. He touched on the subject
in 1949[12] and elaborated on it in 1950:[13] "We have, during the last year,
. . . tried to increase our work especially on certain production or
farm-management problems which are coming to the fore as a result
of the acreage allotment and adjustment problem now facing the American
farmers." In 1951[14] he told Congressman Horan (Republican, Washington)
that he would cut the BAE's economic research before its statistical work:
"I am a research man myself and I hate to say that. But . . . the basic
statistical materials . . . are . . . absolutely essential. And, if we don't

do it, then somebody else is going to, I think at greater cost." Wells's persistent recent preference for crop and livestock estimates over research—preference in terms of priorities in the face of budget reductions—was further clarified before the Senate subcommittee that same year. He professed his worry over what would happen if acreage allotments were reimposed. The "strain that it will put on our county acreage estimates . . . will be extremely great."[15]

The point of this illustration should be underlined. Nothing was more controversial in agricultural policy during these years than the question of production control. The experienced Mr. Wells was convinced that full and authentic statistics were essential to effective acreage allotment programs. The intimate connection between statistical work and controversial issues is obvious. Moreover, Wells's concern over the matter shows that he has not been able entirely to avoid that effort "to forecast emerging problems" which he depreciated in 1948.

Some controversial research was continued, some avoided. — Who gets what share of the consumer's dollar? This is a recurring question. If specific inquiries please one group, they may offend others. Wells said in 1950: "We are now carrying forward 22 separate cost and margin studies under RMA." He hoped to systematize and refine a study of the United States, broken down into marketing areas—"if we are allowed to continue to work in that field."[16]

Cost and margin studies may provoke attacks, but they usually find favor in the farm bloc in Congress and in some farm organizations. Sources of support for other kinds of controversial research are not so apparent, and reports persist that the BAE refused, pushed aside, or "indefinitely postponed" such research. An agricultural economics head in a state college is said to have tried to enlist the BAE's support in research on tenure, only to be rebuffed until he threatened to take the matter up with a prominent senator. If, however, the BAE's leaders leaned over backward to avoid certain controversial issues in the last years of the bureau, they might answer that, had they led the attack, they would have been lonely St. Georges confronting numerous dragons with the help of only a little timorous applause from the sidelines. On the other hand, leadership does not know what support it will get until it takes risks.

Even more disconcerting, in the writer's judgment, are reports that the BAE scrupulously avoided engaging in, or putting its name to, any research which might appear to be critical of other federal agencies. The bureau might well recall its one-sided contests with powerful agricultural action agencies.[17] Moreover, its leaders might think twice before taking on, let us say, the army engineers or the Bureau of Reclamation. Nevertheless, if the principle that one federal agency must not criticize another is allowed to stand, it will go far toward emasculating any contribution that government-supported research might make toward rationalizing the political process.

3. No Escape from Participation in Policy

The BAE is continually called upon for studies and advice bearing upon policy issues; and its members take part in important policy discussions. As Wells told senators in 1948: "The Bureau, as an economic and statistical agency, serves the Secretary's office and various administrators of the Department, constantly. We serve Members of the Congress, constantly. We serve farm organizations constantly. We serve the farm press, constantly."[18] Nearly any day in the chief's office would supply many examples. Introductory hearings on annual appropriations in each house usually involve a ranging discussion of the agricultural situation, with many policy implications which heavily involve economic interpretations. An example of assistance to farm organizations is afforded by the "considerable analysis and calculation" required to calculate parity prices for a wide range of farm commodities according to different formulas.[19]

The BAE has been drawn upon for formal reports of Congress on agricultural policy. An excellent illustration is the report on "Long-Range Agricultural Policy" of the House Committee on Agriculture, which the BAE prepared.[20] Other congressional reports, though not prepared by the BAE, have heavily relied upon its work. Examples are the tenth report of the House Special Committee on Postwar Economic Policy and Planning, Postwar Agricultural Policies,[21] and the report Low-Income Families and Economic Stability, prepared by the staff of the subcommittee on low-income families of the Joint Committee on the Economic Report.[22]

To the reports specifically for Congress should be added more BAE documents which are general releases. The influence of the controversial mimeograph "A Conversion Program for the Cotton South" (1945) has been mentioned. In that year the bulletins, "What Peace Can Mean to the

American Farmer," were issued;[23] of these, Professor L. J. Norton, of the University of Illinois, remarked: "The BAE did an excellent job. . . . Many of us were skeptics about the basic optimism implied in it. I confess I was one. But frankly I believe that the time when price supports will do much, even short-run, economic good for the farmer, is a long way off."[24] The following year Peacetime Adjustments in Farming appeared.[25] If the BAE has not been able to maintain the same amount of interpretive material in its straitened circumstances, it has produced some examples, such as Sherman E. Johnson's Changes in American Farming,[26] which was widely acclaimed in the southern states that the writer visited in 1950. All these documents have important bearings upon agricultural policy.

Consider the function of the BAE in the USDA's contributions to policy-making since 1946. The BAE helped staff seventeen working committees and the four over-all committees in the USDA's appraisal of the long-range agricultural program, which was presented to Congress in October, 1947. According to Wells, the BAE worked "not as planners or directors, but rather as one of the bureaus which had a great deal of statistical and economic material which might be and was useful."[27]

After the 1948 election, when first a large group and then a smaller one conducted intensive seminars out of which emerged the Brannan Plan, the BAE was well represented. It is probably impossible for outsiders to appreciate how profound the split within agriculture became subsequent to the release of the Brannan Plan. Some thought that failure of the BAE spokesmen officially to condemn the proposal root and branch proved that independence of economic thought in the department had fallen to its nadir. Their opposite numbers looked askance on any questions or qualifications voiced by BAE economists after April 7 respecting the Brannan Plan.

The division was long-lasting. In February, 1951, the Secretary issued three memoranda reorganizing the USDA. Memorandum 1279 collected research generally under the Agricultural Research Administration but failed to include the BAE, which was left directly reporting to the Secretary. Some land-grant college spokesmen bitterly denounced the exception of the BAE. They asserted that reliable persons within the USDA had explained the exception as grounded upon the necessity for obligating the economists in the department to support the policies and programs of the Secretary. They warned that the BAE would lose public confidence if its function were confined to marshaling evidence

to support the Secretary's program rather than to engage in an unpreju-
diced search for the truth.

The writer's interpretation of this acrimonious relationship is somewhat different. The effect of the Brannan Plan made it abundantly clear
that the formal transfer of the planning function from the BAE to the
Secretary's office in 1945 was well advised[28]—but it should be recalled
(as Wells pointed out) that the Secretary's office "had never abdicated
as the chief planning agency of the Department." How could it have been
otherwise? At the same time, when some of the country's ablest economists
remained on the staff of the bureau, that agency would inevitably participate in high policy discussions within the department. How influential the
analysis of the bureau would be was another matter.

4. Conclusion

History shows that the BAE was always a controversial agency.
But the controversy over the BAE waxed and waned. Sometimes it waned
(as in the late 1920's and early 1930's) apparently because of a policy
in the BAE to stand aloof from controversy. Such retreat may no
longer be open to the bureau. At times, however, the BAE was able to
maintain a vigorous, critical role respecting agricultural policy, as
during most of Tolley's chieftainship (probably in part because the times
were propitious). Even after Tolley came to grief, the BAE could still
operate in somewhat the same way. Sometimes, again, the limits upon
the BAE's critical function became very narrow. The post=Brannan Plan
period is an example; but so was the post-Wallace-Taylor period of the
1920's, and that passed.

It seems to follow that the BAE had its ups and downs as an analytical
and critical agency for agriculture, organized within the United States
government itself. It is certainly notable that many of the vigorous
and forthright economists of Tolley's heyday remained in ranking positions
in the BAE of 1952-53, even though others had left.[29] If (as the writer
believes) it is good public policy to restore the BAE, this can be done;
but history suggests that sometimes such an agency will be able to
perform an effective and public critical function even respecting important issues in agricultural policy, while at other times its critical function
will have to be more informal. Even so, a significant informal critical
function—in conferences in the Secretary's office, in the committee rooms

of Congress, or elsewhere—can be maintained.[30]

In fulfilling its role, the BAE was extraordinarily vulnerable to a few strategically placed congressmen.[31] As has been shown, the BAE was also especially susceptible to attacks from the AFBF. It seems ironical that the AFBF should have helped diminish the influence of the BAE during 1946, when its leadership was vigorously advancing the case for a flexible price-support policy—a policy similar to that which the AFBF embraced in 1947. Be that as it may, the BAE's vulnerability to strategic attacks was notable, especially when compared to the intrenched position of many other USDA bureaus and agencies with their organized support.

The record establishes (a) that the BAE could maintain a critical, analytical function respecting policy issues; (b) that this function could not always be prosecuted with equal vigor or by the same open means; (c) that the willingness of leadership to take some risks was apparently essential to the bureau's active prosecution of work on controversial problems; and (d) that the BAE was inherently controversial and, intermittently, at least, quite vulnerable. Let us pursue two questions further.

First, is it in the public interest to re-create a BAE strongly oriented toward research on disputed issues? Surely a constitutional democracy founded on the proposition that a decent respect is due the opinions of mankind can give only an affirmative answer to this question. Again, if research is as nearly monopolized as it is in agriculture by public agencies, an agency like the BAE and its counterparts in the colleges of agriculture need to prosecute "programmatic research."[32] The executive committee and the agricultural policy committee of the Association of Land-Grant Colleges and Universities made a strong statement in 1946:

"The agricultural colleges and experiment stations in the several States are convinced that many, if not most, of the major difficulties which will confront American farmers in the years ahead concern economic issues such as: (a) Prices for products sold by farmers and articles purchased by them; (b) readjustment of wartime agricultural production programs to meet changed conditions; (c) provision of adequate employment opportunities for rural people; (d) ways of improving the level of living of farm operators and their families; (e) maintaining urban employment and income, and an abundant world trade.

"Likewise, the land-grant institutions believe that progress in the solution of these economic problems is largely dependent upon finding the facts on which sound economic policies must be based. This in turn means economic research and economic analysis on a national basis."

This quotation buttresses the writer's affirmative answer. Moreover, the same testimony suggests that such research needs to be institutionalized both in the states and in the federal government: "Surely the Congress will not make such a drastic cut in funds for the support of economic research in the face of certain fact that no other agency will be able to make up that curtailment. The individual land-grant institutions already are carrying greatly increased burdens due to enormously expanded veteran enrollments, and the necessity of helping the farmers of their respective States to make necessary adjustments to changed local conditions created by war and the aftermath of war. They have no intention of reducing their programs of agricultural economics research, but they are not in position to absorb with State-funds anything like an additional $500,000 program of agricultural economics research; neither is any State institution in a position to carry on the Nation-wide economic research now conducted by the Bureau of Agricultural Economics."[33]

In 1951 F. F. Hill, head of agricultural economics at Cornell, made the point succinctly—and in keeping with the statesman-like tradition of such previous Cornell spokesmen as A. R. Mann and C. E. Ladd: "The Bureau of Agricultural Economics renders an important service to agriculture not only through the compilation of statistics, which are important, but also through its technical studies. Speaking as a staff-member of a land-grant college, I would like to emphasize the importance of a staff such as that maintained by the Bureau which has a national point of view and is in a position to make studies of its own and to collaborate in regional and national studies with the land-grant colleges of the country which necessarily are primarily concerned with problems in their respective States."[34] It is ironical that the administration which directed the "fragmentization of the BAE" should be heavily staffed and advised by Cornellians.[35]

This leads to the second question: Who would sustain a revived BAE? Farm organization support could probably be written off; indeed, the best that can be hoped is for the Farm Bureau, especially, to be indifferent. The need for inner strength in the BAE's own leaders is obvious.

An important potential source of support would seem to lie in leaders in colleges of agriculture, who may work through influential persons in their own state and in Congress and who may co-operate effectively through the Association of Land-Grant Colleges and Universities. Doubtless there was considerable informal college support for the bureau which does not appear in the record. Unfortunately, the association recorded its support only very sporadically. Formal assistance from individual college officials was equally rare.[36]

On the other hand, land-grant college officials have probably contributed to the difficulties of the bureau. Thus Congressman Clarence Cannon appears to have had a strategic role in the acceptance of the Dirksen-engineered cut of the BAE in 1942.[37] The writer cannot believe that there was no one in the University of Missouri's college of agriculture who could have effectively supported the BAE at this juncture. Again, the controversial Coahoma County report was mimeographed and a few copies distributed for professional criticism in 1945-46. An official of the Mississippi Extension Service reportedly gave it to a congressman. In view of the consequences, this official's action, in the writer's judgment, is deeply to be deplored.[38] But the larger significance of these incidents should not be lost. They suggest that at critical junctures individuals in colleges of agriculture may be able either to harm or to help the BAE very greatly. With all our speculations about institutions of government, there remain many occasions in which there is no substitute for statesmanship in individuals.

Methodological note.—Readers familiar with the writer's article "The Bureau of Agricultural Economics under Fire: A Study in Valuation Conflicts (JFE, August, 1946) may note that the present chapter omits the methodological discussion respecting the role of valuations and beliefs in understanding the controversy over the bureau. The JFE article drew upon the concepts developed by Gunnar Myrdal in An American Dilemma (2 vols.; New York: Harper & Bros., 1944). See Vol. I, "Introduction" and chap. i; Vol. II, Appendix I. The relationships between beliefs about the facts and valuations about what ought to be done were explored as they were manifested in the controversies over the BAE. Some of the interpretations in the present chapter may be better understood by reference to the methodological discussion in the article, which has been omitted partly to save space in a discussion already very long. The use of Myrdal's concepts enables a more penetrating discussion of the troubles that have vexed the BAE; nevertheless, their use is subject to three qualifications which should be briefly mentioned.

In the first place, insistence upon the interpretation of controversies through analyzing the apparent beliefs and valuations of participants may blind the analyst to simpler and more valid interpretations. One of the writer's students made an elaborate explanation of a certain individual's statements in another public controversy (one to which these pages have not referred); his paper was read by some of the participants, who objected on the grounds that the statements concerned were simply lies and that everyone in the controversy knew that they were lies. Clearly an elaborate methodology may be abused if its use gives a false interpretation when a simple, straightforward analysis would give a true one.

In the second place, there is perhaps an inherent assumption in the belief-valuation analysis that, whereas valuations cannot be proved or disproved as such, they may rest on beliefs about facts which can be tested. The inference is that subsequently the values can be rationally attacked. Often this is true, but sometimes it is not. Consider religious beliefs. If the Protestant ethic maintains that the will of God is inscrutable, this is obviously a belief which cannot be tested by examination of "the facts."

In the third place, the belief-valuation concept need not serve to relax the obligation upon the individual for responsible moral judgments -- but it may have this effect. If one applies the belief-valuation concept beyond its limits, he may find himself probing for the explanation of human actions when the time has come to recognize that the situation can never be fully explained but that judgments must, nevertheless, be made. Should Asia or Europe have priority in American foreign policy? Should industry-wide collective bargaining be banned? Under a given set of circumstances, should price controls and rationing be employed to prevent inflation, or is reliance upon fiscal and monetary policy sufficient? All three questions may be illuminated by analyses of the facts, of beliefs about the facts, and of valuations about what ought to be done—but again, in all three questions, decisions will have to be made as judgments and not as inexorable conclusions from impeccable analysis. Respecting the problem set by the present book, the writer fully believes that an inquiry into the experience in agriculture can illuminate the question whether a democracy can effectively maintain a publicly supported "programmatic research" function; but, in the final analysis, whether it ought to maintain that function is a matter of judgment.

In 1948 the Joint Committee on Extension Programs, Policies,
and Goals of the USDA and the Association of Land-Grant Colleges
and Universities declared that "extension has a growing responsibility
to help rural people understand the complex social and economic
problems—local, national, and international—which confront them."
Following twenty years of prodding by determined men, a number of
state Extension Services were then consciously—if gingerly—probing
this field.

1.   Emergence and Scope of the Program

Specific agitation for an Extension Service program in public
policy began early. The Survey of Land-Grant Colleges and Universities
(1930) urged Extension to acknowledge an obligation beyond vocational
training, namely, in the area of "important social and humanistic purposes."
In 1931 Extension Director H. J. Baker (New Jersey) savagely criticized
both Extension and the experiment stations:[2] We are "confining our
thinking too much to state boundaries." Has Extension tackled economic
problems? "The answer . . . is an emphatic negative." Has it given due
attention to social organization in rural communities?"The . . . Service
has almost entirely ignored such problems." "In agriculture, the
extension activities have been mainly service. Many of the county agents
and . . . specialists are incapable of thinking otherwise until they are
yanked out of the ruts of self-esteem and complacency and given a
background through graduate study which will help them think in terms
of human welfare." In 1932 Dean C. E. Ladd of Cornell's college of
agriculture said: "Too many extension programs have attempted to turn
the wheels of progress back, to encourage the development of a particular
farm enterprise because college professors were interested in the
enterprise, and in spite of the fact that economic forces were causing
[its] abandonment."[3]

Then came the New Deal and World War II, both of which strongly stimulated Extension to re-examine its mode of attack. True, Director H. C. Ramsower of the Ohio Extension Service could still declare in 1946 that Extension had been "rather slow to enter into active programs dealing with public policy problems."[4] Nevertheless, when federal Extension Director M. L. Wilson called a meeting on the subject in 1949, representatives from eighteen states attended.

That conference drew up a statement of scope, objectives, and methods of Extension work in public policy.[5] The Farm Foundation immediately offered to sponsor a long-range program to help Extension Services define their function in public policy education. The offer was accepted, a committee established,[6] and a national meeting held in Chicago the following January. Conferences were held in each Extension Service region later in 1950, and four successive annual national conferences followed. Representatives from forty-four states attended the 1954 conference.[7] Despite the inevitable variation among the states in resources committed to the program, outstanding work is being done in some states in every region.

2. Some Problems in Public Policy Education

The genius of public policy programs in Extension is to attack controversial issues. Therefore, the entire previous analysis points up the central difficulty: Can the colleges of agriculture sustain programs of this sort in Extension (and also in research, since there must be something to "extend") in the face of the political pressure that is bound to be generated thereby? As previous chapters suggest, the answer to this question turns upon the intention of the institution to carry on such work, the possession by administrative officials and the faculty of wisdom and of political courage (which should be tempered, but not neutralized, by prudence), the ability to marshal political support, the institutional safeguards (including the definition and acceptance of appropriate roles by the governing board and the president), and public opinion.

A second difficulty is economic. Extension directors, deans, and everyone who shares in making the college's budget must be convinced that the public policy program is significant enough to warrant sizable allocations from scarce resources—and this in the face of competing

demands, many of which are strongly backed by commodity organizations.
Present support of the program may be attributed to its quality and to
the statesmanship of administrators in meeting a general need for which
little specific, organized demand exists.[8] How well the program will be
maintained is debatable. Agricultural Extension work has long justified
itself by concrete achievements—number of farm visits made, of meetings
held, and, especially, of practices changed. Programs like "balanced
farming" have encountered difficulties in their comparative disadvantage
in reporting "progress." How much more this disability attaches to
public policy programs! Even in Michigan, where the effort is extraordinarily vigorous and well staffed, only a handful of farmers apparently
have a "good understanding" of the relationship between support prices
and parity.[9]

A third difficulty is organizational. The program may fail to
penetrate the layers between the college and the farmer. In many states,
during 1950-51, the district Extension agents, through whom any new
departures initiated at the state level must filter to the counties, were
considered bottlenecks which impeded the introduction of innovations
in programs.[10] County staffs present special problems. A successful
county agent is an extremely busy man. Moreover, although his training
has broadened over the years, it is still concentrated commonly in
physical and biological sciences as applied to agriculture. Such training
neither predisposes him to favor the public policy program nor prepares
him to use its materials. He associates with eminently practical and
successful farmers, managers of co-operatives, main-street businessmen,
and others who have made their mark in this "vigorous, driving, and
progressive world." To such people public policy education is likely to
seem impractical ("what's it good for?") and maybe a little suspicious
("some more of that radical stuff from the university"). Finally, he has
to be acceptable to local politicians, who are often scornful of bookish
approaches to public policy problems—and he is aware of the intense
and pervasive intolerance that local politics often generates.

A fourth difficulty arises from the prejudices and biases of Extension
workers. Certain agricultural college officials and professors are really
politicians with academic hats—and yet their drive and ability bring them
close to the top of their scientific fields. Conscious of the "political
prejudices" of others, they often seem quite unaware of their own. On the

other hand are those college leaders who recognize their partisanship on such issues as the orientation and administrative control of soil conservation, rural rehabilitation, and reclamation programs—and who acknowledge tendencies to side with the farmer in controversies with business or labor. Consciousness of antiurban prejudices troubles them; so does the belief that they are identified by others with the "farm bloc."

Aware both of their own tendencies toward partisanship and also of the universal obligations of the land-grant institutions they serve, many agricultural college personnel strive to eliminate the effect of bias in their scholarly work. No aspect of methodology has fascinated the national conferences in public policy Extension work so much as the question of prejudice. All agree that educators should "articulate their values."[11] Purdue ably argues that Extension workers are obligated to present all sides of controversial issues, while scrupulously refraining from presenting their own conclusions about what is right, preferable, more expedient, or the lesser of two evils (as the case may be). Iowa State holds that the duty fully to explore alternatives is matched by an obligation upon the educator to give his own conclusions, if any, and the supporting reasons. While Iowa's approach seems preferable,[12] both have produced excellent programs; but what is most impressive is the effort to be unbiased. For, as men are not born educated, neither are they born objective. Moreover, in at least one state, college leaders have sternly refused—late in 1954, at least—to surrender the public policy program to, or even to share it with, a well-known farm organization. Refusal was based on the proposition that Extension had certain inherent advantages, which the farm organization could not possibly match, in the effort to approximate objectivity.

3. Public Opinion—"a Pervading and Impalpable Power"

Finally, the public policy educational program must deal with the most baffling phenomenon in democratic politics, public opinion. As has been recognized, the problem is quite different from those which beset programmatic research. Who forms the public—all citizens or only some of them? Is it compatible with democracy to assume that an "attentive public" exists (in Almond's term)? Can the existence of this public be ascertained? If so, what kind of information on what subjects should be offered to it?[13]

As if this were not enough, public policy educators must acknowledge the possibility that the most fateful alternatives may confront the citizen at any time. Fortunately, these alternatives slumber through most public policy educational programs in agriculture, dealing as they do with familiar controversies about agricultural prices, conservation, or credit; or reaching out to fiscal, monetary, and tariff policy; or focusing upon local issues involving roads, schools, public health, and the like.[14] Even on these matters, the "pertinent facts and relationships are not self-evident, but must be discovered," as Dr. Wellman noted. The issues are complex and often explosive—as participants in almost any school district reorganization can testify. In these matters, nevertheless (and despite occasional oratory to the contrary), the major characteristics of our political and economic system are ordinarily not in jeopardy.

In a half-dozen countries, however, the last generation has witnessed somewhat shaky constitutional governments overthrown by fascist or militarist dictatorships; in two huge countries autocratic regimes that still might have evolved toward constitutionalism have succumbed to authoritarian communism. In the United States new terrors are being substituted for the old fears of unemployment. Great rifts threaten to open in the consensus necessary to constitutionalism's survival.

How do these developments affect Extension work in public policy? Suppose that from Extension meetings on agricultural price policy the participants emerge with some rather firm choices among alternatives. Is the implication that candidates for Congress who accept these choices deserve the vote, regardless of their positions on other issues? However "right" a candidate was on farm policy, his constituents would probably reject him if he proposed to make peace with the Kremlin by surrendering western Europe. Would they reject him if he opposed those who vilify large numbers of the leading participants in the preceding administration as "soft" toward communism? Should they?

This question requires a decision upon what constitutes good citizenship; and this, in turn, prompts an inquiry into what constitutes good government. For in Communist states good citizens are good Communists; in Fascist states, good Fascists. In constitutional democracies, then, we must re-examine the bases, assumptions, and characteristics of our government and of the rights and duties of its citizens.

All that can be given here is an inkling of this task—of the approach to it, its dimension, and the reasons for its resurgence. Political philosophy has flourished when great questions about the nature of the state, its relationship to other associations, and the role of the citizen have arisen. The incipient decline of Greece in the fourth century B.C.; the medieval controversy over relationships between church and state; the emergence of constitutionalism in England; the rise of nationalism on the Continent; the swift, if uneven, change toward urban, industrial societies; and the French and Russian revolutions—all have set off philosophical inquiries into politics. For Americans an appropriate source is the federal constitutional period, with the debates it induced in Philadelphia, in the state ratifying conventions, and (most handily) in the Federalist Papers. Because its authors combined statesmanship with philosophy, B. F. Wright has written, the Federalist is "still by far the greatest book on politics ever written in America."[15]

Today's tensions demand new inquiries in political philosophy. Economics breeds political problems. Certain Farm Bureau and agricultural college leaders have long feared that the political pervasion of economic life would imperil liberty. They castigated the New Deal and the Fair Deal on this score; and they may well have been alarmed at President Eisenhower's pledge of December, 1953, that his administration would "protect the security, the welfare, and the economic stability of each individual citizen."[16] Can this guaranty be fulfilled without complete economic planning which sets prices, fixes production quotas, and eventually assigns work and issues permits to change jobs? Conservative farm leaders, if they are consistent, will say that this is where we will end if the nation's first office is used to instil such goals as proper ends of government. Such criticisms may fall more congenially on liberal ears than they did under previous administrations—when it was common to assume that anything done in the name of "the people" must be all right. The New Deal responded to political demands by providing a wide range of social legislation and building the implementing programs. One consequence inevitably was greatly to centralize political power. In view of the strength of political demands for governmental action and, above all, in view of international tensions, no informed person will argue that the American community can do without a formidable concentration of power. But the concentration itself was accomplished largely without regard for possible political consequences and even with disdain for those who

occasionally voiced doubts. It is ironical that the power concentrated in
Washington during the New and Fair Deals should serve in the 1950's
as a base for an assault upon many of those identified with the previous
Democratic administrations. Beyond mere irony, these wholesale
assaults contain dangerous threats to fundamentals of the Constitution
by infringements upon freedom of speech and assembly, by effective
denial of due process of law, and by erosion of the consensus necessary
to make a system of balanced powers work. The writer most profoundly
questions whether many agricultural leaders (in the USDA, the colleges,
and the farm organizations) are as intellectually and emotionally
conscious of these dangers as they are of those stemming from economic
regulation.[16a]

The deep divisions in present-day society need not have economic
roots alone. The smallest incident of interracial friction has global
repercussions. Devotees of different religions glare at each other over
armed frontiers. Communism and fascism challenge the philosophy
of constitutional democracy. In this country the prevention of subversion
must be balanced with the protection of constitutional rights of individuals.

These matters provide the ultimate and almost unbearably difficult
test of agricultural Extension's public policy program. The test is
unavoidable if the program is to offer more than training in the application of a few economic principles to agricultural production and
marketing. Nor can public policy educators escape the difficulty by
helping people learn the facts or fearlessly presenting the truth, as
Secretary Benson said in his otherwise admirable statement on the subject.[17] Of course, accurate observation and interpretation are essential
to good research and teaching in this as in other fields. However, was
Walter Lippmann right in late 1953 when he interpreted Attorney General
Brownell's attack upon the Truman administration as an act of unlimited
partisan warfare which, if unchecked, would be fatal to the Constitution?[18]
Was George F. Kennan right in asserting that now in the United States
virtually no one's character is safe from assassination?[19] Is Allan
Kline right when he finds the "American way of liberty and freedom under
law" imperiled by vigorous governmental subsidization, regulation, and
control of the economy?[20] Such judgments compel attention. All of
them should be examined in the light of the evidence; but none is a
geometric proposition finally to be marked Q.E.D.

On such questions, moreover, public policy educators cannot escape by "articulating their values" and then proceeding to factual analysis of alternatives. One may like ham better than cheese, small-town better than city living, or supermarkets better than corner groceries. He may prefer public to private power developments, valley authorities to interagency agreements, Extension to Soil Conservation Service operation of conservation programs, or income to sales taxes. But one does not merely prefer freedom from arbitrary arrest, for example, or freedom of religion. As President Pusey said: "We need to know, but we need also to believe, and what we want especially to do is to believe knowingly and to know with conviction."

XVII / The Politics of Agricultural Research and Extension

How do tax-supported education and research fare in America? In his Apology Socrates told the Athenians that "no man who goes to war with you or any other multitude, honestly striving against the many lawless and unrighteous deeds which are done in a State, will save his life; he who will fight for the right, if he would live even for a brief space, must have a private station and not a public one."[1] John Dewey wrote that a state which "will organize to manufacture and disseminate new ideas and new ways of thinking may come into existence some time, but such a state is a matter of faith, not sight."[2] In rejecting proposals for extending more federal aid to higher education, the Commission on Financing Higher Education found that, especially where study and research have been founded, as in the natural sciences and humanities, upon "a complex network of value judgments," academic freedom "is hard to defend. . . . In these fields public opinion is notoriously given to snap judgments, and in them centralized control could . . . do great damage."[3] Are researchers and educators on the public payroll independent of politics only because they refrain from examining controversial issues? Or can these persons find in institutional safe-guards and educational statesmanship enough protection so that a reasonable amount of work on politically divisive questions becomes an acceptable risk?

This book has sought to throw some light on these questions by examining the record of agricultural research and Extension. The inquiry has had to extend to the political interests of the agencies involved; the manner in which these interests are organized, advanced, and defended; and the effect upon the educational role of the agencies of their immersion in politics. There is no need to detail the conclusions reached in foregoing chapters, but some points should be restated.

1.   Major Inferences

Federal grants-in-aid for agricultural research and Extension have not been the means of federal political control. On the contrary, federal

194

grants have sometimes enabled agricultural colleges to resist state and local political pressures. Agricultural experience suggests, the writer believes, that the principle of federal grants could be safely extended to assist general education; but much informed judgment holds the opposite view.[4]

Political control of tax-supported research and Extension in agriculture operates essentially outside federal grants-in-aid. For one thing, influence stemming from, or associated with, national farm "action" programs has affected the scope and freedom of research and education in both the USDA and the agricultural colleges. On the whole, political influence associated with such programs has had a more obvious effect upon federal agencies than upon the state colleges. Thus the Bureau of Agricultural Economics (BAE) (1922-53) was, superficially at least, more vulnerable to political attack than many of the colleges. Looking deeper, however, one discerns another thing: the great power of state and local politics to influence colleges of agriculture, some of which have been virtually foreclosed from examining certain kinds of issues. On some matters and at some times, the federal BAE enjoyed more freedom of inquiry than many colleges did; on other matters colleges often had a wider latitude.

So far as policy-oriented research is concerned (and in this concept the writer includes the academic counseling of congressmen, administrators, farm leaders, and others who are formulating policy), rather effective roles should be definable and defendable for the USDA bureaus and agricultural colleges. Institutional protection for a considerable degree of freedom of inquiry can be devised. In part, this means the discovery of administrative arrangements and procedures, such as formally separating agricultural economic research in the USDA from the office of the Secretary and from the administration of major action programs—or such as stating and observing an appropriate division of function between land-grant college boards of control and college presidents. In part, this means imprinting upon each generation of researchers, their administrators, and their political overseers the proper conceptions of the function of agricultural research and the skills to defend it. Much more is involved, however, than inculcating the proper habits or conditioning those involved to respond to certain "cues" and to reject others. Also needed is academic statesmanship, in which wisdom and courage are adequately mixed and blended.

But the analysis must go further. Political influence upon publicly
supported research and education cannot be sufficiently considered
by examining organized groups and the more accessible parts of the
policy-making process. Public opinion has long been acknowledged as
an eminent force in politics.

Thus many American farmers are widely believed to favor high,
rigid price supports at about 90 per cent of parity. This interpretation
helps to explain the initial attack upon research in low-nicotine tobacco
in Kentucky in 1951 (chap. vi). It helps account for the Brannan Plan,
the tension within the American Farm Bureau Federation (AFBF) after
it officially indorsed flexible price supports in 1947, and the friction
between the AFBF and the USDA in 1949-52. The state of public opinion
in agriculture has often been considered a limiting factor respecting
policy-oriented research and Extension work. On the other hand, public
opinion has sometimes been marshaled to sustain colleges and universities against political attacks.

Even more important are the subtler aspects of public opinion.
Analysts must look beyond organized pressures and visible political
processes to the "underlying" or "potential" groups. Particularly for
agricultural Extension work in public policy (and for the research
that services it), the addition of these dimensions of "politics in depth"
introduces novel problems. An entire political community, and not
merely a few leaders, must be reached with educational programs. Here
the guides, which seem fairly defensible and adequate for policy-oriented
research, fail. Interpretations of the nature of the problem and how to
deal with it conflict. By defining the scope of the present inquiry to
exclude considering how to reach rural people generally with agricultural
Extension public policy programs, one can escape this vexing problem.
But this is legerdemain, and it is truer to say that a vitally important
aspect of the subject of this book remains most inconclusively handled.

With some assurance, however, one can stress again the importance
of the fact that the agencies here under review are participants in the
political process. Whether analysis is concerned with policy-oriented
research or with citizenship education, the political characteristics of
the public agencies involved are highly significant. It will be appropriate
to close, therefore, with some further treatment of the subject which
introduced the first chapter, the political characteristics of colleges of
agriculture.

2. Decentralizing Influence of Agricultural Colleges

Individually and collectively, the colleges of agriculture have worked to decentralize many parts of agricultural policy formation and execution. In their contacts with federal administrators and (it may be assumed) with various other persons of importance in the system of government (congressmen, farm organization leaders, etc.), college officials consistently criticize the centralization of policy-making and policy execution in Washington. Sweeping recommendations for decentralization were made, for example, in the report of the Association of Land-Grant Colleges and Universities' committee in 1944, Postwar Agricultural Policy.[5]

Certain aspects of agricultural policy formation and execution appear appropriate for decentralization.[6] But the centrifugal effects of the agricultural colleges cannot be properly considered respecting agricultural policy in isolation. A host of other political interests are organized to pull policy-making and administration out of Washington and into the hands of the states. It is certainly plausible that these interests often reinforce each other. Do the decentralizing efforts of the colleges reinforce similar efforts by other political interests in other areas?[7] If so, with what methods and to what effects?

3. Advocacy of an Educational Approach

Agricultural colleges have stressed research and education as effective approaches to the solution or amelioration of human problems. Research and Extension in agriculture are largely predicated upon the ideal of individual and group self-help, with scientific assistance. Efforts to realize this ideal encounter many difficulties. For example, personal service has been called the "bane of agricultural Extension work." County workers are often harried by demands for special services—sometimes the phrase "chicken-culling" is applied to doing favors for those influential in county affairs. Again, an Extension specialist may be assigned to help a group of vegetable farmers market their crop. If this group can collectively afford to pay for the service, is it appropriate for Extension to offer it without charge? If research is done primarily to help a small group of prosperous growers of a particular commodity, does the fact that the research is written up in a way to suggest its general value justify the public subsidy involved?

There are administrative difficulties in realizing the ideal. Some county agents are specialists, e. g., in animal husbandry or agronomy, who are neither equipped by training nor motivated by interest to develop diverse adult educational programs for their clients. Again, the county agent may head an enlarged staff of specialists and become absorbed in administration. Sometimes he must spend considerable time recruiting and holding members in the farm organization who are necessary if his county is to continue with Extension work. Or the program may suffer from unsatisfactory communication between state and county offices.[8] State Extension administrators are often overwhelmed with duties and have to cope with the problem of co-ordinating a staff of specialists each of whom is understandably anxious to push his own program to the hilt. Finally, Extension has a simple method of recording progress by reporting practices changed. In so far as Extension is merely training its clients in the use of fairly simple skills, this method of reporting is probably adequate; but it is insufficient for gauging Extension's success in enabling its clients to make more informed choices among alternatives.[9]

In another vein, the emphasis upon research and education may ignore the fact that this approach is not really sufficient for many farmers who are unable to take advantage of it—through lack of sufficient land, credit, or necessary skills or through physical debilities that could be corrected. Colleges of agriculture have studied the problem,[10] which has also been acknowledged by the Survey of Land-Grant Colleges and Universities (1930),[11] the Joint Committee Report on Extension Programs, Policies, and Goals (1948),[12] and (rather infrequently) in meetings of the Association of Land-Grant Colleges and Universities.[13]

The question of reaching its potential personnel remains a vexing one to the agricultural research and Extension system. An attitude exists among some college personnel that many rural people in poor situations are beyond help; they are shiftless, perhaps, or, simply, they like it that way—it is a "way of life." On this subject, W. E. Hendrix has cogently remarked: "The importance of low-income people's own values as a factor in their low incomes cannot be denied. On the other hand, the ascription of rural poverty essentially to the 'ne'er-do-well' character of the poverty-stricken people is valid only if it can be shown that such people are acting with full knowledge of their production and employment alternatives and that there are no imperfections in the capital and labor markets and no institutional factors barring their entry into other kinds of employment. Such explanation is inconsistent and invalid if people are unaware of their employment alternatives. It is invalid if people know of more productive kinds of production or employment but are unable to finance the change. It is invalid if there are monopolistic and monopsonistic trade policies which operate in a restriction of output and employment. It is invalid if their entry into more remunerative kinds of employment is restricted by considerations of race, color, or creed. In short, one cannot consistently hold only to a 'ne'er-do-well' explanation of poverty and in the same breath damn the labor unions or corporations for their price-fixing policies or the government and farmers for their cotton, tobacco, and other crop-control programs. Rather, admission of imperfections in knowledge or of imperfections in capital or labor markets or of institutional barriers to the mobility of resources postulated in competitive theory shifts some of the responsibility for low incomes and poverty upon our educational and other social and political institutions, or upon society in general."[14]

Still, in the writer's experience, even those who deny that the problem exists never fully convince themselves; they can never eliminate the vestiges of the ideal that education should be a universal birthright. Many others in the colleges of agriculture are painfully conscious of the limited coverage of their program. The differences between what custom or insufficient resources constrain them to emphasize and what they feel they ought to do provide continuing tensions.

The writer believes that considerable value inheres in the vigorous advocacy of the research and educational approach by the colleges. Agricultural action programs—in soil conservation, production and subsistence credit, and production control—tend to develop approaches of "telling the farmer what to do." If a man has a quota of farm loans to make and supervise or of conservation plans to sign up, he is under considerable compulsion to work in this fashion. Against this tendency, the emphasis of the researchers and Extension workers in agriculture upon self-help, upon demonstrations, upon co-operation by farmers in public programs, is wholesome. Moreover, the educational approach is humanistic in that its aim is to arm all people with the ability to act rationally upon their problems, and, up to the point where reason alone must accept the precedence of faith, to orient themselves satisfactorily to their universe. It is not argued that action programs in agriculture and elsewhere fail to embrace humanistic goals. Yet the very concentration upon specific and limited goals which is generally recognized as a weakness of the educational approach is commonly the strength of the action agency.

4. College Conservatism

The personnel of public agricultural research and education has been preponderantly conservative. Jealous of their states' prerogatives, steeped in the "liberal" traditions of the free market, oriented toward those farmers who are normally in the best positions to help themselves — agricultural college administrators have often disliked federal action programs. There are many agrarian radicals in this country, but the writer recalls none among the agricultural deans and directors he has met. The negotiating of hierarchies, which all these men have done, has a sobering influence.

Many agricultural college deans and directors have had natural science backgrounds. Frequently they have been highly skeptical of social science. They have often combined considerable political skill with strikingly superficial conceptions of politics. It has been the rare agricultural college official who could acknowledge the service of the New Deal as a response to irresistible public demands — but a response which helped channel these demands so that the fundamentals of the American constitutional system were kept intact. In recent years many social scientists have been advanced to agricultural directorships, deanships, and sometimes to presidencies of land-grant institutions. None of these newcomers can aspire to be shrewder politicians than many of the "old indestructibles" who have traditionally run Extension Services, agricultural colleges, land-grant institutions, and the Association of Land-Grant Colleges and Universities. In general, however, the newcomers with social science backgrounds have somewhat more sophisticated conceptions of politics than their counterparts, coming out of the natural sciences, have had. And yet this greater sophistication is quite compatible with the conservatism that characterizes (in the writer's judgment) many of the social scientists-become-administrators.

Some examples of land-grant college conservatism are at hand. In

1922 at the Washington agricultural conference called by President
Harding, a prominent agricultural college dean vehemently denounced
organized labor as responsible for society's ills.[15] In his presidential
address to the 1925 convention of the Association of Land-Grant Colleges
and Universities, A. F. Woods considered the farm problem: "The low-
grade inefficient farmer who has demonstrated inability to learn and
cooperate with others must be eliminated. These produce the surplus
by slovenly methods and do most of the howling."[16] The following year
Chairman R. A. Pearson of the association's executive committee
proudly announced that Woods had been named director of research of
the USDA, a post which the association had helped to establish. Pearson's
statement, as the grip of the depression tightened in 1930, that the
engineering experiment station bill was the "most important measure in
Congress . . . in the interests of farm relief" may be recalled;[17] it is
rivaled in fatuity only by the remarks of Extension Director R. K. Bliss,
of Iowa, in the dismal year 1932. Bliss noted that the desperate situation
called for some adventuring: "This is a good time to ask ourselves . . . :
Are we doing everything we can to develop . . . local leaders to work with
and through their neighbors? Are we furnishing these local leaders with
educational material . . . ? Do we have this material prepared in the
most attractive manner? Are we making full use of slides, films, and
charts? Are we making as large a use of radio and newspaper publicity
as we should? Are we cooperating as fully as possible with agricultural
organizations, cooperatives, schools, and churches?"[18] In the succeeding
paragraph, Extension was counseled to help farmers in their search
for recreation.

The continuous skepticism of many college officials concerning
the federal action programs did not provide them with enough insight
to co-operate wholeheartedly in the state and local planning program
of 1938-42 or to defend that program in its extremities. In discussing
the experiment station in postwar planning, R. B. Corbett, of the University of Maryland, declared in 1942 that the "best opportunity this
country has of returning to States' rights and real democracy" was to
carry out agricultural research along traditional lines, making sure
that it was financed by the states rather than by the federal government.[19]

Indeed, the complaints of college spokesmen themselves of the
failure of the land-grant institutions to rise to the challenge of the times

is evidence that the writer is not alone in attributing an essential conservatism to these institutions.[20] Interviews provide further evidence.
There was the land-grant college president who dilated upon the danger
to free institutions of the federal grants-in-aid for agricultural research
and Extension. There was the land-grant college official who described
cities as blots on the body politic, where people lead morbid, unnatural
lives, and are mostly New Dealers. There was the refusal of a state
Extension director to co-operate in a meeting in which the Hospital
Survey and Construction Act of 1946 was discussed. There was, reportedly, the gloom at the Association of Land-Grant Colleges and Universities meeting following the Truman victory in 1948. There was the
depreciation of the Farmers Union by numerous college officials. There
was the characterization of their own college of agriculture as "very
conservative" by two Farm Bureau officials in different states—neither
of them Ohio.

In appraising agricultural conservatism, it is appropriate to examine
the function of conservatism in politics. Frederick Watkins, in The
Political Tradition of the West,[21] follows a discussion of the awakening
of the middle classes and of the emergence of liberal constitutionalism
with a chapter on the conservative reaction. Aristocrats (meaning landed
gentry) combined with farmers (mostly peasants) to counteract the
political drives of the middle classes which had eventuated in the French
Revolution and created widespread ferment in the Western world.

The ideas which, to some extent, informed the conservative reaction
were presented by political philosophers such as Edmund Burke, who
opposed the faith of the Enlightenment in the ability of human reason
to solve all problems. Burke and others argued that "man and nature
alike are so complex that no mortal mind can hope to understand the
full consequences of any given action." Hence they replaced the theory
that progress is the product of concentrated efforts of pure reason
with a theory which stresses the superiority of organic social growth.
This view by no means rejects all social change. It rather argues that
the emergent social order can be swept away only with the direct consequences; that order should be kept, in general, precisely because it
permits orderly change as human reason brings itself to bear upon those
aspects of social relationships which have become unendurably irri-
tating. Watkins remarks: "The value of a conservative theory lay in
the fact that, by inspiring rural resistance to the urban forces of the

Enlightenment, it provided modern society with one of the elements necessary for the establishment of an internal balance of power."

In a similar vein, R. G. Collingwood[22] interprets conservative politics in a typical analysis of power checking power—here, the power exercised by organized political parties which are sufficiently agreed to contest their differences by political, i.e., peaceful, means rather than by resort to violence. Collingwood quotes one conservative who explained that he was a "brake" on the vehicle of progress, continuing that it was essential for any vehicle to have a brake!

Behind both expositions of conservatism lies a distillation of Western political philosophy in two cardinal points. First, while political society is not to be equated with civilization, the complexity of human institutions, the development of an ever more productive human society, and the spreading of the fruits thereof to an ever wider populace all require initially that a political order be established and maintained— and, more recently, that government itself be employed in a positive way to create and distribute goods; all this underwrites the necessity of organizing political power. But, second, political power, on the lesson of history, must be checked; it can be checked only by an antagonist of its own kind, namely, political power; hence, a constitutional system is indicated in which dualities of disagreement within agreement, of government and opposition, can exist.

According to these analyses, conservatism has its uses. Furthermore, as one ponders the conservatism of the colleges, he is forced to recall the representative characteristic of these and other agricultural agencies, discussed in chapters i and ix. above. If the colleges stand between the farmers and the rest of us, they may appear conservative from the standpoint of northern urbanites, while appearing much less so to many influential persons in agriculture.

Are the agricultural colleges conservative in the sense of the "brake on progress"? One can slow down a vehicle with a brake, or he can stop it completely by sabotaging the machinery. If to be conservative is to apply a brake, the perversion of conservatism is to use sabotage. Some of our ultra- or radical conservatives or reactionaries seem willing to risk the destruction of our social machinery in their effort to establish control over it. But many conservatives are as repelled as the liberals by the actions of these worthies.

Where do agricultural college personnel (and agriculturalists generally) stand? In numerous conversations in the South the writer has
encountered only one official of an agricultural college whose savagely
reactionary opinions exploded during the interview. This man's attitude
was as untypical as it was verbally violent. Many of his colleagues
deplored his opinions.

In recent years, moreover, an excellent sign of the radical conservative or reactionary has been his devotion to Senator Joseph R.
McCarthy, of Wisconsin, whose methods have been publicly deplored by
many conservative Americans and who was the target of a motion for
a vote of censure made by Senator Ralph Flanders, of Vermont, in
July, 1954.[23] In a considerable number of the writer's interviews, all
of which predate the Army-McCarthy hearings in the spring of 1954,
Senator McCarthy's name has come up. One prominent farm leader
(though not an officer of a national farm organization) declared that
he considered the senator to be one of the nation's most useful citizens.
All other farm leaders who have expressed themselves to the writer
have been either vehemently opposed to Senator McCarthy, mildly
opposed, or critical but rather indifferent. Among agricultural college
personnel with whom the writer has discussed the question, one approved
the senator "because he is against the same things that I'm against,"
and another had shifted from approval to outspoken opposition. All
other agricultural college personnel who expressed an opinion were
critical of McCarthy, most of them intensely so.

In short, the temper of most agricultural college personnel seems
typically to range from moderately to rather markedly conservative.
But the fire-eating reactionary seems to be an aberration. The writer
finds this conclusion reassuring. Nevertheless, the American political
community is experiencing breath-taking changes. Some interests and
the groups clustered around them are rapidly expanding; others are
remaining stationary or even contracting. Can the American political
institutions, "the arrangements by which we live together," be modified
to accommodate the new distribution of interests which is emerging?
America is fortunate in the temperance of its agricultural leadership;
but, in the present and prospective social tensions, temperance by itself
will prove insufficient. Enlightened and vigorous statesmanship will be
required.

Chapter I

1. Cf. David B. Truman, The Governmental Process (New York: Alfred A. Knopf, 1951), p. 33 and passim.

2. Agriculturalists interested in this problem will find richly rewarding the study of Kurt Riezler, "Political Decisions in Modern Society," Ethics, Vol. LXIV, No. 2, Part II (January, 1954), available at the University of Chicago Press. See also the author's "Farm Politics and Some Problems of American Democracy," in the 50th Proceedings of the Association of Southern Agricultural Workers (1953). The writer has also borrowed Arthur Moore's expressive title, The Farmers and the Rest of Us (Boston: Little, Brown & Co., 1945).

3. Thus the USDA was established in 1862 "to acquire and diffuse among the people . . . useful information on subjects connected with agriculture in the most general and comprehensive sense of that word" (12 Stat. 387, chap. 72, sec. 2); cf. the Morrill Act, establishing the agricultural and mechanical colleges, July 2, 1862 (12 Stat. 504, chap. 130, sec. 4); the Hatch Act, providing the first federal grants for agricultural experiment stations, March 2, 1887 (24 Stat. 440, chap. 314, sec. 1); and the Smith-Lever Act of May 8, 1914, providing the first federal grants for agricultural Extension (38 Stat. 372, chap. 79, sec. 1).

4. Cf. C. J. Friedrich, Constitutional Government and Democracy (rev. ed.; Boston: Ginn & Co., 1950), p. 344, and Robert K. Merton et al., Reader in Bureaucracy (Glencoe, Ill.: Free Press, 1952), passim.

5. Federalist, No. 51 (see Douglas Adair, "The Authorship of the Disputed Federalist Papers," William and Mary Quarterly, I [April and July, 1944], 97-123, 235-65).

6. The phrase is Pendleton Herring's (The Politics of Democracy [New York: Rinehart & Co., 1940], p. 111). Efforts to pin political labels on groups or organizations are often ill-advised. The writer does not suggest that many or most college officials embrace a common ideology the well-articulated principles of which can be applied to answer virtually any political question that arises. Still, a common point of view seems to exist that is distinctly worth noting and that can be suggested by using Herring's phrase without implying that agricultural college folk are in anything like an intellectual lock step on crucial issues.

7. Land-grant colleges and universities number sixty-nine, including the forty-eight institutions mentioned, seventeen colleges for Negroes, three territorial universities (Alaska, Hawaii, and Puerto Rico), and the Massachusetts Institute of Technology. Until November, 1954, the seventeen Negro colleges were not members of the Association of Land-Grant Colleges and Universities. This study includes neither the Negro colleges, the territorial universities, nor M.I.T.

8. 12 <u>Stat</u>. 504, chap. 130, sec. 4.

9. It seems best to capitalize "Extension Service" (or, simply, "Extension") throughout; often the Extension Service will be discussed in relationship to other agricultural agencies which will be capitalized, such as the Soil Conservation Service (SCS) of the USDA. Moreover, to capitalize "Extension Service" helps to distinguish it from the general college or university extension activities.

10. The significance of the agricultural experience for the problem of publicly supported research and education as it is brought to bear upon controversial issues can be understood without special study of resident teaching in colleges of agriculture. A compelling aspect of the study is the possible political influence deriving from federal grants-in-aid; whereas (as will be seen) the federal grants for Extension and research in agriculture are large, the grants for resident teaching are relatively small ($50,000 annually to each state and territory [act of August 30, 1890, 26 <u>Stat</u>. 417, chap. 841, sec. 1]), and the money is made generally available in the land-grant colleges and universities rather than concentrated in agriculture; hence its effects are diluted.

11. House <u>Hearings</u>, Agricultural Appropriations, fiscal 1954, Part 3, p. 989. Territories are included; also note that in "the majority of the States, Alaska, Hawaii, and Puerto Rico, 4-H Club work is conducted by county agents, county home demonstration agents, and assistants," so that the figure for boys' and girls' club agents is misleading.

12. <u>Ibid</u>., p. 978.

13. <u>Ibid</u>., p. 982.

14. <u>Ibid</u>., Part 2, p. 379.

15. For the reorganization see the writer's "The Republican Department of Agriculture—a Political Interpretation," XXXVI, <u>JFE</u>, No. 2 (May, 1954), 210-27. The six major research bureaus are the Bureau of Agricultural Industry (established in 1884); the Bureau of Agricultural and Industrial Chemistry (established as now constituted in 1943); the Bureau of Dairy Industry (1924); the Bureau of Entomology and Plant Quarantine (consolidated from previous agencies in 1934; federal work in entomology dates from 1854); the Bureau of Human Nutrition and Home Economics (established as now constituted in 1923); and the Bureau of Plant Industry, Soils, and Agricultural Engineering (as the Bureau of Plant Industry, it dates from 1902). The $30,000,000 is calculated from House <u>Hearings</u>, Agricultural Appropriations, fiscal 1954, Part 2, pp. 460, 493, 593, 647, 707, and 797; the Bureau of Animal Industry's work in "animal disease control and eradication," spending some $8,000,000 in the fiscal year 1952, and work comparable thereto was not counted as research.

16. CF. David B. Truman, op. cit., "Rules of the Game," Index, and "The Democratic Mold," pp. 129 ff.; Walter Lippmann, The Phantom Public (New York: Macmillan Co., 1925).

17. Whether public institutions are subject to more pressure than private ones need not be argued. Certain agricultural officials have vigorously denied this proposition to the writer, while others in the same colleges have said that the writer could not hope freely to pursue

his own studies as a staff member in their institutions. Numerous examples of overt pressure upon private institutions exist, and the more subtle pressures upon them may be very restrictive. Thus private institutions may be "free" to study controversial issues, if such research is not crowded out of the budget. On December 12, 1952, Benjamin Fine wrote:

"American colleges and universities will spend a record total of more than $350,000,000 for research projects during this academic year. Most of this money—about $300,000,000—has been granted by the Federal Government. Business foundations and individual donors are providing the rest. [Query: What of state governments?]
"Ninety per cent of the money is earmarked for research in the physical and biological sciences. Only a fraction is set aside for research in the humanities. Virtually none of the Government's funds will be devoted to the social sciences or liberal arts.
"This 'imbalance' is causing concern among educational leaders" (New York Times, sec. 1, p. 1).

18. This does not mean that great multitudes of people are marshaled to support the college; it is more likely to be the "attentive public"; cf. Gabriel Almond, The American People and Foreign Policy (New York: Harcourt, Brace & Co., 1950), Index; and see Kurt Riezler, op. cit., Secs. V and VI, on opinion leaders.

Chapter II

1. S. E. Morison and H. S. Commager, The Growth of the American Republic (2d ed.; New York: Oxford University Press, 1937), I, 158-62, 172.

2. 4 Wheat. 316; cf. Morison and Commager, op. cit., pp. 330-31, 337.

3. See below, chap. vii.

4. John D. Black, Agricultural Reform in the United States (New York: McGraw-Hill Book Co., 1929), chap. i and Appendix B, pp. 493-94. See this source for the pre-New Deal period generally; see also Theodore Saloutos and John D. Hicks, Agricultural Discontent in the Middle West, 1900-1939 (Madison: University of Wisconsin Press, 1951); articles by Chester C. Davis, F. F. Elliott, and others, in Farmers in a Changing World (United States Department of Agriculture Yearbook [Washington, D.C.: Government Printing Office, 1940]).

5. Chester C. Davis, op. cit., and J. K. Galbraith, "The Farm Bureau," Fortune, June, 1944.

6. When price supports are at 90 per cent of parity, readers may wonder why prices can fall to 84 per cent (or even considerably lower). A number of reasons are offered as explanations. There are inconveniences in applying and qualifying for loans on grains. A farmer must have approved storage himself or he must put his grain in a warehouse approved by the Commodity Credit Corporation (CCC), in which event he pays storage charges; or, if the farmer makes a purchase agreement with the government, he assumes all risks involved in being able to deliver grain of the stipulated grade on the due date. Bumper crops usually overflow storage space, and the excess grain drives prices down. Variations in quality—the existence of a great deal of low-quality grain—

drives prices down. There are other reasons as well. See the statement by the USDA, in Senate Hearings, S. 3052, "General Farm Program," (83d Cong., 2d sess. [March, 1954]), Part 1, pp. 25-26.

7. Marketing quotas on tobacco were upheld in Mulford v. Smith, 307 U.S. 38 (1939); the extension to excess wheat produced but fed to livestock on the home farm was in Wickard v. Filburn, 317 U.S. 111 (1942).

8. The sixteen steps were as follows: (1) collecting basic data on planted acreage and yields; (2) reconstituting farms; (3) contacting farmers to obtain basic data; (4) computing "war crops" credit (for a number of years farmers were encouraged to grow crops declared to be needed for the war effort; it was provided that the acreages shifted from the basic crops to "war crops" would not be subtracted from their historical bases of the basic crops); (5) computing diversion credit (in subsequent years provision has also been made not to penalize farmers who shift from basic to other crops, under certain circumstances); (6) determining individual farm allotments and yields by local committees; (7) preparing listing sheets and allotment notices; (8) preparing allotment regulations, procedures, and forms; (9) preparing forms, etc., for the marketing quota referendum; (10) holding the referendum; (11) considering appeals; (12) developing farm marketing quota forms; (13) measuring farms; (14) computing acreage; (15) preparing and issuing marketing quota notices; (16) receiving, recording, and processing marketing quota reports, etc. (House Hearings, Agricultural Appropriations, fiscal 1954, Part 3, pp. 1478-79).

9. U.S. v. Butler, 297 U.S. 1 (1936).

10. House Hearings, Agricultural Appropriations, fiscal 1954, Part 1, p. 24.

11. Charles M. Hardin, The Politics of Agriculture (Glencoe, Ill: Free Press, 1952), chap. ii, sec. 4. Reference to "grants-in-aid" in the text is not to federal grants to states for research, education, etc., but to subsidies in cash or kind to farmers to induce them to follow conservation practices or to make production shifts.

12. The agreement is printed in John M. Gaus and Leon A. Wolcott, Public Administration and the United States Department of Agriculture (Chicago: Public Administration Service, 1940), pp. 463-65, and see pp. 157-59; see also below, pp. 32-34, 48, 144, 160, 216.

13. House Hearings, Agricultural Committee (H.R. 8402; 73d Cong., 2d sess.), Serial I, p. 161.

Chapter III

1. By the Hatch Act of 1887 and the Smith-Lever Act of 1914. The land-grant colleges benefited from land grants under the Morrill Act of 1862. Subsequent federal grants-in-aid for agricultural research in the states were authorized by the Adams Act, the Purnell Act, the Bankhea Jones Act, and the Research and Marketing Act (Hope-Flannagan).
Additional grants-in-aid for agricultural Extension in the states were

provided by the Capper-Ketcham Act, the Bankhead-Jones Act (with amendments), the Clarke-McNary Act, the Norris-Doxey Act, Title V of the Housing Act of 1949, and the Research and Marketing Act. In 1953 Congress passed H.R. 4677 to consolidate previous acts authorizing grants-in-aid for agricultural Extension. See House Hearings, Committee on Agriculture, "Extension Service Consolidation" (83d Cong., 1st sess.), Serial J.

The Office of Education of the Federal Security Agency administers funds appropriated for land-grant colleges by the Second Morrill Act, the Nelson Amendment, and the Bankhead-Jones Act.

This report is not designed to reproduce and analyze the details of grants-in-aid administration in this field. Basic laws are available in the Revised Edition of Laws Applicable to the United States Department of Agriculture (Washington, D.C.: USDA, 1945), Vol. I, chaps. xiii and xiv (with supplements); cf. U.S. Code, secs. 301 et seq. and 361 et seq. Brief accounts of federal administering agencies appear in the U.S. Government Manual and in the annual reports of the appropriate federal agencies.

Analytical accounts may be found, among other sources, in the following: Survey of Land-Grant Colleges and Universities (directed by Arthur J. Klein; United States Department of the Interior, Office of Education, Bull. 9 [2 vols.; Washington, D.C., 1930]), cited below as the "Survey"; A. C. True, A History of Agricultural Extension Work in the United States, 1785-1923 (Washington, D.C.: Government Printing Office, 1928); Gladys Baker, The County Agent (Chicago: University of Chicago Press, 1939); Russell Lord, The Agrarian Revival: A Study of Agricultural Extension (New York: American Association for Adult Education, 1939); V. O. Key, Jr., The Administration of Federal Grants to States (Chicago: Public Administration Service, 1937); George A. Works and Barton Morgan, The Land-Grant Colleges (Staff Study No. 10, prepared for the President's Advisory Committee on Education [Washington, D.C.: Government Printing Office, 1939]); Council of State Governments, Federal Grants-in-Aid (Chicago, 1949).

2. Report of the OES for 1923, p. 3.

3. Reports of the OES for 1924, 1926, 1928, and 1931.

4. II, 591. This is affirmed in a later study, which showed that the states spent $20 for every federal dollar for the function of general direction and planning of state research (Research and Related Services in the USDA [prepared for the House of Representatives Committee on Agriculture (81st Cong., 2d sess)], III, Chart "A").

5. The critical function of the OES might be strengthened. First, the legalistic accounting function of ascertaining whether a state is conforming to the relevant legal provisions attached to federal grants would be separated from the critical, advisory function respecting the experimental program in the states. A small, permanent staff, not necessarily qualified themselves as research scientists, would perform the former function. The latter function would then be performed by outstanding scientists in the several fields, who would be recruited for brief terms, perhaps a year at a time, from panels nominated by professional societies. Researchers in the states might welcome an occasional critical examination of their programs on their home grounds by eminent scientists so recruited from other institutions, from the federal government, or

from private institutions, foundations, or industries. At the same time, such outstanding figures would not want to commit themselves to long periods of employment by the OES, although many of them would surely welcome a year's tour of this kind of duty. The writer discussed this kind of examination with many state research administrators in 1950 and 1951, and the general reaction was favorable.

6. Charles M. Hardin, The Politics of Agriculture (Glencoe, Ill.: Free Press, 1952),chaps. ii, iv-vi.

7. An experiment station director said in 1951 that during the 1930's the increases in research appropriations for federal bureaus compared to funds available for experiment stations led to some friction arising out of the inauguration of federal research in the states; however, an agreement was negotiated about 1940 under which all federal research in the states would be conducted co-operatively with state experiment stations. A search of the annual reports of the experiment station organization and policy committee of the Association of Land-Grant Colleges and Universities from 1939 to 1944 disclosed no mention of such agreement. When research relationships were reported, they were praised as highly satisfactory.

8. The six research bureaus in the Agricultural Research Administration, USDA, received $23,600,000 in appropriations for fiscal 1943 and $35,400,000 in fiscal 1951. In 1943-51 the funds available for state agricultural experiment stations from both state and federal sources increased from $21,000,000 to $60,000,000 (House Hearings, Agricultural Appropriations, fiscal 1952, Part 1, Table 5, p. 59; see also Research and Related Services in the USDA, III, 2614, Chart "B").

9. Cf. True, op. cit., pp. 119-20; see Works and Morgan,op. cit., Appendix C, for a reproduction of a typical memorandum between the USDA and a college of agriculture.

10. Sec. 6 of the Smith-Lever Act and sec. 4 of the Adams Act of March 16, 1906, chap. 951.

11. The Hatch, Adams, and Purnell Acts for research grants called for no state offsets, whereas $4,200,000 of the $4,700,000 (approximately) of Smith-Lever grants for Extension have to be matched, dollar for dollar, by the states. In the Bankhead-Jones Act of 1935, Congress reversed itself by authorizing an additional $12,000,000 of Extension grants without matching and an additional $2,863,000 of research grants with matching. The Bankhead-Jones Amendment of 1945 added $12,500,-000 for Extension with matching. The matching requirement may coerce states by forcing them to budget more funds for agricultural research and Extension than they otherwise would. For "low-income" states, the effect may be to distort the state budget in favor of agricultural interests. State legislatures, however, are normally overrepresentative of rural and small-town areas, so that a question is appropriate whether legislatures are "coerced" when they are constrained to do what their predisposition directs. Further, no "coercion" of the content of educational programs is involved.

12. In 1942 R. E. Buchanan, dean and director of the Iowa Experiment Station, reported on "Grants to Federal Bureaus and Agencies for Co-operation with States": "It was emphasized that the Extension Services

of the various states are related to the Department of Agriculture in quite a different way than are the Agricultural Experiment Stations; that there is a marked tendency to reduce the autonomy of the State Extension Services. . . . [A] similar tendency on the part of federal agencies to limit the autonomy of the . . . Experiment Stations must be carefully scrutinized. At present there is satisfactory decentralization on the part of Experiment Stations; but the constant tendency to increase centralization of Extension work constitutes a grave menace to the Stations" (Proceedings of the Association of Land-Grant Colleges and Universities [hereafter cited as "Proceedings"],LVI [1942], 128 [abstr.]). While any remarks of Dean Buchanan must be accorded great weight, the present chapter indicates that on this occasion his forebodings were ill founded.

13. Based on interviews.

14. March 21, 1950. The debate dealt with proposals for extending federal grants to support education generally.

15. These findings agree with previous conclusions. The Survey had reports from forty states respecting the administration of grants-in-aid for agricultural research. All approved existing methods of inspection and approval of accounts. Thirty-eight approved administrative procedure under the Purnell Act, but two states would have preferred fewer restrictions. The Survey stressed that only few states had complaints; all the complaints apparently turned upon matters of annoyance rather than upon questions of interference by the federal government in the formulation of state research programs. Some complaints were registered respecting limitations on Adams and Purnell projects, others respecting delays required to get federal approval, and others respecting expenditures of time for occasional projects which, when prepared, failed to find federal approval. But it was emphasized that criticisms were not leveled against federal domination of state programs. In the opinion of the colleges, the Survey indicated, the OES policy of a relationship "of participation rather than control" accurately described the situation (II, 589-91). The Survey's report on federal-state relations in agricultural Extension was similar. Nine states commented respecting the use of subject-matter specialists by the federal office. Six states questioned the utility of the specialists to the states in developing programs of work; but two states requested the use of more specialists, particularly in home economics. Four states questioned the requirement of annual reports by county workers—criticizing the number of questions involved, the amount of time devoted to answering them, etc. One cannot discover, however, a criticism of federal Extension's domination of state programs and activities (ibid., p. 409).

In 1939 Works and Morgan declared, respecting administration of the Adams Act, that, despite the "delicate" nature of personal relationships involved, "fine cooperation has existed between the Federal Government and the States in the administration of the experiment stations, and their work has been one of the most successful of the Federal-State enterprises" (op. cit., p. 35). Compare their statement respecting Extension work: "The memorandum of understanding between the Federal Department and each agricultural college, drawn up in 1914 and setting forth the policies stated above, has remained in force, unmodified; and no appeal has been made to Congress to rescind any of the regulations made by the Secretary of Agriculture, as provided in the Smith-Lever

Act" (p. 73). The authors quote Benson Y. Landis and John D. Willard, Rural Adult Education (New York: Macmillan Co., 1933), pp. 22-24, 110-11, and Clarence B. Smith and Meredith C. Wilson, The Agricultural Extension-System of the United States (New York: John Wiley & Sons, 1930), p. 69.

F. B. Mumford, long dean of the College of Agriculture of the University of Missouri, wrote in 1940: "The experience of the land-grant colleges in the expenditure of federal funds for education has not been of such a nature to support the argument that federal administration is dangerous. Evidence is lacking of harmful interference with the states in the administration of these institutions. Local initiative has not been destroyed. The states have determined all major questions involving educational policies. The federal authorities do require, and properly so, a strict accounting of all expenditures" (The Land-Grant College Movement ⌈Agricultural Experiment Station Bull. 419 (University of Missouri, 1940)⌉, p. 76; cf. pp. 78, 90-91, 92, 97-98).

Also compare the questionnaire submitted by the Council of State Governments to (among others) officials of agricultural experiment stations and agricultural Extension Services in the several states. Question 3 asked, "Has federal aid led to federal interference in state affairs?" Thirty-four states replied: 28 experiment stations and 29 Extension Services said "No"; 2 experiment stations and 3 Extension Services said "Yes"; 4 experiment stations and 2 Extension Services said "To a minimum degree." A comparison with replies from other state services receiving grants-in-aid indicates that the experiment stations and Extension Services were least critical of all, excepting administrators of state vocational education programs (Federal Grants in Aid ⌈Washington, D.C.: Council of State Governments, 1949⌉, Appendix A, p. 275).

16. House Hearings, Agricultural Appropriations, fiscal 1936, p. 88. The OES has published vigorous criticisms of state experiment stations only once, it is believed. See Proceedings, XLII (1928), 197 ff.

17. The percentage for state and local Extension work from federal funds has fluctuated from 41 in 1914 to 62 in 1919 to 34 during the prosperous 1920's up to 58 in 1936-37 and down to 40 in 1952. In 1941-42 only twelve states provided an amount for agricultural Extension equal to what they received from the federal government; by 1947-48 only twelve states failed to provide at least an equal amount. Chart "B" in Research and Related Services in the USDA (loc. cit.) shows the stabilizing effects of federal grants for research. State grants for agricultural research fell every year from 1930 to 1934, while federal grants held steady. Federal grants were increased in 1936-40. State sources provided $2.78 for every federal dollar in 1930; this ratio was not attained again until 1946.

18. Similar criticisms were advanced in several states. On the other hand, the writer was also told more than once of the possibilities that federal grants may insulate state Extension directors from administrative control either in the state or in Washington. The current tendency to make agricultural college deans also directors of research and Extension has been mentioned. One such dean discussed with the writer the Extension version of the "old Army game." He said that full Extension directors, only nominally responsible to their deans, exercised power through their de facto control of Washington grants. If they do not want to co-operate with their deans, they cite Washington regulations or policy against it;

if they do not want to co-operate with Washington, they cite state policy to support their position.

19. See Hardin, op. cit., chap. iii.

20. See chap. xii below.

21. V. O. Key, Jr., op. cit., p. 80, and, generally, chap. vii.

22. Proceedings, XVIII (1904), 17-18. In 1916 Congress provided authority to the USDA to "coordinate the work of the Department . . . with that of State agricultural colleges and experiment stations in lines authorized in said acts." Essentially similar language is still retained. Note, however, that it says nothing about "coordinating the work of the several stations."

23. The claims of the association respecting passage of the Smith-Lever Act of 1914 are recorded in the Proceedings for relevant years and in True, op. cit., pp. 279-82. The research of Joseph Cannon Bailey, however, indicates that the act was eventually passed in considerably different form from that proposed by the colleges and stresses the role of other interests in securing congressional action. Final passage was supported by the National Soil Fertility League, rested upon the work of Theodore Roosevelt's Country Life Commission, and was associated with the shift in congressional control with Lever, of South Carolina, as chairman of the House Committee on Agriculture and Hoke Smith, of Georgia, as chairman of the Senate committee. Much credit was due the persistent work of Knapp (Seaman A. Knapp, Schoolmaster of American Agriculture [New York: Columbia University Press, 1945], chap. xii.

24. The memorandum is reprinted in Works and Morgan, op. cit., Appendix C.

25. The Adams Act of 1906 contained the provision respecting research grants (34 Stat. 64, chap. 951, sec. 4); the Smith-Lever Act of 1914, that for Extension grants (38 Stat. 374, chap. 79, sec. 6).

26. The position in the text is opposed to the conclusion reached by the distinguished Commission on Financing Higher Education (Nature and Needs of Higher Education [New York: Columbia University Press, 1952], pp. 151-64). The commission unanimously opposed the introduction of new programs of direct federal aid to colleges and universities or the expansion of scholarship aid to individual students. The commission found the strength of higher education to be in its freedom, which has thrived in our pluralistic political community—a community of diverse interests and preferences, wherein power is widely distributed. Intrust the fortunes of higher education to the federal government (with its "overwhelming financial resources and tremendous potential power"), and freedom would be lost. The commission saw especial danger in federal aid to the social sciences:

"In the natural sciences, where federal aid has been largely concentrated, there is not normally the danger of public hostility to the studies performed, such as that which lies in wait for the social scientist who challenges emotional bias, traditional modes of thought, or long-accepted values. The natural sciences have not founded their study and research upon . . . a complex network of value judgments. Where proof is difficult to establish as it is in the social sciences and humanities, freedom is hard to defend, yet all the more valuable. In these fields public opinion is notoriously given to snap judgments, and in them centralized control could . . . do great damage."

The commission argued that, whereas higher educational institutions could defend themselves with the present amount of federal aid, they could not do so if federal subsidy became "a major factor in financing higher education." The report cited "constant controversy between the representatives of the Veterans Administration and those of higher education in the operation of the admittedly desirable veterans educational program. Only alert and constant vigilance by university and college officials prevented the adoption and enforcement of rules and regulations which would have contradicted the deeper principles of higher education."

The distinguished commission buttressed these powerful arguments with others. The British experience with governmental grants to higher education was set aside on the grounds that the British have "entrusted the formulation of educational and scientific policies and the expenditure of government funds to nongovernmental agencies and individuals to a degree not conceivable under the American system." The commission also pointed to the difficulty of developing criteria to prevent pork-barreli in making congressional grants to higher education. Finally, it countered the argument that government is especially obligated to help higher education in inflationary periods by asserting that government should rather "adopt fiscal policies which will halt inflationary trends." Their position is very persuasive in its argument against the extension of centra control so that educational institutions "would act as Congress wills." They knew of no one who advocated such control. "But those who advocate the extension of federal financial support are treading down this path."

No doubt it is a dangerous path; yet the writer would be inclined to risk it. It is not clear from the commission's report what real alternative other than the federal government exist to provide higher education with the additional financial support that it needs. "Under today's conditions industry is the last untapped source to which educators may look— except government," said the commission (p. 176). It suggested that business might increase its philanthropic gifts from about 0.6 per cent of net income before taxes to 3 per cent. Assuming that higher education would get a similar proportion of this increased gift, its industrial benefice would rise from $40,000,000-$50,000,000 (in 1940, estimated) to $325,000,000. This would have been enough to "close the gap in higher education's current financing. It would not, however, meet all the vast range of needs from scholarship funds to capital plant." Business has had a tax incentive to make such contributions (up to 5 per cent of net income before taxes) since 1936. In unprecedented prosperity, however, business was giving only 0.6-0.7 per cent for these purposes. The commission's proposal to increase this sum six- or seven fold seems highly unrealistic—yet even this increase would be insufficient.

Finally, the writer believes that, despite the dangers from governmental control, our constitutional democracy must learn to finance even controversial research and teaching by government and, at the same time, to institutionalize within governmental processes themselves the means of protection for researchers and educators. As this book shows, the writer further believes that this end is gained partly by the adaptation of institutional devices but that an important component also depends upon educational administrators' and politicians' being able to act like statesme

Chapter IV

1. The incident described in the text was the one on which the issue
was joined, or nearly joined, between the USDA and Pennsylvania State
College. Another incident will be reported briefly here, however, lest it
be confused with the first. In 1943, the Agricultural Adjustment Administration (AAA) having become involved in partisan and electoral politics,
Congress cut off its funds for information work, placing the obligation
for information about the AAA program upon the Extension Service.
See David C. Knapp, "Agricultural Policy Formation in the Appropriations
Process" (Doctor's dissertation, University of Chicago, 1953), and Charles
M. Hardin, The Politics of Agriculture (Glencoe, Ill.: Free Press, 1952),
p. 138.
      After a shakeup in its leadership, the AAA complied so promptly
and vigorously with the ban against informational activities that the
Extension Service was hard put to it to carry on the extra burden of
work with resources already heavily strained by the demands of war food
production. The federal Extension director, M. L. Wilson, naturally
requested state Extension directors to assume the responsibility for
information work previously handled by the AAA. There was some
grumbling but general compliance; in Pennsylvania, however, Director
Fry refused to comply with the request; he acted upon a declaration
by the Pennsylvania State College Board: "It is the consensus of the
Board that the College should not be committed to the administration
or endorsement of any program sponsored by any department of the
Federal Government except in respect to such helpful and far-seeing
programs as may be specifically approved by the board."
      The Philadelphia Record published an article by Edwin Kemp,
"Treasury-supported Extension Service Turns Down AAA" (August 28,
1943), whereupon the Tribune-Republican of Meadeville, Pennsylvania,
editorialized (September 2, 1943): "The whole performance is a bold
attempt by the federal government to dictate policy to the Pennsylvania
State College, to circumvent a specific Congressional directive by forc-
ing the state extension organization to spread New Deal farm propaganda,
and an unveiled threat to either play the game the way Washington wants
it played, or go hungry."
      The federal Extension Service, of course, was carrying out the
mandate of Congress. Despite this, there was no threat, veiled or
otherwise. Pennsylvania was not deprived of federal funds. Rather than
demonstrating federal coercion, the incident really shows the ability of one
state to refuse to co-operate in the "co-operative" agricultural Extension
Service program, even in wartime. The possibility exists that the stand
of the Pennsylvania State College Board merely reflected the position
of the Pennsylvania agricultural Extension Service. In 1943, the writer
was told by an informed person, who was neither a Democrat nor a
USDA employee, that the Pennsylvania agricultural Extension Service
had set out systematically to put its friends on the state college board.
Of this story, one can say, at least, that the board is well constituted
for the success of such an endeavor. Nine of its members are chosen
by a group composed of the executive committee of the Pennsylvania
State Agricultural Society and three representatives from each county
agricultural society; presumably the Extension Service could capture
many of these positions. Nine more members are elected by the alumni;
presumably the Extension Service might capture some of these. The
governor also nominates six members, who are confirmed by the state
senate, and there are five or six ex officio members (P.L. 863, sec. 1,
June 24, 1939; Purdon's Pennsylvania Statutes [annotated permanent ed.,
1950], title 24, sec. 2536).

2. House Hearings, Agricultural Appropriations, fiscal 1935, p. 77.

3. Cf. Senate Hearings, Committee on Agriculture and Forestry (S. 2228; 74th Cong., 1st sess.), esp. pp. 37-39.

4. Cf. chap xiv below and John M. Gaus and Leon A. Wolcott, Public Administration and the United States Department of Agriculture (Chicago: Public Administration Service, 1940), Index, s.v. Land-use planning and Mt. Weather Agreement.

5. So Dean S. W. Fletcher, of the School of Agriculture, presented the statement of the president and trustees of Pennsylvania State College to the Subsection on Experiment Station Work of the Association of Land-Grant Colleges and Universities in 1939 (Proceedings of the Association of Land-Grant Colleges and Universities, LIII [1939], 143-44).

6. U.S. Code, sec. 341; act of May 8, 1914, 38 Stat. 372, chap. 79, sec. 1 (emphasis supplied).

7. In the Bankhead-Jones Act, Congress had, as noted, authorized additional appropriations to Extension for precisely this kind of work; it also had approved the state and local land-use planning program by implication in the provision of appropriations to finance the USDA's part in it.

8. See George A. Works and Barton Morgan, The Land-Grant Colleges (Washington, D.C.: Government Printing Office, 1939), p. 69. Iowa is an exception; its law provides for creation of "farm aid associations" with minimum membership and contribution of annual dues, whereupon county funds are directed to be appropriated in certain amounts to the farm aid association. The association, among other things, may employ "one or more teachers, experts, or advisers" (Code of Iowa, Vol. I [1950], chap. 176, esp. 176.7, 176.8.

9. Purdon's Pennsylvania Statutes (annotated permanent ed., 1950), title 24, sec. 2546.

10. Proceedings, XXXIII (1920), 140-43.

11. Cf. recommendations of the Survey of Land-Grant Colleges and Universities (1930), II, 540; Report of the Joint Committee on Extension Programs, Policies, and Goals (Washington, D.C.: Association of Land-Grant Colleges and Universities, 1948), p. 46. Recommendations are for payments of salaries from federal and state sources, with local funds used for office and other expenses.

12. Cf. Report of the Joint Committee, p. 54.

13. It is interesting to note the correspondence in viewpoint between McDowell and the late B. S. Crocheron, long-time director of the California Extension Service. The latter declared in 1925 that the value of the county agent to the local people lies in his unbiased judgment as not representing a local situation or a local constituency and in the fact that his appointment and tenure are not dependent upon the "favor of local politicians, or even of a certain influential organization of farmers" (Proceedings, XXXIX (1925), 211 ff. Both Pennsylvania and California Extension Services have frequently been characterized to the writer,

by state as well as by federal workers, as examples of aloofness and indifference toward Washington combined with highly centralized organization and operation within the state. Cf., on Pennsylvania, Gladys Baker, The County Agent (Chicago: University of Chicago Press, 1939), pp. 134-35.

14. Cf. Proceedings, 1920-41, Index. S. W. Fletcher, as director of the Pennsylvania Experiment Station, participated frequently in land-grant college activities during the 1930's.

15. His comments on the significance of the 1930 Survey were unrecorded.

16. Annual Report of the Agricultural Extension Service of Pennsylvania State College (1922), p. 10.

17. To be sure, acknowledgments occur in some Pennsylvania circulars, such as L. C. Madison's expression of appreciation to the Bureaus of Animal Industry and Public Roads, USDA, for pictures and plans used in Circular 152 (1934). But compare New York Bulletins 83, 87, 96, 124, 277, 284, 362, 406, and 443 (from 1924 to 1940).

18. Pennsylvania Extension Circular 123 (1929).

19. Pennsylvania Extension Circular 151 (1934).

20. Cf., particularly, New York Bulletin 443 (1940), Extension Work in New York in Agriculture and Home Economics. See, however, R. W. Kearns, How To Lead Discussions ("Pennsylvania Extension Series," No. 236), published in April, 1942 (after McDowell's retirement)—a broad-gauged statement.

21. Purdon's Pennsylvania Statutes (annotated ed., pocket suppl., 1949), title 3, sec. 852.

22. House Hearings, Committee on Agriculture, "Long-Range Agricultural Policy" (80th Cong., 1st sess. [Lancaster, Pa., 1947]), Part 7, p. 834.

Chapter V

1. The college president's statement was made to the writer in an interview. The dean's statement was reported by Carlyle Hodgkin, "Agriculture's Got Troubles," Successful Farming, March, 1943, p. 22.

2. Above, p. 17; see also below, pp. 40 ff., 151, 159 ff., 199-200.

3. Generally, after the removal of the Agricultural Adjustment Administration in the mid-1930's, this has been the only action program administered by the colleges. The farm labor program was handled by Extension from 1943 to 1947. See Wayne D. Rasmussen, A History of the Emergency Farm Labor Supply Program ("Agricultural Monographs," No. 13 [Bureau of Agricultural Economics, USDA, 1951]). A critical interpretation of the operation of the decentralized Extension and research administration in agriculture during World War II is found in Bela Gold, Wartime Economic Planning in Agriculture (New York: New York University Press,

1949), pp. 287-91. Contrast Walter W. Wilcox, The Farmer in the Second World War (Ames: Iowa State College Press, 1947), pp. 89 ff.

4. A number of examples of threats to leading administrative personnel in agricultural colleges have been reported; but our interest here is in allegations of actual dismissals.

5. Some readers may recall the purge by the AAA in (or about) 1938 of employees who had come from agricultural Extension Services. This, however, was an internal personnel action; to reverse a current expression in public adminstration, it was "unstaffing to get rid of a point of view." It was an incident in the political competition of two organized groups rather than an example of pressure upon public educational personnel.

6. The Role of the Land-Grant College in Governmental Agricultural Programs and Education for Action Programs in Agriculture (XXXVIII, Nos. 2 and 28 [Ames, Iowa, 1938 and 1939]). Cf. chap. xi below.

7. See below, chap. x.

8. Many would attribute the reluctance of some federal officials to their patterned or learned or habitual or conditioned responses rather than to self-restraint. Let us merely note this philosophical difference without attempting to discuss it.

9. The SCS is something of an exception because of its close relationship to state associations of soil conservation districts which are organized to bring pressure upon state legislatures.

10. See Charles M. Hardin, The Politics of Agriculture (Glencoe, Ill.: Free Press, 1952), p. 138; David Knapp, "Agricultural Policy Formation in the Appropriations Process" (Doctor's dissertation, University of Chicago, 1953); and, for the travail of the Farm Security Administration, Grant McConnell, The Decline of Agrarian Democracy (Berkeley: University of California Press, 1953).

11. On the TVA see Philip Selznick, TVA and the Grass Roots (Berkeley: University of California Press, 1949), and Norman I. Wengert, The Valley of Tomorrow (Knoxville: University of Tennessee Press, 1952). The writer prefers Wengert's interpretation. On earlier relationships to the USDA see Hardin, op. cit.; on the 1953 reorganization see Hardin, "The Republican Department of Agriculture—a Political Interpretation," JFE, XXXVI, No. 2 (May, 1954), 210 ff.

12. Examples include problems involving soil conservation (such as relative merits of different systems of erosion control under different conditions, the effect of soil conservation programs on the economy of farms, availability of appropriate lines of credit for soil improvements, etc.); agricultural adjustment (agricultural prices and farmers' responses thereto, the relative merits of different methods of supporting farm prices, distribution of benefits of farm adjustment programs; effect of programs for feed grains on livestock production, etc.); farm credit; reclamation; and rural electrification.

13. Agricultural college officials may take some comfort from the experience of the Labour party in England. The Labour party could not

shake off or refute by argument the suspicion held by many that its
professions of constitutional rectitude concealed a willingness to make
a violent revolution if the time became ripe; all it could do was to live
the suspicion down. Cf. K. B. Smellie, A Hundred Years of English
Government (London: Duckworth, 1950), p. 234.

14. Hardin, The Politics of Agriculture, pp. 149-55.

15. For this and the following paragraph see the writer's "The
Republican Department of Agriculture—a Political Interpretation." See
also USDA Release No. 1534-1954 (June 15, 1954) on changes affecting
local ASC committeemen.

16. House Hearings, Agricultural Appropriations, fiscal 1953, Part 1,
p. 237.

17. Ibid., p. 239.

18. The annual appropriations for regular activities of the USDA
ranged from $1,054,900,000 in 1940 to $731,200,000 in 1953 (estimated).
Although the decrease was due largely to decreases in sums for action
programs, e.g., elimination of the parity payments of $225,000,000, action
programs still accounted for some 80 per cent of the total in 1953.
(Action programs here include the Forest Service, flood prevention, SCS,
the Agricultural Conservation Program of PMA, the sugar program,
the Federal Crop Insurance Corporation, the administrative funds
of REA, FHA, and FCA, and the School Lunch Program.) In 1953, moreover, participation in the International Wheat Agreement cost the
government $182,000,000. If this sum is added to the $731,000,000, the total
is $913,000,000—not so very much less than the budget for 1940 (House
Hearings, Agricultural Appropriations, fiscal 1954, Part 1, pp. 24 ff.

19. Congressional Record, C, 4863; Andersen was Chairman of the
Subcommittee on Agriculture of the House Committee on Appropriations.

20. It was a logical consequence, the writer believes, rather than
an inevitable one. The situation was ripe for the program, but agricultural
administrators contributed by recognizing the situation and devising
an appropriate program.

21. In this usage, to "educate" means to equip with the means of
making rational choices. The writer recognizes the philosophical
difficulties inherent in this simple statement and will rely upon the
discussion of education in Collingwood, The Great Leviathan (London:
Oxford University Press, 1947).

22. John D. Black, Parity, Parity, Parity (Cambridge, Mass.: Harvard
Committee on Research in the Social Sciences, 1942), p. 46; Agricultural
Reform in the United States (New York: McGraw-Hill Book Co., Inc.,
1929), p. 153. Figures in the text are from these books, but the argument
was expressed in more polemical sources.

23. The Aiken Bill of 1948 had provided for flexible supports of
60-90 per cent of parity on the basic crops, in inverse proportion to
the size of the crops; however, if marketing quotas were announced and

accepted by farmers, the support could not be lower than 72 per cent of parity.

24. The problem of ascertaining what public opinion actually is on a given subject is notoriously difficult. Do Iowa farmers want 90 per cent supports for corn? The Iowa Farm and Home Register reported on November 1, 1953, that 47 per cent of a sample of Iowa farmers preferred supports on corn at 90 per cent of parity and 13 per cent preferred supports at 100 per cent of parity—or 60 per cent favored high supports. The alternatives were "flexible supports" 75-90 per cent, favored by 22 per cent of the farmers; supports to "prevent hardship" favored by 9 per cent; and no supports favored by 6 per cent. Responses on supports for other farm products differ. It is not clear precisely when the sample was polled, but it was certainly after June and before October, 1953, and it was probably in August or September (see mimeographed "Report of the Farm Policy Survey" [Des Moines, 1953], esp. p. 4). In a second report, however, results of interviews in April, 1953, of a sample of Iowa and northern Illinois farmers produced strikingly different answers. The question was, "Do you think support levels should be fixed or should they be varied according to supply so that farm incomes remain stable?" Of the type of farm called "field crop" in Iowa, only 15.4 per cent of those reporting said that they preferred fixed price supports. Here the alternatives were merely between fixed and variable (and the report noted that the question was misleading, as variable supports would not stabilize income for individual producers). Even so, the differences between the responses and the first poll are very great (see "Views of Iowa and Illinois Farmers on Price Support Policy," Preliminary Report No. 1, Project 1229 [Ames: Iowa Agricultural Experiment Station, 1953]). Finally, Wallace's Farmer and Iowa Homestead reported results of a poll of a sample of Iowa farmers who were probably interviewed in September, 1953. The hypothetical alternatives offered to the farmers and the percentages of farmers favoring the various alternatives were (1) a 20 per cent cut in corn acreage and a 90 per cent corn loan—28 per cent favored; (2) a 15 per cent cut and an 85 per cent loan—favored by 11 per cent; (3) a 10 per cent cut and an 80 per cent loan—favored by 21 per cent, etc. (issue of October 3, 1953). All these polls were thoughtfully and carefully done and followed scientific sampling methods. To be sure, some reconciliation of the divergence in results is possible—fewer farmers in the Register poll might have favored 90 per cent if they had had to accept the acreage cut of 20 per cent and if they had had a cafeteria of choices as presented by the Farmer and Homestead poll. The Iowa State poll might have produced different results if taken in September rather than April; but this kind of reconciliation acknowledges the instability of public opinion or, at least, of what passes for public opinion in the reports of attitude tests. An excellent criticism of the use of opinion polls in political interpretation is given in Lindsay Rogers, The Pollsters (New York: Alfred A. Knopf, 1948).

Thus the problem of ascertaining public opinion is acute. But politicians must judge it, or, in fact, they must judge something much more difficult, namely, the relationship between farmer opinion and farmer voting. Many midwestern congressmen appear to have decided that enough of their farmer constituents to control their election want 90 per cent supports on corn and want it badly enough to vote them out of office if they refuse to approve it. The evidence for this is in the vote of the House of Representatives on June 30, 1952, to extend

price supports on the basic crops through 1954. Midwestern rural
congressmen voted overwhelmingly for this bill. Every one of the Iowa
congressmen, all of whom were Republicans, was present and voted
for the bill—in spite of the fact that the American Farm Bureau
Federation and the Iowa Farm Bureau were both opposed to the bill.

This vote is probably explained by belief on the part of midwestern
congressmen that the farmers really elected President Truman in
1948. The writer considers that this widely circulated view is greatly
exaggerated. A comparison of the vote in the Iowa farm, small-town,
and urban counties in 1944 and 1948, as well as in the cash-corn counties,
deflates the claim that the farmers swung the election. Again, while
Mr. Truman won Iowa in 1948, all the Iowa congressional districts
were electing Republicans—and by almost the same comfortable margins
of victory that they had in 1944. Note also that Loveland, the symbol
of 90 per cent support prices, was defeated by Senator Hickenlooper,
who received 55.1 per cent of the total vote in 1950. The congressmen
seem to have been overcautious; but an excess of caution is a prominent
characteristic of most congressmen who succeed in getting re-elected.
On this issue, at least, if we had had disciplined political parties,
congressmen might well have estimated the situation differently and
have voted for a flexible price-support program. But to pursue that
question would take us outside the problem of this book.

25. The SCS, especially in the late 1930's, sought to and did influence
some legislatures to pass state soil conservation district laws or to
amend such laws in line with SCS policy. But this is a far cry from a
threat by the SCS against an appropriation for a department in a state
agricultural college. For the concept of "access" see David B. Truman,
The Governmental Process (New York: Alfred A. Knopf, 1951).

Chapter VI

1. Federal Register, XII (1947), 4144, 4879, 5478, and 8041.

2. For an analysis of the Washington and field operations of the
PMA see Charles M. Hardin, The Politics of Agriculture (Glencoe,
Ill.: Free Press, 1952), chaps. vii-ix.

3. From a copy of the bill provided by the Legislative Research
Commission of the Commonwealth of Kentucky.

4. Cf. Louisville Courier-Journal, February 23, 1950; Lexington
Herald, February 26, 1950; and Lexington Leader, February 26-28, 1950.

5. Lexington Herald, March 4, 1950; Louisville Courier-Journal,
March 14, 1950.

6. Cf. C. J. Friedrich on the rule of anticipated reactions, in
Constitutional Government and Democracy (Boston: Ginn & Co.,
1950), pp. 49, 398. Analysis is indebted to A. F. Bentley's The Process
of Government (Chicago: University of Chicago Press, 1908; Bloomington,
Ind.: Principia Press, 1949), esp. chap. xix; David B. Truman, The
Governmental Process (New York: Alfred A. Knopf, 1951); and Earl
Latham, "The Group Basis of Politics: Notes for a Theory," American
Political Science Review, XLVI, No. 2, 376 ff., and The Group Basis of
Politics (Ithaca, N.Y.: Cornell University Press, 1952).

7. For background see Harold B. Rowe, Tobacco under the AAA (Washington, D.C.: Brookings Institution, 1935); Glenn L. Johnson, "Burley Tobacco Control Programs" (University of Kentucky Bulletin 580 [Lexington, February, 1942]); B. U. Ratchford, "Federal Agricultural Policy in Relation to Tobacco," Journal of Politics, August, 1949.

8. Not all possibilities with respect to where the threat comes from and what motivates it are fully explored in the foregoing account. Business interests, anxious for competitive reasons to impede research in low-nicotine tobacco, may have stimulated the attack. Differences in personalities and cultural backgrounds among the antagonists probably aggravated the controversy.

Chapter VII

1. Survey of Land-Grant Colleges and Universities, I, Table 4, pp. 88-89. The Survey's tables include the fifty-two non-Negro institutions, of which total receipts in the two years compared grew from just under $40,000,000 to over $142,000,000. Private gifts, institutional funds, and earnings and miscellaneous revenue make up the balance. Federal receipts comprised 9.5 per cent of the 1928 total; state appropriations, 50 per cent; private gifts, 5.2 per cent; student fees, 10.8 per cent; other institutional receipts, 7.5 per cent; earnings, 12.1 per cent; miscellaneous receipts, 4.9 per cent (p. 93).

2. Ibid., p. 92.

3. E. D. Ross, Democracy's College (Ames: Iowa State College Press, 1942), p. 96. He continues: "President W. O. Thompson, misled apparently by the agitation of farmers' organizations in Ohio, was led to assert that the movement sprang not from the social reformers and professional educators 'but from the rank and file of the people themselves.' The evidence is all directly to the contrary. The invariable experience of administrators and educators was that the farmers themselves were the hardest to convince of the need and possibility of occupational training; and editorials, letters to agricultural papers, and discussions in state and local societies and by other farmers' meetings were all to the same effect—an indifference, suspicion, or open contempt for the new-fangled methods of learning to farm."

4. Afterward, better farm prices, more mechanized and scientific (hence more attractive and exacting) farming, and added opportunities for agricultural specialists increased enrolments. In 1910 colleges of agriculture had 6,255 students; in 1915 they had 15,669. But the farm depression of the 1920's caused a decline in enrolments to 11,179 in 1926-27. "Farmers themselves advised and urged their sons not to go into agricultural work" (Survey, I, 775-78).

5. Survey, I, 15.

6. L. B. Caswell, quoted in A. C. True, A History of Agricultural Education in the United States, 1785-1925 (Washington, D.C.: Government Printing Office, 1929), p. 150.

7. Ibid., p. 167.

8. Ibid., p. 175; and see pp. 152, 155, 157 (Iowa); 185 (Illinois).

9. True, op. cit., p. 149.

10. O. W. Firkins, Cyrus Northrop: A Memoir (Minneapolis: University of Minnesota Press, 1925), chap. xx. Cf. the experience of President Adams of Wisconsin, described in J. F. A. Pyre, Wisconsin (New York: Oxford University Press, 1920), p. 280.

11. Jonas Viles, The University of Missouri: A Centennial History (Columbia: University of Missouri Press, 1939), chap. ii.

12. "During the administration of President Daniel Read (1866-76) who made the transition from college to university" (ibid., chaps. iv-vii).

13. In 1868 the board was made appointive by the governor, with senatorial confirmation; it had been elected by the legislature. In 1875 the constitution reduced the board to nine members, of whom one-third were members of the state board of agriculture.

14. The opposition on the board capitalized upon the criticism of President Read in Boone County, as evidenced by an adverse visiting committee's report in 1872. Viles, op. cit., pp. 164, 170.

15. Ibid., p. 173.

16. William Carlyle Etheridge (ibid., chap. xi).

17. Ibid., pp. 178-79, 190-91, 198-200, 222-23.

18. From a letter written in 1890, quoted ibid., p. 230. Cf. the qualifications of Andrew Sloan Draper and Edmund J. James, in Allan Nevins, Illinois (New York: Oxford University Press, 1917), pp. 153, 211; O. W. Firkins, op. cit., p. 355; M. C. Fernald, History of the Maine State College and the University of Maine (Orono: University of Maine Press, 1916), p. 77.

19. Viles, op. cit., p. 255.

20. Ibid., pp. 234-40.

21. E. D. Ross, A History of Iowa State College (Ames: Iowa State College Press, 1942), p. 85.

22. It is interesting to recall the sectarian attacks which, though "made on all state institutions, were especially concentrated on the A. and M. group, as with their scientific emphasis—even to the Darwinian arch-heresy—they were regarded as of all secularized organizations of higher education, the most godless" (ibid.).

23. Ibid., pp. 197-200. The December 12, 1890, issue argued that Iowa State College should be "managed by Iowa men—from the president down to the janitor—men whose every interest is in Iowa."

24. Ross, A History of Iowa State College, pp. 203-4.

25. See the inaugural address of President A. B. Storms in 1903, the "general science controversy" of 1913, the report on duplication of activity with Iowa University of 1916 (Bureau of Education). In the 1920's sharp increases in enrolment and the emergence of social problems which prompted emphasis upon the social sciences both contributed to liberalization of college objectives. Cf. Ross, A History of Iowa State College, pp. 197, 210-11, 235-36, 262, 265, 283-85, 298, 326-30, 368. See also chap. x below.

26. Ross, A History of Iowa State College, p. 86.

27. Much to the disgust of J. B. Turner, "who had never hesitated to express his dislike of 'old hunker presidents'" and now groaned "O Lord, how long, how long? An ex-superintendent of public instruction and a Baptist preacher! Could anything be worse?" "But [adds Nevins] no better man could in reality have been chosen" (Nevins, op. cit., pp. 44-45.

28. Ibid., pp. 63-65.

29. Ibid., pp. 72-73, 121, 123, 175·

30. Further evidence, it may be noted, for the present writer's contention that federal aid has been a source of strength to state-supported institutions of higher education rather than a threat to their independence.

31. Nevins, op. cit., pp. 101, 104, 159-61, 199.

32. Ibid., p. 196.

33. Ibid., pp. 173-77, 199, 213, 224-25.

34. See J. T. Willard, History of Kansas State College of Agriculture and Applied Science (Manhattan: Kansas State College, 1940), pp. 93 ff.

35. "It was abundantly demonstrated that a Board . . . of members . . . selected because of their known attitude on disputed political questions could not convincingly put in effect a faculty reorganization that would be generally recognized by the other party as non-partisan" (ibid. p. 101). The blanket resignations were obtained under a law of 1897, apparently passed for that purpose.

36. Ibid., p. 105.

37. Ibid., pp. 106-7.

38. It should be said, however, that Ward, a Unitarian minister, apparently had introduced his religious views into his instruction. For this series of events see ibid., pp. 119-27.

39. As evidenced by the 350 per cent increase in state appropriations between that year and 1928, already noted.

40. Charles McCarthy, The Wisconsin Idea (New York: Macmillan Co., 1912). See also F. L. Paxson and Walton Bean, The Rise of American State Universities (to be published).

41. Pyre, op. cit., chap. xii, esp. pp. 364 ff. Mead's article (Survey, December, 1915) is quoted on p. 357.

42. Op. cit., final chap.

43. The dispute within the college turned on the merits of Keynesian economics but apparently also assumed the aspects of a power struggle. Charges were made that the school of commerce abridged academic freedom by discriminating against other than Keynesians. A committee of the university examined the situation, reported that academic freedom was not involved, but found such severe conflict between the two opposing groups that no prospect of reconciliation appeared. It proposed (among other things) a sweeping reorganization of the college. The attack from outside, however, appears to have been part of a campaign to remove President George D. Stoddard by identifying him as an extreme left-winger.

44. Nevins, op, cit., pp. 96-97, 121-22, 126, 138-39, 194-95, 262-65.

45. While a number of issues were cited as underlying the dismissal, krebiozen (the secret-formula drug on which Stoddard had forbidden further research) was the detonator. Partisan politics appeared to play a certain role, however. Instead of following the alumni recommendations for nominations for university regents, the Republican slate-makers preferred Grange in 1950. (The substitution reportedly was made in an atmosphere of smear charges that the university faculty harbored "50 Communists, socialists, or pinks." To this, President Stoddard was able to retort that thorough investigation had not discovered even one Communist on the faculty.) But Grange was elected and, as noted, made the motion of no confidence. The vote was six to three, with five Republicans and one Democrat voting against Stoddard and two Republicans and one Democrat voting for him; one Democrat was absent. While a number of issues had been developed over the years and Stoddard had become a "controversial" figure, this is to be expected from a vigorous educator. No man can effectively preside over a great modern state university without making enemies and becoming "controversial." Considerable controversy can be sustained as the price of an outstanding president. At the same time, the apparent partisan manipulation of the presidency of the University of Illinois in the summer of 1953 is greatly to be deplored. See the Chicago Daily News for July 30, 1953 (editorial), and the Chicago Sun-Times, news stories, July 25, 27, 29, and 30, 1953. It is ironical that, when Governor Stevenson offered a bill to provide for a single, appointive state board for higher education, Stoddard had declared against it: "It seems foolish to me to change something that has worked so well. . . . The record of the University of Illinois board . . . has been distinguished for decades" (Chicago Daily News, May 19, 1951).

46. Willard, op. cit., pp. 232-35, 321.

47. Ross, A History of Iowa State College, pp. 336-37 (emphasis added); see also pp. 86-90, 263-64, 271, 293 ff., 331, 333-34. Cf. Willard, op. cit., pp. 35-36, 112.

48. Survey, I, 52-62.

49. Writing with the advantage of having been president of Iowa State College, R. M. Hughes, in his <u>A Manual for Trustees of Colleges and Universities</u> (Ames: Iowa State College Press, 1943), expressed a preference for boards ranging from seven to fifteen members (pp. 5, 8).

50. The <u>Survey</u> thought such representation of alumni "undoubtedly advantageous." Cf. Nevins, <u>op. cit.</u>, final chap., and W. M. Hepburn and L. M. Sears, <u>Purdue University</u> (Indianapolis, Ind.: Hollenbeck Press, 1925).

51. A number of other provisions in various states favored some sort of representation of agriculture on the boards, however (<u>Survey</u>, I, 58).

52. Hughes, <u>op. cit.</u>, p. 6.

53. <u>Ibid.</u>, p. 159. Cf. Hepburn and Sears (<u>op. cit.</u>, p. 135), who praise the Purdue board for its "role . . . of guardianship rather than . . . active participation" in the details of university management.

54. <u>Survey</u>, I, 62, 64. Compare R. M. Hughes's remarks on board members: "Too often men are appointed for political reasons. These are sometimes merely unimportant and useless people. Often they are highly injurious to the institutions, introducing political prejudices and pressures into the control of educational institutions. On the whole, however, the men and women on these boards are capable, conscientious, and deeply concerned to serve usefully" (<u>op. cit.</u>, p. 5).

55. <u>Survey</u>, I, Part II, chap. i, 35-46; table, pp. 54-55. Twenty-eight of forty-four institutions reported for the year 1928. The <u>Survey</u> also found that in sixteen institutions the presidents and the governing boards had the right to appear before budget hearings; in seventeen institutions the president had the right. In sixteen states college staff members other than the president were forbidden to contact either state legislatures or budget agencies on budgetary matters. From interviews the writer would surmise that informal relationships involved in the process of getting and spending appropriations are often equally as significant as the formal procedure and are sometimes of greater significance.

56. <u>Ibid.</u>, I, 39.

57. <u>Proceedings of the Association of Land-Grant Colleges and Universities</u>, XXXVII, 463 ff. Cf. the strong criticism of Eugene Davenport, of Illinois, in <u>Proceedings,</u> XLII (1929), 38-41. As the next chapter indicates, legislative earmarking continues to be a problem in a number of states, and "gentlemen's agreements" about how the budget shall be spent may provide controls almost as rigorous as outright earmarking.

58. Mann, <u>op. cit.</u> In Minnesota the state board of control tended to dominate the university in 1901-8 (Firkins, <u>op. cit.</u>, chap. xxv). In Missouri the state board of agriculture was given normal functions of the board of curators in 1897-1900 (Etheridge, in Viles, <u>op. cit.</u>, pp. 303-13). See also E. A. Bryan, <u>Historical Sketch of the State College of Washington, 1890-1925</u> (Spokane, Wash., 1928), chaps. i, ii, iv, v.

Chapter VIII

1. The term "colleges of agriculture" is convenient and sufficiently exact. To be sure, some of the illustrations which follow record pressure on the entire land-grant college or university; some of them, merely on the experiment station or the Extension Service; but what importantly affects either its mother-institution or its parts also affects the college of agriculture.

2. Calling the decentralization of American parties their most important characteristic, E. E. Schattschneider wrote: "He who knows this fact, and knows nothing else, knows more about American parties than he who knows everything except this fact" (Party Government [New York: Farrar & Rinehart, 1942], pp. 131-32).

3. Southern Politics (New York: Alfred A. Knopf, 1949), p. 55.

4. Modeled, reputedly, upon a statement of policy by the University of Florida. In another southern state a written policy was debated but rejected in favor of a verbal policy—"any written statement would give the demagogues something to work on."

5. The Mississippi constitution, article 8, sec. 213-A, ratified in the November, 1942, election.

6. See above, chap. v, pp. 47 ff. While the general effects of the power struggle are indirect, occasional examples of quite direct pressure upon agricultural research and Extension have partisan overtones. Thus protection for county agents from local partisans who identified them with the "New Deal" was advanced as a reason for passage of Missouri's law requiring county sponsoring organizations for Extension programs. The margarine incident described in chap. x set off some partisan comment in local newspapers identifying Iowa State economists as "New Dealers." In another state a pioneering program to stimulate the democratic examination of political issues failed to get refinanced from a private donor on the grounds that in its early years it had not "damned the New Deal and all its works." In a fourth state a leading agricultural economist appears to have failed of appointment to the college of agriculture's faculty because of his previous service with agencies established by the Democratic administration in the national government.

7. Washington Post, December 15, 1953.

8. See above, pp. 71-73. Stoddard led in the formation of the United Nations Educational, Scientific and Cultural Organization and headed the American delegation to it in 1950. Two prominent Republican board members, however, not only voted confidence in Stoddard but publicly objected to the procedure of his dismissal. Herbert B. Megran called the procedure "ignoble and improper," and Wayne Johnson termed it "terrible and ridiculous" (Chicago Daily News, August 4, 1953). For the circumstances surrounding the appointment of Stoddard's successor, David D. Henry, see the New York Times, November 24 and December 5, 1954.

9. See chap. xi below.

10. In the general distribution of political power in a given state, legislatures vary considerably in relative significance. Again, V. O. Key, Jr. (op. cit.), brings this fact out clearly, especially in chaps. ii-xii; but in the political processes affecting agricultural research and Extension most state legislatures appear to be quite significant.

11. Above, p. 65.

12. Washington Post, March 7, 1952.

13. The writer has listened to vehement complaints about more than one president who has reportedly bragged that he "kept the budget down"; envious contrasts are usually made with President _____ of _____, who "sold his institution to his state and built it up."

14. Gentlemen's agreements are sometimes contracted outside legislative halls. In one state in which an organization of farm groups in effect presents the budget of the college of agriculture to the legislature, an annual meeting is held on the budget with this organization's officers. Sometimes commitments are made in this meeting which amount practically to earmarking, it is reported.

15. See above, p. 74.

16. See below, chap. ix, n. 30.

17. A useful theoretical discussion of the different groups and the manner in which they become activated politically is given in chap. xix of A. F. Bentley, The Process of Government (Chicago: University of Chicago Press, 1908; Bloomington, Ind.: Principia Press, 1949). See also David B. Truman, The Governmental Process (New York: Alfred A. Knopf, 1951). An example occurred a few years ago in a related policy field. An official of the Forest Service made a speech to an urban businessmen's group in which he criticized stockmen for abusing the public range and deplored proposals to increase their grazing upon forest preserves. He bespoke multiple use of the forests and stressed their utility for recreation, for protection of the water supply so vital to further urban development, and as an attraction for tourists. Livestock leaders denounced him at once and called for his discharge. All this was reported in the newspapers, whereupon the Izaak Walton League and other groups representing hunting and recreational interests as well as conservationists and publicists concerned about the supply of water all came to the support of the Forest Service. Probably considerable discussion and other signs of political awareness of the problem grew among the wide numbers of citizens who are normally outside such controversies—"the underlying interests," in Bentley's terms. What had begun, as it were, as an exclusive fight in a private club suddenly found its contestants squared off in front of a large and growing crowd in Madison Square Garden.

18. See the Preface.

19. Another commodity will illustrate some of the stereotypes in such cases. The writer was amused by a wall chart showing the historic production costs of the commodity; the chart also showed prices, always well below costs. But it also showed production of the commodity steadily

increasing! Discussing the apparent absurdity in this chart (prominently
displayed on the wall of an agricultural college official), the writer suggested an alternative analysis to the president of a state farm organization. He replied: "Listen; we learned to make that analysis you saw
from Professor ____. We like it. We don't want to know about any other
analysis that would shake our confidence in it." The writer could never
be sure whether he was being informed or being hoaxed in this con-
versation.

20. Some distinguished agricultural college figures have participated
in studies of migratory labor, however—notably, Noble Clark, associate
director of the Wisconsin Agricultural Experiment Station, and J. Earl
Coke, Assistant Secretary of Agriculture (1953), formerly Extension
director of the College of Agriculture, University of California. Clark
was a member of the President's Commission on Migratory Labor, which
reported in 1951 (Migratory Labor in American Agriculture [Washington,
D.C.]). Coke was chairman of Governor Warren's Committee To Survey
the Agricultural Labor Resources of the San Joaquin Valley; see its
preliminary report (Sacramento, Calif., 1950).

21. The Farm Foundation has greatly aided colleges of agriculture
to move into this area. See Joseph Ackerman and Marshall Harris (eds.),
Family Farm Policy (Chicago: University of Chicago Press, 1947); Harold
Hoffsomer (ed.), Land Tenure in the Southwestern States (sponsored also
by the General Education Board; Chapel Hill: University of North Carolina
Press, 1950); Improving Farm Tenure in the Midwest (Agricultural
Experiment Station, University of Illinois, Bull. 502 [1944]); reports
of the Farm Foundation; etc.

22. Reluctance of agricultural colleges on this matter seems somewhat inconsistent with the eminently satisfactory relationships between
the colleges and the TVA (see p. 48). Part of the explanation, the writer
believes, lies in the identification of influential members of some of
the colleges with private utilities; part of it appears to lie in the considerable political power which private utilities, reinforced by their
allies in and out of government, exercise in many states.

23. The Survey of Land-Grant Colleges and Universities (1930) lightly
touched this problem (I, 602-4).

24. For examples see Julien Benda, La Trahison des clercs (Paris:
B. Grosset, 1927); Robert S. Lynd, Knowledge for What? (Princeton:
Princeton University Press, 1939); Charles E. Kellogg, "The Scientist
and Social Policy in the Democratic State," Scientific Monthly, Vols.
LIV-LV (May-July, 1942).

25. See the thoughtful discussion in Truman, op. cit., pp. 38-39.

26. Indifference may have a positive value in politics, of course;
cf. Pendleton Herring's remark, in another context: "If all are partisans,
who is to umpire?" (The Politics of Democracy [New York: Rinehart &
Co., 1940], p. 32).

27. Readers should be apprised that a reputable line of political
interpretation is quite opposed to the emphasis upon individual power
and influence that this implies. The power even of the President,
they insist, is the power of the Presidency; such power can only be

understood by an analysis of the process by which the President, a departmental secretary, the speaker of the House, or any other high official is <u>empowered</u>. This is a very useful interpretation; nevertheless, it should not be embraced so fully that all personal responsibility is eliminated. Reference is to Bentley, <u>op. cit.</u>; Truman, <u>op. cit.</u>; and Earl Latham, <u>The Group Basis of Politics</u> (Ithaca, N.Y.: Cornell University Press, 1952), chap. i.

28. Examples may be found for the Illinois Agricultural Association in W. Bruce Storm, "An Analysis of the Illinois Agricultural Association as a Pressure Group" (unpublished Ph.D. thesis, University of Chicago, 1950), and Arthur Moore, <u>The Farmer and the Rest of Us</u> (Boston: Little, Brown & Co., 1945); and for the North Dakota Farmers Union in Ross B. Talbot, "The Politics of Farm Organizations in North Dakota" (unpublished Ph.D. dissertation, University of Chicago, 1953).

29. Such identifications are fairly common phenomena on agricultural college campuses. The writer has met several individuals who made no bones about their loyalties and has heard about many others. Some years ago an agricultural "elder statesman" characterized one agricultural college dean as "an upright man, in many ways; but so identified with the _____ interest that much of his value on public matters is lost."

30. Cf. the remarks of R. M. Hughes (<u>A Manual for Trustees of Colleges and Universities</u> [Ames: Iowa State College Press, 1943]). Repeated reference to these remarks is made in part because they characterize the conclusions that many experienced men in other states had come to, regarding proper relationships between presidents and boards.

31. North Carolina's use of research foundations is an example of a device to raise money from interested groups for large areas of research, such as dairy problems or tobacco, with direction of the research in the college.

32. Cornell University's college of agriculture has a policy, which is representative of a number of such institutions, covering the acceptance of outside funds. The research must be appropriate to undertake using other moneys if the gift concerned were not available; the university exercises complete discretion on publication; and results are published for all to use freely and are released at the same time.

33. On the high political level, abuses of executive veto power, judicial review, and legislative investigating power have occurred. In the present context the best design for selection of a governing board plus the best statement of the board's and the president's functions can both be nullified if the president fails to act his part; or a research foundation of an agricultural college can become a means for direct group domination of research—if one of the donors becomes dominant in the sense of providing the bulk of the finances and then, after the research program is under way and the college has made personnel commitments, suddenly decides to "call the tune."

Chapter IX

1. An examination of the forty-eight state Extension directors in

the United States as of 1947 showed that thirty-three had held the same
position in 1941 and seventeen in 1934. With one or two exceptions, the
directors named during 1934-47 were promoted from within the same
institution. Twelve of these had been in the same Extension Service—
six as assistant directors in 1934. Fourteen of them had been in physical
or biological sciences—heads of animal husbandry departments or
professors of agronomy, dairy husbandry, etc.; two had been agricultural
economists. These figures demonstrate both the long incumbencies in
these positions and the tendencies to promote from within the institution.
(Several Extension directors in 1947 were also deans of agricultural
colleges—in thirteen states at that time the dean was also director of
both the Extension Service and the experiment station; in three states,
he was also Extension director.)

2. A History of Iowa State College (Ames: Iowa State College Press,
1942), p. 90; cf. pp. 94-95. Cf. J. T. Willard, History of Kansas State
College of Agriculture and Applied Science (Manhattan: Kansas State
College, 1940), p. 170. For an analogy see Ernest S. Griffith's discussion
of "government by whirlpools," in Congress: Its Contemporary Role
(New York: New York University Press, 1951), pp. 37-38, 45, 112.

3. George A. Works and Barton Morgan, The Land-Grant Colleges
(Washington, D.C.: Government Printing Office, 1939), pp. 40-43, and E. A.
Burnett, Proceedings of the Association of Land-Grant Colleges and
Universities, XXXII (1919), 229.

4. E. W. Allen, Proceedings, XXXIII (1920), 91 ff.

5. Experiment Station Organization and Policy Committee, Proceedings, XXXVI (1922), 157.

6. Proceedings, XL (1926), 209-10. Cf. Mumford's remarks in
1922: "Unfortunately . . . there has been a quite general tendency for
the extension service to attempt to justify itself as an independent
institution, and in that overzealous attempt methods have been used
which have placed the college and the experiment station on the defensive,
and the recognized three-field function of our agricultural institutions
[resident teaching, experimentation, and extension] have, not infrequently, been placed on a competitive rather than a co-operative basis.
Sometimes indeed [extension workers have tried] to establish confidence
in extension work by destructive criticism of representatives of the
experiment station and agricultural college" (Proceedings, XXXVI [1922],
198). On the other hand, Dean W. C. Coffey testified to co-operation
between Extension and the station in Minnesota, giving examples (Proceedings, XLI [1927], 208-55).

7. Training and Recruiting of Personnel in the Rural Social Studies
(Washington, D.C.: American Council on Education, 1941), pp. 34-36, 62.
The writer was first referred to this study by a college dean with whom
he was canvassing Extension-station relations in 1943; the dean deplored
the situation in his own state, which he said was similar to that in several
others.

8. One ranking land-grant college official cited the 1950 bulletin
of his institution. This showed an experiment station with 11 subject-
matter departments and 87 scientific positions, of which 29 were Ph.D.'s,

45 were Masters of Science or of Arts, and 13 were Bachelors (usually Bachelors of Science). In contrast, the Extension Service had 7 supervisors, 6 with Bachelor's degrees and 1 with no degree; and it also had 45 specialists, 10 with Master's degrees, 33 with Bachelor's degrees, and 2 with no degrees. In this institution the Extension Service is notably independent—but, it should be added, the caliber of its employees at the county level has drawn considerable praise.

9. In these efforts at integration the ideal is easier to express than to realize. Joint appointments and rotation are difficult in that both research and effective Extension work often require concentrated application. However, research-Extension relationships are also being affected by the growing education of the farm clientele. A research worker in Washington State remarked that his first meeting with orchardists amazed him: "It was like a graduate seminar in physics." In Florida, where commercial agriculture rests upon exotic plants (a researcher explains) and profound ecological problems are created, research assumes great burdens: "The farmers don't stop at the county agent; they go directly to the substation to see the Ph.D. in charge of the experiment which interests them." Some persons quarreled with these statements, but more were inclined to agree; the upshot is a belief that the balance is tending to shift toward the experiment station, at least in the kind of work that Extension has traditionally done.

10. Alabama, Colorado, Indiana, Iowa, Kansas, Michigan, Mississippi, Montana, New Mexico, North Carolina, North Dakota, Oklahoma, Oregon, South Carolina, South Dakota, Texas, Utah, Virginia, and Washington. States with separate agricultural and mechanical schools for Negroes are not counted. In addition, a number of states in which the college of agriculture is on the state university campus have separate experiment stations (e.g., Georgia and Ohio). It should also be pointed out that numerous other institutions of higher education are claimants for funds in many states; here, however, the concern is with the major division between university and "A. and M." school. Cf. John D. Millett, Financing Higher Education in the United States (New York: Columbia University Press, 1952), pp. 241-5

11. The president of a state university was recently questioned by a legislative finance committee on his hiring policy. He described his investigations and use of references in determining the fitness of prospective faculty members. "But," he was told, "the president of the state college informed us that he uses [a standard reference work on financial standing] to check not only a prospective appointee's financial integrity but also his social and political views. Why don't you do the same?' The university president was flustered. Apparently neither he nor the legislators knew that the reference work in question provides no information on "social and political views." This incident, which is probably characteristic of the continuous jockeying for advantage between two such institutions, would be quite humorous if it did not suggest that a vague and general inquiry into the "social and political views" of a prospective professor is an appropriate preliminary to hiring him.

12. House Hearings, Agricultural Appropriations, fiscal 1953, Part 1, pp. 348-49. The experiment station committee on organization and policy of the Association of Land-Grant Colleges and Universities was trying (with some success) to establish communication between the state committees and national advisory committees under the Research and Market-

ing Act. The Research and Marketing Act and its administration have been analyzed in Research and Marketing Administration (RMA) reports, Agricultural Research Administration reports, <u>JFE</u> articles, agricultural appropriation hearings, and elsewhere. Lewis Mainzer is preparing a Ph.D. thesis at the University of Chicago on the subject.

13. See above, pp. 68-69. In 1926 appropriations were being made to the university rather than to the advisory interests themselves, as they had been initially. Cf. Dean H. W. Mumford's description, in <u>Proceedings</u>, XL (1926), 212-13. Interviews over the last decades indicate that a valued advisory relationship continues, but both the growth and maturity of the experiment station and the tremendous refinement of research processes have markedly changed it. One also observes that the Illinois Agricultural Association (IAA) (the Farm Bureau) has become the largest and best-financed state farm organization in the nation; it contributed $1,257,000, or more than 40 per cent of Extension's budget in Illinois in fiscal 1953, where county agents (farm advisers) are chosen by county farm bureaus from legally qualified nominees of the state Extension Service. The IAA is considered to be one of the most effective lobbies in Springfield, and its agenda includes funds for the college. On the IAA see W. Bruce Storm, "An Analysis of the Illinois Agricultural Association as a Pressure Group" (unpublished Doctor's dissertation, University of Chicago, 1950). See Preface, above.

14. The present Montana and North Dakota councils had predecessors. In this discussion of state councils it should be made clear that the common reference is to organizations essentially created to advise the college, or part of it, on its program and to help get legislative appropriations; but some organizations, although created for other purposes, are significant both as councils and as sources for support in the legislature. Again, readers should be reminded that councils of agriculture in a number of states (twenty-six in 1951) are affiliates of the National Council of Farm Cooperatives. Some of these councils are doubtless of considerable significance in state politics, and some probably scrutinize agricultural research along lines of interest to their member organizations. The Wisconsin Council of Agriculture, formed in 1928, with a membership of eighty to ninety organizations which included some 120,000 individuals (1951), has been a powerful factor in Wisconsin state politics. It has counseled with the college of agriculture and supported its programs; but college spokesmen maintain that this has not meant the "approval" of projects.

15. Missouri has a state advisory committee for agricultural Extension (such as several states are now developing) but no council for the experiment station.

16. For Illinois see above, n. 13. In appraising the advantages of councils in states like New York, Illinois, and California, one must remember that they rank first, fourth, and fifth in per capita income payments and first, second, and third in total personal income (1950); that all three states have had exceptionally vigorous leadership in their agricultural colleges for long periods; and that in all three states the rural districts are overrepresented in the legislatures. The advisory councils had fertile fields and excellent tilling machinery!

17. Cf. the remarks of N. E. Dodd, given in Charles M. Hardin, <u>The Politics of Agriculture</u> (Glencoe, Ill.: Free Press, 1952), p. 177.

18. Kerr was long president of Oregon State, Bryan of Washington State, Thompson of Ohio State; and Davenport was the celebrated early dean of the Illinois college of agriculture. For their speeches see Proceedings, XLV (1931), 82 ff.; for Coffey's remarks, Proceedings, XLVII (1933), 148.

19. The French Revolution (quoted in R. J. S. Hoffman and Paul Levack [eds.], Burke's Politics: Selected Writings and Speeches [New York: Alfred A. Knopf, 1949], p. 318). For an excellent general discussion of the problem, see Don K. Price, Government and Science (New York: New York University Press, 1954).

20. Difficulties are recognized in fastening upon the proper subject matter. In a sense, political significance pervades actions of agricultural college personnel. The county agent distributes a bulletin on fertilizing pastures; the research, publication, and dissemination are all tributes to the ability of agricultural interests to secure public services. Define politics this broadly, however, and it can be conveyed only through stream-of-consciousness novels. Again, the distinction between research and education upon controversial issues and active politics is hard to make, especially at the margin; but a difference exists between writing a controversial bulletin and sitting down with a commodity group to help draft a bill or map a drive to keep present legislation on the books.

21. After one controversy, an official of the college declared: "The charge that the college had taken sides was absolutely false, but we did have to discipline one man for playing politics." Respecting the objectivity and quality of analysis in a college "fact-finding" report in another controversy, an official of the college was scathingly—and properly—critical.

22. College-Grange relationships have probably been most co-operative and productive in North Carolina, Ohio, Oregon, New York, and Pennsylvania, although the writer is somewhat doubtful about the last two. In one state with a powerful Grange unusually active in policy matters, a ranking college official reported a meeting with the state Grange executive committee, whose members expressed surprise to learn that the college was active in some fields which the Grange had accused it of neglecting. "We should know more about what the college does," they said; whereupon, the college official rejoined: "This is the first time that I have ever been invited to meet with your executive committee." Theodore Saloutas and John D. Hicks write: "The typical Union member of the western Middle West displayed a belligerent attitude toward the existing agricultural colleges" (Agricultural Discontent in the Middle West, 1900-1939 [Madison: University of Wisconsin, 1951], p. 229). Interviews suggest that the relationship has improved a little in Montana and North Dakota and perhaps in one or two other states, but the relationship, except for unusual faculty members, remains cool at best and is often mutually antagonistic.

23. As is strikingly illustrated in V. O. Key, Jr., Southern Politics (New York: Alfred A. Knopf, 1949), esp. chaps. ii-xi, each devoted to a separate state.

24. Among the numerous studies of this situation, an outstanding recent one is Robert Kramer (ed.), Legislative Reapportionment (Law and Contemporary Problems, Vol. VII, No. 2 [spring, 1952]); examples

are taken from the article by David G. Farrelly and Ivan Hinderaker.

25. V. O. Key, Jr., <u>Politics, Parties, and Pressure Groups</u> (3d ed.; New York: Thomas Y. Crowell Co., 1952), p. 275.

26. Frederic A. Ogg and P. Orman Ray, <u>Introduction to American Government</u> (10th ed.; New York: Appleton-Century-Crofts, Inc., 1951), p. 819.

27. W. Brooke Graves, <u>American State Government</u> (3d ed.; Boston: D. C. Heath & Co., 1945), p. 232.

28. <u>Southern Politics</u>, p. 155, n. 28.

29. Russell Lord, quoted in H. R. Tolley, <u>The Farmer Citizen at War</u> (New York: Macmillan Co., 1943), pp. 116-17.

30. An incident in Nebraska in November, 1953, shows the ideal roles of the board, the administration, and the professor involved. C. Clyde Mitchell, head of the department of agricultural economics of the University of Nebraska, published an article in the November <u>Capper's Farmer</u> entitled, "Let's Not Go Back to 1920." In an economy (said Mitchell) with numerous controls (both public and private) on production processes and the market, agriculture's support price legislation is both understandable and defensible: "Crop loans and associated production restrictions," Mitchell wrote, "have placed farmers on more even terms with America's industrial economy . . . farmers have fixed supports because they provide a solid basis for planning."
The Hall County Farm Bureau concluded that Mitchell's views on price supports "are the exact opposite of ours" and appointed a committee to call on the university's board of regents and "take any further action they deem advisable." Regent J. Leroy Welsh welcomed the Hall County Farm Bureau's complaint and said: "I have no brief for anyone in a tax-supported institution who favors the destruction of the free enterprise system."
The board of regents met, heard Dean W. V. Lambert of the college of agriculture present the case for academic freedom and analyze its application in this incident, expressed their confidence in the dean's administration, dismissed the Mitchell affair, and adopted a statement of principle, part of which read:
"The right, as a professional person, to freedom in research and publication of the results thereof, limited only by the precepts of scholarship and the faithful performance of other academic duties. . . .
"The right, as a professional person, to free and thorough discussion in the classroom.
"The rights to uphold, to discuss and dissent are the moral fiber of America's greatness. They are likewise the strength of a great University."
Furthermore, Dean Lambert made excellent use of Secretary Benson's November address to the Association of Land-Grant Colleges and Universities (see below, p. 192). See the <u>Lincoln</u> (Nebraska) <u>Journal,</u> November 22, 1953, article by Jack Hart; the <u>Nebraskan</u> (University of Nebraska student newspaper) for November 13, 1953.

31. Arguable viewpoints include the very wide range of positions compatible with free government. Presumably, no board will knowingly employ either a Communist or a Fascist, or urge that these extreme

positions be represented. The question is, of course: What of the crypto-comrades and the undeclared worshipers of Hitler's "leadership principle"? If a few of these brethren get faculty employment, their colleagues can be counted on to answer them. It is really absurd to worry about a handful of subversives when the flaming words of the <u>Communist Manifesto</u> and <u>Mein Kampf</u> are freely available—and, if we retain our faith in free institutions, free discussion, and freedom in education, it is unthinkable that such documents should not be available. Poisons should be kept away from small children; but the maturing individual has to learn to handle them properly.

32. Winston Churchill, <u>The Second World War</u>, Vol. II: <u>Their Finest Hour</u> (London: Cassell & Co., 1949), p. 15.

33. See pp. 123-24, 168, 192.

Chapter X

1. The foregoing account is primarily based upon published materials; a number of interviews and discussions of the matter were held in 1943 and at various times since then, but material from these interviews has not been consciously employed in this account. See the <u>Des Moines Tribune</u>, July 13 and November 5, 1943; the <u>Des Moines Register</u>, September 24, 1943; and the <u>Cedar Rapids Gazette</u>, September 19, 1943.

2. Cf. p. 91 above.

3. The formal organization of political power was actively concerned; the board of education, the governor, the speaker of the house of representatives in Iowa—all were involved. But informal political interests were also apparent, especially those which A. F. Bentley called the "wide, weak interests." or the "underlying groups" (The <u>Process of Government</u> [Chicago: University of Chicago Press, 1908; Bloomington, Ind.: Principia Press, 1949]) or which David B. Truman called "potential groups" (<u>The Governmental Process</u> [New York: Alfred A. Knopf, 1951]).

4. In the May, 1947, issue of the <u>Journal of Farm Economics</u>, the writer referred to an exodus from Iowa State College which broke up one of the most active, productive, and influential social science groups in the country. This statement has been criticized as implying that Iowa State College's social science work was subsequently reduced to ineffectiveness. The inference is incorrect. Social science in Iowa State continues to have an able group, and those who constitute it probably enjoy a happier situation because of what happened in 1943—even including the resignations (again we return to imponderables). But it is no disparagement of those who remained or who have since been recruited to emphasize the ability of those who left or even the eminence of some of them or the degree to which the pre-1943 department enjoyed <u>esprit de corps</u>.

Chapter XI

1. W. I. Jennings wrote, "To find out whether a people is free it is necessary only to ask if there is an Opposition and, if there is, to ask where it is" (<u>The British Constitution</u> [Cambridge: At the University Press, 1942] , p. 78).

2. "What Makes a Strong President?" New York Times Magazine, December 13, 1953; Cf. Hyman, The American President (New York: Harper & Bros., 1954).

3. Pendleton Herring, The Politics of Democracy (New York: Rinehart & Co., 1940), p. 32.

4. This way of putting the question requires acknowledgment of a professional debt to Professor W. Y. Elliott, whose "co-organic" theory of the state and of other social organizations stresses both the politics of survival (including internal organization and economy as well as external relationships, defense measures, alliances, etc.) and the politics of purpose (the ends toward which men aspire) (The Pragmatic Revolt in Politics ⌈New York: Macmillan Co., 1928⌉).

5. Charles M. Hardin, "Programmatic Research and Agricultural Policy," JFE, Vol. XXIX (May, 1947).

6. Proceedings of the Association of Land-Grant Colleges and Universities, XLIII (1929), 245.

7. November 12, 1953. See Proceedings, Vol. LXVII (1953).

8. Proceedings, LI (1937), 26; cf. p. 28.

9. Proceedings, LV (1941), 28; emphasis in original.

10. Proceedings, Vol. LXII (1948), esp. p. 40; and Proceedings, LVII (1943), 29 ff., esp. p. 31. For similar sentiments see "Federal-State Relationships in Agriculture," papers by M. L. Wilson, then Undersecretary of Agriculture, and H. R. Tolley, chief of the Bureau of Agricultural Economics, in Proceedings, LIII (1939), 92-105; F. J. Sievers, of Massachusetts, "Some Essentials and Non-essentials of Agricultural Research," Proceedings, LIV (1940), 145-47; President C. A. Dykstra of the University of Wisconsin, in his address "The Problem of Survival," Proceedings, LV (1941), 42-43; President Edmund Ezra Day of Cornell, in his address "Science and Social Progress," Proceedings, LV (1941), 58-59; J. E. Carrigan, of Vermont, "The . . . Extension Service . . . in the Enlarging National Agricultural Program," Proceedings, LVI (1942), 136 ff.; President H. C. Byrd of the University of Maryland, in State Government, February, 1944; President Lewis Webster Jones of Arkansas University, "The Challenge of the President's Commission," Proceedings, LXII (1948), 41 ff.

11. Even as statesman-like a figure as the late H. E. Babcock gave expression to this idea ("The Place of Cooperatives in Developing and Preserving Free Enterprise," American Cooperation, 1942-45, pp. 49-50).

12. See below, pp. 143, 145 ff., 197.

13. Proceedings, LXI (1947), 82-88.

14. Cf. David Riesman's provocative analysis of the "inner-directed" generation, in which he would put many persons prominent in agriculture (The Lonely Crowd ⌈New Haven: Yale University Press, 1950⌉).

15. Proceedings, XXXVIII (1924), 282 ff., and Oregon Farms (Extension Circular 524 ⌈Corvallis: Federal Cooperative Extension Service, Oregon State College, 1948⌉). Maris was then director of the Oregon Extension Service. Later he ably directed the Farm Security Administration's farm-ownership program.

16. Cf. Basic Facts about Montana's Agriculture (Bull. 81 ⌈1926⌉), and Bull. 1000 (1949), of the same title (Bozeman: Extension Service, Montana State College).

17. "A Farm Program for North Carolina" (Raleigh:Agricultural Extension Service, North Carolina State College ⌈USDA co-operating⌉ , 1948).

18. "North Carolina Accepts the Challenge."

19. See the appraisal of Dean H. W. Mumford of the Illinois college of agriculture, in Proceedings, XXXVIII (1924), 299-310. More recently, verbal criticisms of one of the several state planning documents characterized it as a countermove to the USDA's proposal for agricultural postwar planning; "its intrinsic value, if any, was in improved public relations." A similar, if somewhat less brutal, self-criticism was made in a second state. In general, the writer believes that state and local planning is most successful when forced by grinding necessity—as in the Oregon, Montana, or North Carolina illustrations; but this by no means suggests that "grinding necessity" will be matched by the leadership and ability necessary to produce the plans. See the writer's discussion, in "Reflections on Agricultural Policy," APSR, Vol. XLII (December, 1948).

20. Winston Churchill, The Second World War, Vol. III: The Grand Alliance (Boston: Houghton Mifflin Co., 1950), p. 602; cf. p. 24.

Chapter XII

1. It was first called the "Association of American Agricultural Colleges and Experiment Stations." The present title dates from 1927. It is often called the "Land-Grant College Association." Its annual Proceedings were published by the Office of Experiment Stations (USDA) until 1909; subsequently, by the association.

2. Negro land-grant institutions were not included during the period of this study, although territorial ones were. In its annual meeting in Washington, D.C., November, 1954, the association voted to admit Negro institutions to membership.

3. Proceedings of the Association of Land-Grant Colleges and Universities, L (1936), 91. The statement was prompted by the Soil Conservation and Domestic Allotment Act of 1936, which provided for transition to the states of the administration of the Agricultural Conservation Program (ACP) and authorized the designation of the colleges as agents of the states for this purpose. Actually, the colleges have not been employed as state agents in the ACP; the first proposal that a college should administer a state plan was made by Mississippi in 1952. See the writer's "State Administration for National Soil Conservation?" in the Farm Policy Forum for May, 1952; see also the Appendix and chap. ix of The Politics of Agriculture (Glencoe, Ill.: Free Press, 1952), as well as chaps. iii and iv above.

4. J. L. Hill, "The Builders of the Association," Proceedings, XLII (1928), 26 (presidential address).

5. Proceedings, XXXII (1919), 69-74.

6. In the light of these remarks, it is curious that the charge was made in 1921 that few presidents attended association meetings (Proceedings, XXXV [1921], 352).

7. Four of the six members were presidents during eight of the years 1921-35; R. A. Pearson, president of Iowa State and the University of Maryland, in that order, was chairman of the executive committee during these years. In 1938-45 there were six presidents in every year except 1941 (four presidents) and 1940 and 1945 (five presidents).

8. The president is chosen annually and does not succeed himself. Institutional presidents are usually chosen, but occasionally a dean is honored.

9. Though the past tense is used in this paragraph, the executive committee retained many of these powers and functions after 1945.

10. The secretary of the executive committee has also been of great importance; Thomas P. Cooper, of Kentucky, noted in his presidential address in 1946 that he had served sixteen years as secretary-treasurer; he also noted that only nine men had served as chairman of the executive committee since the formation of the association (Proceedings, LX [1946], 28 ff.).

11. Proceedings, LX (1946), 28 ff., 50 ff.

12. Perhaps not too much stress should be laid upon this interpretation. The association has been employed by institutional presidents before to protect their roles in federal-state relationships in agriculture; presumably, it may be so employed again. In 1920 several presidents objected to a proposed national conference of Extension workers, and it was abandoned in favor of regional conferences (Proceedings, XXXIV [1920], 286). In 1928 the executive committee objected that agricultural transactions had often taken place from beginning to end without the president's knowledge; it secured an agreement with the Secretary of Agriculture that copies of all correspondence would be sent to the presidents (Proceedings, XLII [1928], 78).

13. Proceedings, LX (1946), 107.

14. Director C. W. Creel, of Nevada, was the first Washington representative; he was followed by W. A. Lloyd, retired from the federal Extension Service, who died in 1946. Since then, Russell J. Thackrey, of Kansas, has served. Of his service, Dean Cooper remarked that literally dozens of college presidents now said that for the first time they knew what was going on in Washington of interest to the association.

15. Proceedings, XLII (1928), 30.

16. V. O. Key, Jr., The Administration of Federal Grants to States (Chicago: Public Administration Service, 1937), p. 180.

17. Reference has been made to the association's activities on
behalf of the second Morrill Act, the Adams and Smith-Lever acts,
and the Nelson Amendment (above, p. 213). The association also
supported the Capper-Ketcham Act (1928), the Bankhead-Jones Act (1935),
the Hope-Flannagan Act (1946), and other measures, and it fought
to protect appropriations authorized by these. While the association
supported the Newlands Reclamation Bill, it also moved to protect
the interest of land-grant institutions in revenues from public land
sales, which were used to support reclamation (Proceedings, XVI
[1902], 13-14). In 1905 the Adams Bill was under consideration
along with other measures, and the executive committee recommended
a strategy which has consistently been followed, namely, to select
one measure at a time for political support (Proceedings, XIX [1905],
17-18, 42-44). Sometimes conflict between the agricultural and engineering schools of member institutions has broken out in the association.
In 1919 President W. M. Riggs of Clemson College noted that the
association felt that its request for federal aid for engineering research
was justified but cautioned that Congress was unreceptive: "The
average Congressman scents in this matter a contest between the
Agricultural College and the State University. . . and passes the buck
to the Legislature" (Proceedings, XXXIII [1919], 144 ff.). In 1928
representatives of the agricultural Extension Service sought the
association's support for the Capper-Ketcham Bill. The executive
body of the association noted that the engineering experiment station
bill had precedence but voted to leave the matter to the executive
committee, which elected to support the Capper-Ketcham Bill.
Farmers outnumbered engineers (Proceedings, XLII [1928], 565).

18. Proceedings, XXXIX (1925), 63-68.

19. Proceedings, XXXV (1921), 163, 170-71, 349.

20. Proceedings, XXXVII (1923), 519.

21. Proceedings, XXXVII (1923), 67-69; cf. pp. 255-56.

22. Above, p. 29.

23. V. O. Key, Jr., op. cit., pp. 184, 189.

24. Proceedings, XVIII (1904), 19; Proceedings, XIX (1905), 17.

25. Proceedings, XXXV (1921), 183.

26. Proceedings, XXXII (1919), 130-31.

27. See the testimony of a number of states to the efficacy of the
association in this regard (Proceedings, XVII [1903], 31-32, 84).

28. Proceedings, XXII (1908), 47.

29. Proceedings, XXVI (1912), 95-98. The Office of Foreign
Agricultural Relations was created in the USDA in 1945, apparently
without benefit of further association promotion.

30. Proceedings, XXXVII (1923), 486-87.

31. Proceedings, XV (1901), 41.

32. Proceedings, XV (1901), 57-58.

33. The Politics of Agriculture, chap. ii, sec. 3.

34. Proceedings, XXXII (1919), 68.

35. Proceedings, XXXII (1919), 114-20; see also the 1919 report of the committee on college organization and policy (Proceedings, Vol. XXXII [1919], Index).

36. Individuals had, of course, been active. With his usual insight, A. R. Mann, of Cornell, urged action by the association on the agricultural situation in 1923 (Proceedings, XXXVII [1923], 308 ff.). T. P. Cooper, of Kentucky, did likewise in 1924 (Proceedings, XXXVIII [1924], 236 ff.).

37. Proceedings, XLI (1927), 85-86, and following pages for the report itself.

38. Proceedings, XLII (1928), 76.

39. Agricultural Reform in the United States (New York: McGraw-Hill Book Co., Inc., 1929), pp. 77-80.

40. "Development of Agricultural Policy since the World War," in Farmers in a Changing World (yearbook, USDA, 1940), p. 312.

41. President A. F. Woods took part in the hearings on agricultural relief in 1925 but confined his remarks to discussions of grants for agricultural research and education. See the remarks of Congressman Fulmer (South Carolina) in Congressional Record, LXVI (1925), 4668, and House Hearings, Committee on Agriculture, "Agricultural Relief" (68th Cong., 2d sess.), Serial CC, p. 348.

42. House Hearings, Committee on Agriculture, "Farm Relief" (71st Cong., 1st sess.), Serial A, Part 2, pp. 95-104; see also Senate Hearings, Committee on Agriculture and Forestry, same subject, same session, pp. 175-79.

43. Proceedings, XLIV (1930), 127; these remarks should be read in the light of the slow and late development of economic personnel in the Extension Service. See chap. x.

44. House Hearings, Engineering Experiment Station Bill (71st Cong., 2d sess.), Serial G, p. 99. Compare his report of the meeting on the agricultural situation called by the AFBF (Chicago, 1931) in which the association was represented by Dean Mumford (Illinois). Pearson said later that the "most important" of the great many aspects of the agricultural situation to be considered was an agreement as to the manner of paying Extension salaries! (Proceedings, XLV [1931], 26).

45. Proceedings, XLIII (1929), 35, 73-97.

46. Proceedings, XLIV (1930), 81 ff.

47. Cf. the report of Director H. C. Ramsower, of Ohio, in *Proceedings*, XLV (1931), 302 ff., and the analysis of H. R. Tolley in *Proceedings*, XLIV (1930), 108 ff.

48. Federal Farm Board Bull. 4 (Washington, D.C., 1930) and *2d Annual Report* (1931).

49. Theodore Morgan, "The Federal Farm Board" (unpublished Ph.D. thesis, Harvard University, 1939), chap. xix.

50. *Proceedings*, XLV (1931), 43.

51. Federal Farm Board, *2d Annual Report* (1931), pp. 66-69; *3d Annual Report* (1932), pp. 59-60.

52. *Proceedings*, XXXVII (1923), 27.

53. *Proceedings*, XLV (1931), 27.

54. *Proceedings of the National Conference on Land Utilization* (Chicago, 1931).

55. *Proceedings*, XLVI (1932), 87-92, 317-18, 325 ff.

56. *Proceedings*, XLVI (1932), 276.

57. Later the National Resources Board; still later the National Resources Planning Board.

58. In 1942 the request was for establishment of a conference between the USDA and the association on the functions of the Agricultural War Boards (*Proceedings*, LVI [1942], 202-3); for the Agricultural War Boards see Hardin, *The Politics of Agriculture*, pp. 134-35. The second request, also in 1942, was for the association to establish a special committee on wartime agricultural problems to make analyses and prepare recommendations for policy-makers. The organization and policy committee had in mind such things as facilitation of agricultural production without "irreparable damage" to the soil and stimulation of milk production in the face of the fact that farmers could make more money raising hogs (*Proceedings*, LVI [1942], 197-99, 213).

59. M. L. Wilson, then director of the Subsistence Homesteads Division, United States Department of the Interior, and Chester C. Davis, then chief of the Agricultural Adjustment Administration's production division, also spoke. See *Proceedings*, XLVII (1933), 47, 103, 112.

60. See pp. 32-34, 48, 160, 216. The association's committee briefly described how the Mt. Weather Agreement was reached and reported the agreement (*Proceedings*, LII [1938], 285-87).

61. In 1943 a well-known state Extension director told the writer that a recent meeting with the war food administrator had marked the first time in five years that he and his colleagues had been consulted on "the farm program." Interviews in a number of other states brought out the same complaint.

62. A verbal report was mentioned in 1941. After 1939 the Proceedings ceased to list members of the USDA committee. When the executive committee moved the discharge of the committee on relationships in 1944, it reported that relationships with the USDA were so cordial that it was no longer needed—a statement of doubtful perceptivity, in view of subsequent developments. The executive committee assumed the relationship function, which, in fact, it had never relinquished (Proceedings, LVI [1942] , 85; LVIII [1944] , 70). Interviews which appraised the effectiveness of the committees on relationships varied from "The subject was too hot to handle" to "The committees were not worth a damn."

63. Proceedings, LXI (1947), 155-56; LXII (1948), 257.

64. Proceedings, LXIV (1950), 312.

65. Proceedings, LXV (1951), 156.

66. Proceedings, LXV (1951), 155.

67. Cf. chap. v above and Hardin, The Politics of Agriculture.

68. Proceedings, LXV (1951), 156, 158-59.

69. Cf. Hardin, The Politics of Agriculture, chap. iii. The association indorsed the general objectives of the Granger Bill, designed to bring about the divorce, although it objected to specific provisions of the original version (Proceedings, LXIV [1950] , 304).

70. A series of conferences on phosphates by groups in the association antedated the committee; indirectly, its formation was stimulated by the Tennessee Valley Authority's agricultural program and the activities of Dr. H. A. Morgan, once president of the University of Tennessee and later (1933-48) a member of the TVA board, and J. C. McAmis, who had come from the Tennessee agricultural Extension Service to head TVA's agricultural relations division. The interest of the association reflected the satisfaction of its members with their TVA relationships as well as their concern over the phosphate situation.
Another important issue which was similarly rooted in members' interests is reflected in the work of the association's committee on irrigated agriculture and water resources. This activity grew largely out of dissatisfactions with the three-way relationships between agricultural colleges, the Bureau of Reclamation of the United States Department of the Interior, and the USDA. See Proceedings, LXIV (1950), 297.
For another issue which stimulated considerably less interest in the association, however, see references to a proposed agricultural marketing bill for the establishment of marketing facilities (S. 2212 [71st Cong.]), Proceedings, LIII (1939), 266-67; LIV (1940), 254-55.

71. Proceedings, LVII (1943), 239 ff.

72. The National Soil Fertility Bill (S. 1251 [80th Cong., 1st sess. (1947)] was partly an outgrowth of this committee's work.

73. The report appears in Proceedings, LVIII (1944), 233 ff. For background see Proceedings, LV (1941), 317; LVII (1943), 243. (For subsequent developments, unless otherwise noted, see Proceedings, LIX (1945), 59-69, and LX (1946), 192-214. The report was also published as a brochure. It was made clear that the committee did not speak for the association, but, of course, its stature is a reflection of its appointment by that body.

74. In 1945 a second report amplified some points made in the first one. In 1946 a third report was released, as well as statements on "Strengthening Research and Education in Public Policies Related to Agriculture" (by Noble Clark); a statement criticizing the reduction in funds for the Bureau of Agricultural Economics by the House of Representatives (by the executive committee and the committee on agricultural policy); and one on "Agricultural Policy in Relation to International Cooperation" (by the committee on agricultural policy).

75. The committee or its members appeared at meetings in the USDA, before the National Association of County Agents, etc. A conference in Chicago (June, 1945) on extending social security to the farmers was stimulated by the committee.

76. House Hearings, "Long-Range Agricultural Policy" (80th Cong., 1st sess.), Parts 3 and 15. Noble Clark was chairman of the committee on agricultural policy until June, 1947, when he was succeeded by Professor O. B. Jesness, of the University of Minnesota.

77. Proceedings, LX (1946), 192 ff.

78. Proceedings, LXII (1948), 127-29.

79. Proceedings, LXII (1948), 260; the resolution was presented by the special committee on federal legislation and grew out of a senate request in 1947 for clarification of association policy to provide "reasonable safeguards against committing the Association to a position which will not be in accord generally with that of its individual members" (Proceedings, LXI [1947] , 169).

80. "A Religion for Now," Harper's Magazine, December, 1953.

81. See, e.g., the analysis of problems of dairy farms in John D. Black, The Rural Economy of New England (Cambridge, Mass.: Harvard University Press, 1950), chap. xviii, and the bulletins undertaken in the North Central Farm Management Research Committee's project in the economics of soil conservation, available at the Farm Foundation, 600 South Michigan Avenue, Chicago, Illinois.

82. Compare President J. L. Coulter of North Dakota State, in Proceedings, XLII (1928), 108 ff.; Dean Marston's presidential address in 1929 (Proceedings, XLIII [1929] , 245); Secretary Hyde's remarks in 1930 (Proceedings, XLIV [1930] , 102, 107); Dean C. B. Hutchinson's analyses in 1931 (Proceedings, XLV [1931] , 236); and A. R. Mann's address in 1932 (Proceedings, XLVI [1932] , 149-61).

83. Proceedings, XXII (1908), 16.

84. Proceedings, XXXII (1919), 113.

85. Proceedings, XXXVII (1923), 463 ff.; XXXVIII (1924), 453 ff.; XXXIX (1925), 370-78.

86. Thus the writer now believes that a previous suggestion that the association might provide an active collective agency for the protection of freedom of education and research in member institutions is unworkable ("Programmatic Research and Agricultural Policy," JFE, May, 1947).

87. It asked the USDA to appoint an undersecretary to correlate scientific research and requested the joint committee to develop the case for co-operative research. The latter complied with a recommendation for research conferences, both general ones to be held regionally and specific problem conferences which might be either regional or national (Proceedings, XXXIII [1919], 126 ff.; cf. C. R. Ball's remarks, Proceedings, XXXV [1921], 158-62).

88. Proceedings, XXXVI (1922), 155 ff.; the joint committee again asked the association to support closer federal-state collaboration in research (pp. 160 ff.); and cf. Dean Mumford of the Illinois college of agriculture (pp. 199-200).

89. Quoted in Persia Campbell, American Agricultural Policy (London: P. S. King & Son, 1933), p. 63.

90. Proceedings, XXXIX (1925), 169 ff. The six committees were discharged with honor in 1931 (Proceedings, XLV [1931], 268-69).

91. Proceedings, XLII (1928), 205-9.

92. Proceedings, XLIII (1929), 202 ff.

93. Proceedings, XLIII (1929), 246-47.

94. It is not argued that there was a consensus in the land-grant institutions themselves with the joint committee, Dean Ladd, and others mentioned. To the contrary, when the Survey of 1930 asked the state stations to estimate the relative importance of different lines of experiment station work, thirty-five of them responded. Three groups of policies were listed, in order of declining importance. Timely coordination of research among stations and with the USDA was in the third group (Survey, II, 666-67).

95. Federal Relations to Education (2 vols.; Washington, D.C., 1931).

96. Proceedings, XLVI (1932), 485-87.

97. Proceedings, XLVII (1933), 83-85. Frank warned that, if the control of the destiny of agriculture were not to be "ripped out" of the college's hands and "lodged in Washington, we must develop and discipline a farm population that has had something more than a few weeks of quick coaching in the tricks of the trade of running a dairy or a creamery, . . . we must evolve a type of education that will not only equip the farmers of the next generation to do their job technically, but will give them an

insight into the moving complex of political, social, and economic forces that are beating about their heads and controlling their destinies."

98. Proceedings, XLV (1931), 514 ff.

99. It supported, and proposed a means to realize, Professor Emil Truog's suggestive proposal for decennial, evaluative summaries in the chief areas of agricultural research to help the harassed specialist remain abreast of his field (Proceedings, LII ⌈1938⌉, 288 ff.; LVI ⌈1942⌉, 206-7). A history of this committee occurs in Proceedings, LI (1937), 274 ff.

100. V. O. Key, Jr., op. cit., p. 189.

101. Proceedings, XXXIX (1925), 152 ff.; XL (1926), 158 ff.; and XLII (1928), 197 ff.

102. See the annual reports of the Office of Experiment Stations, under the heading "Coordination and Cooperation," for 1931-36; cf. Proceedings, LIV (1940), 304.

103. See the writer's article, "Political Influence and Agricultural Research," American Political Science Review, XLI (August, 1947), 668 ff.

104. Proceedings, LXI (1947), 155-58; LXII (1948), 257-58; and LXIII (1949), 129-30, abstract of paper by W. A. Minor (USDA).

105. See above, pp. 144-45.

106. Based on an examination of the annual reports of the executive committee of the association, 1939-52; of the reports of the organization and policy committees of Extension and the experiment stations, 1938-45; an examination of the business of the division of agriculture and of the senate since the constitutional revision through 1952. In 1946 Chairman Milton Eisenhower of the executive committee proposed a commission to prepare a statement respecting the purpose and function of the entire area of higher education in America (Proceedings, LX ⌈1946⌉, 107). In 1939 the committee on institutional organization and policy praised relationships with the TVA and recommended an increase in regional co-operation. This committee also recommended a survey to redefine and reaffirm college and university objectives in the light of economic and social developments; a survey was undertaken, but it was rather inconclusive. Recommendations were continued, but the committee itself was dissolved on its own motion in 1946. See the relevant Proceedings.

107. Proceedings, LXIV (1950), 140; the division of agriculture heard an excellent symposium on agricultural policy by members of its committee of that name in 1947 (Proceedings, LXI ⌈1947⌉, 81 ff.). The section on agricultural extension work heard a thoughtful survey and discussion of Extension programs in the public policy field in 1950 (Proceedings, LXIV ⌈1950⌉, 137-44). The section on agricultural experiment station work had sessions on regional co-operation and the social sciences in experiment station research; but only one of the papers was summarized in the Proceedings (LXII ⌈1948⌉, 135).

108. As advocated by Noble Clark and O. B. Jesness, respectively.

Chapter XIII

1. Secretary Ezra Taft Benson reorganized the USDA on November 2, 1953, among other things, by splitting the Bureau of Agricultural Economics (BAE). Research on farm management and costs, land economics, and agricultural finance was assigned to the Agricultural Research Service; all other research and statistical work of the BAE was assigned to the newly created Agricultural Marketing Service (Memo. 1320, suppl. 4 ⌈Washington, D.C.: Office of the Secretary, USDA, 1953⌉). The writer regrets this step for reasons implicit in the argument of these pages as well as in the paper by John D. Black et al. and, in a separate statement, by T. W. Schultz in the symposium, "The Fragmentation of the BAE," JFE, Vol. XXXVI (1954); in view of the penchant for secretaries of agriculture to reorganize the USDA, however, the BAE may be reincarnated some day. Meanwhile, the analysis of these chapters is strengthened rather than disturbed by the dismemberment of the bureau.

2. Chaps. xiii-xv draw heavily upon the writer's article, "The Bureau of Agricultural Economics under Fire: A Study in Valuation Conflicts," JFE, Vol. XXVIII, No. 3, August, 1946; see, however, the "Methodological Note" at the end of chap. xv.

3. House Hearings, Agricultural Appropriations, fiscal 1953, Part 1, pp. 41 ff., 211 ff.

4. House Hearings, Agricultural Appropriations, fiscal 1951, Part 1, p. 358; fiscal 1952, Part 1, p. 174.

5. Senate Hearings, Agricultural Appropriations, fiscal 1952, p. 910.

6. House Hearings, fiscal 1953, Part 1, p. 180. In his first appropriation hearing as chief of the BAE Wells explained that "most of the work in economic investigations is designed to turn out statistics. There are statistics that require a more analytical approach, that have not been routinized like the crop and livestock estimates." Examples included estimates respecting land values, food consumption, gross and net farm income. Wells also heavily stressed his belief that "most of our farm management work is . . . very closely related to statistics." But such work is not subject to complete routinization: "Some analysis is also needed" (House Hearings, Agricultural Appropriations, fiscal 1948, Part 1, pp. 352-53).

7. Wells's statements, however, permit other inferences which, though less directly germane to this study, should be noticed. First, the intimate relationship between economic research and statistics is clear; but Wells ably suggests the gradations between the two. Second, it follows that statisticians and analysts can work more productively together than they can separately—and not merely because statistics gives analysis a protective cover against congressional attacks. Third, one may have to stretch the inference by reading even the fine print between the lines, but Wells's statement suggests a way of effectively including the wide range of professional abilities in one organization. Much professional work requires precision and training but not necessarily great imagination. On a rather high level, it can be routinized in a manner that fits the considerable abilities of many researchers who

do better in employing and refining given concepts and techniques than they do in discovering new ones. This idea permits one to accommodate the essential assumption that every budding economist is a potential Alfred Marshall to the obvious fact that most Ph.D.'s in economics are not Alfred Marshalls.

8. Drawn from House Hearings, Agricultural Appropriations, fiscal 1953, Part 1, pp. 184-93.

9. While many of these functions continue, the past tense is used because the BAE has been abolished.

10. House Hearings, Agricultural Appropriations, fiscal 1953, Part 1, pp. 211-27, esp. pp. 223-25.

11. House Hearings, Agricultural Appropriations, fiscal 1948, Part 1, p. 352.

12. Wells laid the stress on this orientation of the BAE; but he neither could claim credit for development of the BAE's considerable coverage of the economic picture in agriculture nor would presume to.

13. Senate Hearings, Agricultural Appropriations, fiscal 1948, p. 118; emphasis supplied. Formal transfer of the BAE's planning functions to the office of the Secretary followed recommendations of the Milton Eisenhower reorganization committee of eighteen in 1945.

14. The Wallaces of Iowa (Boston: Houghton Mifflin Co., 1947), chaps. viii and ix.

15. Lord prints Taylor's version of one of the classic agricultural political stories, the colloquy between Secretary Howard M. Gore and Taylor in February, 1925, wherein it is shown that the moutaineers know how to face the music.

16. Taylor went to a professorship at Northwestern University. The USDA has sometimes been a haven for political refugees from the land-grant colleges; the writer would be interested in knowing examples of the colleges' furnishing employment to refugees from the USDA.

17. For the BAE consult John M. Gaus and Leon O. Wolcott, Public Administration and the United States Department of Agriculture (Chicago: Public Administration Service, 1940), Index; Arthur W. MacMahon and John D. Millett, Federal Administrators (New York: Columbia University Press, 1939). See especially pp. 365-72 for the career of Howard R. Tolley. See also John D. Black, Agricultural Reform in the United States (New York: McGraw-Hill Book Co., Inc., 1929); Persia Campbell, American Agricultural Policy (London: P. S. King & Son, 1933).
Outlook work could produce local controversy as well. In 1922-23 V. B. Hart analyzed the potato outlook in Steuben County, New York. Potatoes were selling locally for 41 cents. Farmers wanted to know whether to sell. With much qualification, Hart suggested that the chances were about twelve to one against a price rise. But he warned them that he had not advised selling. He wrote above the meeting-room

door the date and the words: "Hart did not say to sell potatoes." Many
farmers did sell, however; and the price did go to 70 cents later. When
Hart returned for a dairy situation meeting the following year, he was
greeted as the man who had told them to sell potatoes. Fortunately, he
could show his statement still written above the door; but this did
not reimburse the farmers who expressed themselves as "all caught
up" with outlook (V. B. Hart, "Encouraging the Use of Outlook Material,"
JFE, January, 1929, quoted by Herbert C. Kriesel, "Redirecting
Efforts of the Extension Service To Educate Farmers in the field of
the Social Sciences" [typed MS, University of Chicago, 1947]).

18. The writer has read but not fully exploited the searching
study of the state and local planning program by Ellen Sorge Parks,
Experiment in the Democratic Planning of Public Agricultural Activity
(unpublished Ph.D. thesis, University of Wisconsin, 1947). Among the
questions she raises which deserve more attention than the text gives
are whether any program of this sort can be carried on by the USDA
without the acquiescence of the Farm Bureau (chap. i); whether such
programs can hope to succeed in the face of Extension resistance (chap.
vi); and whether a planning program can long hold the interests of
farmers unless they can see the results of talk carried over into action.
Some of the difficulties in BAE-college co-operation are suggested
above, pp. 32-33. See also H. R. Tolley, The Farmer Citizen at War
(New York: Macmillan Co., 1943); the annual reports of the chief of the
BAE through 1943; House Hearings, Agricultural Appropriations, fiscal
1942, pp. 258-77. See also Neal C. Gross, "A Post-mortem on County
Planning," JFE, August, 1943. For Pennsylvania's insularity in this
period, see above, chap. iii.

19. House Hearings, Agricultural Appropriations, fiscal 1942,
Part 2, p. 417.

20. The cut was made in the appropriation bill for fiscal 1942.
The Department of Agriculture recommended $5,714,000 for the BAE's
economic investigations. The Bureau of the Budget cut this by $2,500,000.
The House, on recommendation of the Committee on Appropriations, cut
the figure to $2,620,000. The Senate restored this last decrease, but the
conference committee returned to the House figure (Congressional Record,
LXXXVII, 2881 and 5400 [April 2 and June 20, 1941]).

21. Ibid., p. 1671 (March 3, 1941); and Senate Hearings, fiscal 1943,
p. 120 (April 21, 1942).

22. House Hearings, Agricultural Appropriations, fiscal 1942, pp.
280, 286-87.

23. Other House managers were Cannon (Missouri), Tarver, Leavy,
Lambertson, Dirksen, and Plumley (Congressional Record, LXXXVII,
5400). In 1942 Dirksen was the chief individual factor in wiping out
the remainder of the planning program. Lambertson was traditionally
for economy (cf. his remarks in Congress, June 8, 1940 [ibid., LXXXV,
5762]). Leavy and Tarver were apparently favorable to the BAE planning program at this time.

24. Report of the chief of the BAE, 1940, pp. 65-68.

25. See Charles M. Hardin, The Politics of Agriculture (Glencoe, Ill.: Free Press, 1952), pp. 134-35.

26. Senate Hearings, Agricultural Appropriations, fiscal 1942, pp. 370 ff. Director Creel was well informed and extremely favorable in his remarks. He described the Mt. Weather conference of 1938 and a follow-up meeting at Roanoke, Virginia, in September, 1940. At Roanoke there was general agreement among representatives of state Extension Services that the work was progressing satisfactorily; the only criticism he could recall was that the program was perhaps being pushed too rapidly. He informed senators of a special committee of the Extension committee on organization and policy, which had reported favorably on the planning program, the report of which had been received by the appropriate committees of the association. Furthermore, Simons had wired state Extension directors, asking that they communicate their attitudes to Congress. He received wires from thirty-seven directors favoring restoration of the $500,000 cut. Only four directors opposed the program, and these included three from states which had signed no memoranda of understanding with the BAE (apparently Pennsylvania, Illinois, and California). A few directors, such as D. W. Watkins, of South Carolina, approved the program but urged its transfer to the Extension Service. The telegrams to Simons (printed ibid., pp. 379-91) are for the most part highly commendatory, although a few, such as that of R. K. Bliss (Iowa), were rather negative. Simons also presented favorable letters from the New York State Conference Board of Farm Organizations; the New York State Grange had resolved separately in favor of the program. A number of North Dakota officials also attempted to help the BAE, including Governor Moses. President Talbott of the North Dakota Farmers Union also favored the BAE (ibid., pp. 217 ff.).

27. House Hearings, Agricultural Appropriations, fiscal 1943, p. 620; cf. Senate Hearings, Agricultural Appropriations, fiscal 1943, p. 730.

28. Congressional Record, LXXXVIII, 1890 (March 3, 1942).

29. Ibid., p. 1895, and cf. pp. 1992-93. For example, Dirksen discussed war production goals. His suggestion was to give the farmer a fair price and he would produce. A return argument might fairly cite the importance of the pattern of farm prices in determining what farmers would produce as well as the degree to which farm prices had, by congressional direction, become governmentally administered by this time. Again, besides prices, production goals involved consideration of fertilizer, machinery, and labor shortages as well as problems involved in shifting crop rotations and problems of storage, transportation, and the like. Dirksen attacked attaining of required production by citing the wheat referendum of the AAA, ascertaining whether farmers desired to reduce wheat production; it may be fairly asked what the BAE had to do with the routine performance by the AAA of functions directed by the Agricultural Adjustment Act of 1938.

30. Congressional Record, LXXXVIII, 1993; at other points, in answer to members' queries; Dirksen was wont to quote the attitude of the Farm Bureau (pp. 1995 and 1997).

31. To put it in its most kindly light, Dirksen was at least misinformed on these issues. While the BAE had set up regional offices, it

had not created "area" offices within the states, as both the Farm
Security Administration and the SCS had done. Nor could it be
fairly said that the BAE had made an attempt to set up county offices.
Extension directors of the several states generally were chairmen
of state land-use planning committees; Extension county agents were
frequently chairmen of county committees. Nowhere was a BAE employee assigned to work permanently with a county planning committee.

32. These pages contain the formal written presentation of its
work that the BAE made to the committee.

33. Congressional Record, LXXXVIII,1997. Before the Senate subcommittee on agricultural appropriations, Tolley attempted to show
how important AFBF influence had been in the action of the House.
He desired to read a statement from the Farm Bureau's Official News
Letter of March 24, 1942. Senator Bankhead interrupted him, saying
that he was uninterested in anything that had not occurred on the floor
of the House—"Regarding the House cut of $1,000,000, I don't care
anything about what was back of it" (Senate Hearings, Agricultural
Appropriations, fiscal 1943, p. 120).

34. Tarver's opposition to Dirksen was supported by Hare, Barden,
and Leavy. Cannon, of Missouri, stated that he had voted against the
amendment but after further study believed that the cut could be made.
Dirksen's supporters were May and Jennings. The House accepted
Dirksen's amendment, 76 to 55. The Senate restored $500,000 of the re-
duction, but in conference the restoration was halved, so that the BAE
wound up with a slice of $800,000 for economic investigations, $750,000
of which was derived from Dirksen's amendment. See the Congressional
Record, LXXXVIII, 1993, 1997, 4183, 5057, 5061, 5624.

35. E. J. Haselrud (director of Extension, North Dakota), Senate
Hearings, Agricultural Appropriations, fiscal 1943, p. 127 (April 21,
1942). See also the favorable testimony of Glenn J. Talbott, president
of the North Dakota Farmers Union, ibid., pp. 913 ff., and an editorial
from Wallace's Farmer, March 21, 1942, entitled "Don't Put a Blind-
fold on Farmers," ibid., p. 125.

36. The cut of $500,000 for fiscal 1942 was followed by a decrease
from $573,000 to $150,000 for co-operative employees.

37. On February 17, 1943, in response to a question from Tarver
whether the BAE had received complaints from farmers or others about
the discontinuance of this program, Tolley replied: "Mr. Chairman, at
the beginning of the fiscal year, when . . . we served notice upon the
people with whom we had been working that we would not be able to
work on it any more, a great many from the colleges, directors of
experiment stations, and farmers on the State and county committees
expressed to us their regret that we would not be able to work with
them any more. They gave us oral and written statements—there were
many of them—as to how valuable the work has been and how valuable
a part the Bureau of Agricultural Economics had played in it; and
in a considerable number of States and counties they are carrying on
the work as best they can" (House Hearings, Agricultural Appropriations,
fiscal 1944, p. 168).

Chapter XIV

1. Memo. 782, Secretary H. A. Wallace, October 16, 1938, quoted in Gaus and Wolcott, Public Administration and the United States Department of Agriculture (Chicago: Public Administration Service, 1940), pp. 466-77.

2. Congressman Taber (Republican, New York) objected to this language as legislation in an appropriation bill; Congressman Cannon (Democrat, Missouri) made a categorical denial. The chair ruled in favor of Cannon (Congressional Record, LXXXIV, 3307).

3. John D. Millett makes a useful distinction between policy planning and operational planning. The former includes clarifying the "basic policy decisions or value judgments upon which proposed operations rest." The latter involves the organization and procedure to carry out policies. As he notes, the two cannot be arbitrarily divided; bureaus, for example, must and will be concerned with policy. But the functions should be kept separate in the minds of all concerned (The Process and Organization of Government Planning [New York: Columbia University Press, 1947] , chap. i; and cf. pp. 79 ff. for his treatment of the BAE). Cf. Gaus and Wolcott, op. cit., chap. xv, and Paul Appleby, Big Government (New York: Alfred A. Knopf, 1946).

4. The Secretary's Memo. 1139, December 12, 1945, included the provision, effective January 1, 1946: "5. The responsibility for leadership in general agricultural program planning, including direction of the interbureau committees and working groups both in Washington and in the field, is hereby transferred to the office of the Secretary" (House Hearings, Agricultural Appropriations, fiscal 1947, p. 132). Remarks of Secretary Clinton Anderson appeared to indicate that the staffwork and advisory functions were transferred not to his office but to the research divisions of the national farm organizations, chiefly the American Farm Bureau Federation (AFBF) (ibid., pp. 20-21). This interpretation is in keeping with his remarks as United States senator on "Who Shall Speak for Farmers" at the AFBF convention in Chicago in 1949.

5. Jones was War Food Administrator; Vinson was Director of Economic Mobilization. Both were former congressmen.

6. House Hearings, Agricultural Appropriations, fiscal 1945, p. 153 and passim.

7. Congressional Record, XC, 2941 (March 22, 1941). The House provided $2,325,326 for economic investigations; the Senate made this $2,475,236. The conference committee provided $2,375,326 (ibid., p. 4575).

8. House Hearings, Agricultural Appropriations, fiscal 1946, p. 182, passim.

9. This cut was probably due as much to Dirksen as to anyone. It was predicated upon the five-year census of agriculture, "because . . . information developed by the impending farm census will render unnecessary the collection of many types of statistics

which have . . . been collected" by the BAE (Congressional Record, XCI, 2548, 2680-81). Dirksen was the only member of the subcommittee to raise the issue in the hearings (House Hearings, Agricultural Appropriations, fiscal 1946, p. 216).

10. Congressional Record, XCII, 2117 (March 8, 1946) (daily ed.).

11. Specific questions on this point were asked and answered in the hearings (House Hearings, Agricultural Appropriations, fiscal 1947, p. 284).

12. Unless otherwise noted, all material here is drawn from House Hearings, Agricultural Appropriations, fiscal 1947, pp. 234-42, 282, 286. Thus eighteen of one hundred and thirty pages of Hearings upon BAE appropriations are concerned with this issue; in addition, there are one or two indirect references on the floor of Congress.

13. The suggestion on the floor of the House was that the cost of the surveys was much more than these figures indicate (Congressional Record, XCII, 2117 [March 8, 1946] [daily ed.]; cf. remarks of Abernethy and Whitten).

14. In addition, some excerpted paragraphs were more widely circulated by someone outside the BAE.

15. When Whitten asked whether the document was to "raise the race question and make it something of a problem," Tolley said, "No: with respect to the matter of population and . . . the matter of returning veterans, with respect to the matter of what use farmers will make of their wartime savings, if any. That is part of our general effort to keep a running picture of the agricultural situation."

16. This paragraph caused Tarver to remark: "I think that the treatment accorded Negroes in industrial centers of the North is much worse than that which is accorded to Negroes in the agricultural sections of the South in which they are dealt with, on the whole, with sympathy and understanding. Therefore, this is very probably entirely without justification, untrue, and shows an incorrect statement of the situation. It stresses the importance of leadership, so-called militant northern Negro leadership, which in my judgment is a most unfortunate thing and which is doing a greater injury to the Negroes of the South than anything else when it comes to the handling of racial problems which exist in the South, problems which in the main are stirred up by these northern agitators, who seem to take every opportunity of stirring up things of this character" (House Hearings, Agricultural Appropriations, fiscal 1947, p. 241).

17. This is a widely accepted criterion for the ascertaining of "social facts"; see Talcott Parsons, The Structure of Social Action (New York: McGraw-Hill Book Co., Inc., 1937), pp. 41-42, "Note on the Concept 'Fact.'"

18. For a discussion of the "Southern Plantation Economy and the Negro Farmer" see Gunnar Myrdal, An American Dilemma (New York: Harper & Bros., 1944), Vol. I, chap. ii.

19. The American Farm Economic Association's contest called

forth many critical essays on the subject. See JFE, November, 1945. See also, e.g., Report of the Committee on Post War Agricultural Policy of the Association of Land-Grant Colleges and Universities (October, 1944); John D. Black, Parity, Parity, Parity (Cambridge, Mass.: Harvard Committee on Research in the Social Sciences, 1942); and Food Enough (Lancaster, Pa.: Jaques Cattell Press, 1943); T. W. Schultz, Redirecting Farm Policy (New York: Macmillan Co., 1943); and Agriculture in an Unstable Economy (New York: McGraw-Hill Book Co., Inc., 1945).

20. House Hearings, Agricultural Appropriations, fiscal 1947, pp. 18-19. Compare remarks of Earl C. Smith, in the annual address to the Illinois Agricultural Association (Chicago, November 28, 1945), who regarded the "prize winning essays as a challenge to the Departments of Economics of our Land-Grant Colleges to offer proposals that recognize the fundamental importance of a sustained, contented and prosperous agriculture" (pp. 23-24; emphasis supplied).

21. Secretary Wickard's statement, "Post War Problems of Cotton," was presented to the Special Committee of the House Committee on Agriculture on Post-war Farm Programs. The BAE analysis is "A Conversion Program for the Cotton South" (mimeographed), for administrative use.

22. See Tolley's remark: "The Bureau of Agricultural Economics does not decide upon the volume of production of the various commodities that will be asked for in the years ahead, nor do we decide upon the price policy, or the price support policy of the Department" (House Hearings, Agricultural Appropriations, fiscal 1947, p. 184). When Tarver asked whether a "recommendation" had not been made in favor of the let-prices-fall policy, Tolley replied: "If I may answer precisely, we suggested that consideration be given to that possibility." Whereupon Tarver said: "I wish to express my own opinion . . . that in fostering the promulgation of such a policy, in my judgment, your Bureau is doing a disservice for agriculture" (p. 187).

Compare ibid., pp. 248 ff., colloquy with Dirksen and others, probing where the authority lay. References were made to speeches of Secretary Anderson. The authority of the department under present legislation, particularly sec. 303 of the Agricultural Adjustment Act of 1938 (parity payments) and the "intent of Congress" were canvassed. Dirksen remarked that the Treasury Department goes "on the theory that there is no such thing as Congressional intent and that it is for them to fashion what it is their fancy to have been the intent at some anterior date. It is really amazing how they do that." Whereupon Tolley replied: "Economists are not supposed to be experts on the intent of Congress." Dirksen asked whether consideration was given any alternative to the policy that he liked to characterize as "letting prices dribble down to a world level." Tolley answered: "No. . . . The consequences of prices supported by act of government are being given just as serious consideration. One is being weighed against the other" (see esp. p. 259).

The extent of the questioning on this point may be indicated by a colloquy between H. Carl Andersen, of Minnesota, and Tolley. Andersen inquired why he should vote for a BAE appropriation or have any confidence in its work if all it had to offer was a proposition of putting farmers "on the same level with farm labor throughout the world." Tolley said: "I do not know whether it would be worthwhile to further answer. You have heard all this. . . . Speaking of the entire work of the Bureau, . . .

it has been pointed out here repeatedly that facts and statistics, with reference to agriculture, and a summarizing and analysis of those facts and statistics, make up a great part of the work that we do. It is for people in positions such as yours to judge as to how much, if any, of those they want" (ibid., p. 264 [January 16, 1946]).

23. Tolley certainly came close to such an "admission." In doing so, he gave credence to either of two beliefs: first, that the "innermost convictions" of supposedly objective social scientists necessarily color their findings and that in turn these findings are foisted upon ingenuous policy-makers; second, that, given the nature of present and prospective agricultural programs, an important part of an agency charged with "program formulation" is to be able to look squarely at the eventualities any course of policy may entail. Tolley said: "The point I want to make . . . is that holding the price at which cotton moves into the world market away above the world price is going to do two things. One of them is to dry up the export market, unless we have export subsidies or something like it. The other is to dry up part of the domestic market on account, on the one side, of competition from substitutes, and on the other side just the economic fact that the higher the price the less the market will take. So, to have a market for cotton, what we can produce and what we should produce in this country, and to have a market mechanism so that cotton will clear the market and not get piled up and make it necessary for us to have strict and rigid production control, cutting down the amount of cotton that is produced in future years, it seems to me that serious considera- tion should be given to letting the going market price of cotton be at or near the price that will clear the market, both domestically and foreign; that loan operations and all other operations should be in that way; and that the difference between what a farmer gets for his cotton or other commodities and what has been determined to be the parity return should be made up of payments, if you please, in the way they were made up in 1933, 1934, 1935, 1936, and 1937" (House Hearings, Agricultural Appropriations, fiscal 1947, p. 226; emphasis supplied; compare pp. 230, 231, 255).

24. House Hearings, Agricultural Appropriations, fiscal 1947, pp. 19-20, 33, and 50-58. Much was made of the fact that the let-prices-fall policy had no authoritative political sponsorship. Tarver asked Tolley: "So far as you know . . . no farm organization, no farm leader, no State commissioner of agriculture has suggested this plan of yours with reference to allowing agricultural products to be disposed of at world prices and making up the difference between that and parity prices from the Federal Treasury." None that he had seen, Tolley replied (House Hearings, Agricultural Appropriations, fiscal 1947, p. 261). Cf. Tarver's remarks in the House, Congressional Record, XCII, 2048 (March 7, 1946) (daily ed.).

25. Congressional Record, XCII, 2106 (March 8, 1946) (daily ed.); cf. Tarver's remarks, ibid., p. 2048 (March 7, 1946).

26. House Hearings, Agricultural Appropriations, fiscal 1947, pp. 191-203, 225-34.

27. Ibid., pp. 202-3.

28. For Whitten compare p. 225: "Actually you just drift along and do not care to get into conflict with Administrator Bowles . . . with the Labor Department nor with the CIO or the labor organizations, and for that reason you just do what you are called on to do, and let it go at that."

29. It is probably unnecessary to point out that the Fair Labor Standards Act made no such "guaranty."

30. House Hearings, Agricultural Appropriations, fiscal 1947, pp. 189, 260 ff.

31. Ibid., pp. 277-78.

32. Ibid., pp. 288-96.

33. Ibid., p. 50.

34. Congressional Record, XCII, 2048 (March 7, 1946) (daily ed.).

35. See the list of fifteen basic laws "To Stabilize Agriculture," Nation's Agriculture, October, 1945.

36. See T. W. Schultz, Redirecting Farm Policy, pp. 20, 66.

37. For the way this worked see the writer's articles in John D. Black (ed.), "Nutrition and Food Supply: The War and After," Annals of the American Academy of Political and Social Science, January, 1943, pp. 191 ff., and "The Tobacco Program: Exception or Portent?" JFE, November, 1946.

38. See House Hearings, Agricultural Appropriations, fiscal 1947, pp. 279-82, for all citations in this discussion.

39. Ibid., pp. 279-82.

40. Congressional Record, XCII, 2116-2117 (March 8, 1946) (daily ed.). Andersen's effort lost by eight votes.

Chapter XV

1. The American Farm Bureau Federation (AFBF), which had assisted in cutting the planning program in 1942, was instrumental here. Shortly before Tolley resigned, a land-grant college official expressed doubts to the writer that the BAE could survive under present leadership, since "Ed O'Neal no longer has any use for Tolley." President O'Neal testified that the BAE should be confined to statistical and fact-finding research. The significance of the AFBF's position may be inferred from the correspondence between their recommendations and the language of the appropriation act, already noted. The AFBF proposed that the BAE "should be prohibited from conducting social surveys, agricultural planning and promotion, and opinion polls (except bona fide factual marketing studies and surveys of consumer attitudes and preferences with respect to the consumption of agricultural commodities). All funds for this type of work should be eliminated. The regional office

should also be eliminated as this is a needless expense" (emphasis
supplied; House Hearings, Agricultural Appropriations, fiscal 1947,
pp. 1644, 1653-55; Congressional Record, XCII, 2116 [March 8,
1946] [daily ed.]). It should be added that in none of the years 1941-46
was the BAE the chief target of Farm Bureau criticism. In 1941 the main
emphasis was upon the shortcomings of the Farm Security Administration
(FSA) and the Soil Conservation Service (SCS). An all-out attack was
leveled at the FSA in 1942; in 1943 emphasis appears to have been upon
reforming the Agricultural Adjustment Administration (AAA); in 1944,
AAA, FSA, SCS, and departmental information offices were chief
subjects of criticism.

2. House Hearings, Agricultural Appropriations, fiscal 1948,
Part 1, pp. 351 ff.; Senate Hearings, Agricultural Appropriations, fiscal
1948, pp. 119 ff. Respecting conferences with the committees of the
Association of Land-Grant Colleges and Universities, Wells said: "I
do not conceive it to be their function to tell me what to do, but I
want advice, and I am certainly more than willing to tell them what the
Bureau is doing."

3. House Hearings, Agricultural Appropriations, fiscal 1948,
Part 1, pp. 351-52.

4. House Hearings, Agricultural Appropriations, fiscal 1951, Part
1, p. 366. Cf. Senate Hearings, Agricultural Appropriations, fiscal 1948,
pp. 117-18; House Hearings, Agricultural Appropriations, fiscal 1950,
Part 1, pp. 290, 309-10; and House Hearings, Agricultural Appropriations,
fiscal 1952, Part 1, p. 169.

5. House Hearings, Agricultural Appropriations, fiscal 1951, Part 1, p. 320.

6. House Hearings, Agricultural Appropriations, fiscal 1953, Part
1, p. 178.

7. House Hearings, Agricultural Appropriations, fiscal 1951, Part
1, p. 320.

8. Chester I. Barnard, The Functions of the Executive (Cambridge,
Mass.: Harvard University Press, 1938).

9. It is interesting how often this phrase, which Pendleton Herring
used to characterize the alternatives offered by the two political parties
in the United States, is applicable in other political situations (The
Politics of Democracy [New York: Rinehart & Co., 1940]).

10. John D. Black, Parity, Parity, Parity (Cambridge, Mass.: Harvard Committee on Research in the Social Sciences, 1942), p. 51.

11. House Hearings, Agricultural Appropriations, fiscal 1953,
Part 1, pp. 7, 41-52, 211-27. Wells has recognized the point being made:
"You cannot even publish straight statistics without running into some
criticism, to be perfectly honest" (Senate Hearings, Agricultural Appropriations, fiscal 1948, p. 118); and, of the colloquy between Wells, Congressman Dirksen (Republican, Illinois), and Congressman Whitten
(Democrat, Mississippi) respecting a survey of consumer preferences for
cotton and competing fabrics, Wells said: "We are not interested here . . .
in whether people should have cotton or rayon." Whitten said that he

would probably be interested in trying to get them to use cotton, where-upon Wells replied: "If I am in that position, then the survey is no value to you or to anybody else" (House Hearings, Agricultural Appropriations, fiscal 1948, Part 1, pp. 372-73).

12. House Hearings, Agricultural Appropriations, fiscal 1950, Part 1, p. 320.

13. House Hearings, Agricultural Appropriations, fiscal 1951, Part 1, pp. 364-65, and cf. Senate Hearings, Agricultural Appropriations, fiscal 1951, p. 233.

14. House Hearings, Agricultural Appropriations, fiscal 1952, Part 1, pp. 173-74.

15. Senate Hearings, Agricultural Appropriations, fiscal 1952, p. 122.

16. House Hearings, Agricultural Appropriations, fiscal 1951, Part 1, p. 365.

17. See above, p. 161.

18. Senate Hearings, Agricultural Appropriations, fiscal 1948, pp. 115-16.

19. Ibid. Cf. J. T. Sanders of the national Grange, testimony in Senate Hearings, Agricultural Appropriations, fiscal 1948, p. 761.

20. 80th Cong., 2d sess. (1948); cf. House Hearings, Agricultural Appropriations, fiscal 1950, Part 1, p. 301.

21. House Report No. 2728 (79th Cong., 2d sess. [1946]), e.g., p. 23.

22. 81st Cong., 1st sess. (1949); see acknowledgments on p. ix, and note use of reference material.

23. "USDA Miscellaneous Publications," Nos. 562, 570, 582, and 589 (prepared by postwar committees of the department).

24. USDA Miscellaneous Publication No. 595 (prepared by the interbureau committee on postwar programs, in co-operation with the land-grant colleges). But see John D. Black, "The Bureau of Agricultural Economics—the Years in Between," JFE (proceedings number, November, 1947), p. 1036.

25. North Central State Conference for Extension Workers, "Discussing Public Policy," special circular (University of Wisconsin Agricultural Extension [January, 1951]), p. 62.

26. BAE, USDA Miscellaneous Circular No. 707 (1949).

27. House Hearings, Agricultural Appropriations, fiscal 1949, Part 1, p. 355. Cf. "USDA Testimony Proposing Long Range Agricultural Policy and Programs . . ." (mimeographed; Washington, D.C.: USDA, April 21, October 6-8, 1947).

28. Cf. John D. Black, "The Bureau of Agricultural Economics—the Years in Between," pp. 1033 ff.

29. This is not to depreciate the personnel problem of the BAE. Wells stressed the competition the BAE faced from other governmental agencies, colleges of agriculture, etc. He could make proper use of funds only if he could recruit professionally qualified persons: "I just cannot take anyone" (House Hearings, Agricultural Appropriations, fiscal 1952, Part 1, pp. 147-48).

30. The network of influence in agriculture—and, correspondingly, the policy-forming process—is extremely complex. In numerous formal and informal conferences, the BAE has been well represented. Take the American Farm Economic Association. In the years 1939-52 its presidents included F. F. Elliott (1939), Sherman Johnson (1943), Eric Englund (1944), F. V. Waugh (1946), and O. V. Wells (1949). All were, had been, or were to be ranking officials in the BAE. Moreover, the annual meetings of the association are significant forums for the ventilation of policy issues. Examination of the Proceedings of these meetings will impress the reader with the contribution to these discussions by members of the BAE; and an even more vivid impression remains with those who can recall some of the unrecorded contributions of BAE officials.

31. See Charles M. Hardin, "The Bureau of Agricultural Economics under Fire: A Study in Valuation Conflicts," JFE, August, 1946, p. 639, n. 7.

32. Charles M. Hardin, "Programmatic Research and Agricultural Policy," JFE, May, 1947.

33. Senate Hearings, Agricultural Appropriations, fiscal 1947, pp. 529-31.

34. Letter to Senator Irving M. Ives (Republican, New York) in support of the BAE's appropriations (Senate Hearings, Agricultural Appropriations, fiscal 1952, p. 910). Hill became provost of Cornell University in 1952.

35. During February and March, 1954, Alan E. Emory published an interesting series of articles (which ought to be made generally available) on the influence of the college of agriculture of Cornell University in the Benson USDA (Watertown Daily Times, February 25 and following days).

36. Only the statement of E. J. Haselrud in 1942 and F. F. Hill in 1951 have been found (see above, pp. 156, 162, and 183).

37. See above, pp. 161-63, 184.

38. Not having the Coahoma County report, the writer is in no position to pass judgment upon it. Tolley, it will be remembered, repudiated some of the paragraphs. It is unbelievable, however, that the BAE would have published a report which would have inflamed racial relations

in the South. At the same time, the freedom to reproduce and circulate manuscripts for professional criticism is essential to an effective research agency. The distinction must be made clear: it is this limited but necessary freedom which was at stake—the need for which was lost upon the official who passed the preliminary document into hands where it did not belong.

Chapter XVI

1. II, p. 539.

2. Proceedings, of the Association of Land-Grant Colleges and Universities, XLV (1931), 119 ff.

3. Proceedings, XLVI (1932), 281-82.

4. Proceedings, LX (1946), 140-43.

5. "Educational Work in Public Policy Problems and Their Relationships to Agriculture" (mimeographed; Washington, D.C.: Extension Service, USDA, July, 1949), 691.

6. The writer has been an advisory member of the committee.

7. The Farm Foundation (600 South Michigan Avenue, Chicago 5, Illinois) has published or duplicated materials of all conferences. The 1951 national meeting illustrates the approach. Committees reported on four policy areas—foreign policy, inflation, agricultural production policy, and interrelationships between agriculture and other segments of the national economy. Presentations have typically stressed subject matter and methodology. Most of the analysis of subject matter has been in economic terms. Most problems considered have important economic aspects, and virtually all the participants are primarily trained as economists. In 1951, however, the analysis of foreign policy dwelt heavily upon political problems, and in 1953 a day was devoted to political analysis which was designed to be relevant to the public policy programs.

8. The contribution of the Farm Foundation should also be stressed. Credit should also go to former President Allan B. Kline of the AFBF for moving, in the Farm Foundation board, that the program be supported.

9. Dale E. Hathaway, E. E. Peterson, and Lawrence Witt, "Michigan Farmers and the Price Support Program. II. Farmers' Attitudes . . ." (Agricultural Experiment Station Technical Bull. 235 [East Lansing, Michigan, December, 1952]). A sample of five hundred farmers was questioned in the late summer of 1950. Only 8 per cent had a "good understanding"; 12 per cent had "some understanding, not in detail"; 14 per cent thought they understood but "gave answer entirely wrong"; and 64 per cent answered "don't know" (p. 15).

10. In extenuation of the district agents, one may cite their special burdens after World War II in many states where they had to try to stimulate county appropriations and also to find replacements for the stream of Extension workers who found higher-paying jobs. Both these activities were so demanding that little time remained for studying and passing on innovations in the program.

11. Cf. reference to Gunnar Myrdal, An American Dilemma (New York: Harper & Bros., 1944), in the "Methodological Note" at the end of chap. xv (p. 184). See also Leo Strauss, Natural Right and History (Chicago: University of Chicago Press, 1953), chap. ii; David Easton, The Political System (New York: Alfred A. Knopf, 1953), passim; and W. Robert Parks, in the report of the 1953 annual Conference of Agricultural Extension Workers (Green Lake, Wisconsin), distributed by the Farm Foundation.

12. In the first place, public policy educators can safely give their own conclusions if they can make it clear that the emphasis in the educational process is upon the reasons why these, and not other, conclusions were reached. See Louis Hartz, in "Goals for Political Science," American Political Science Review, XLV, No. 4 (December, 1951). Second, social life requires decisions. Even Hamlet's soliloquies had to end. Some issues are postponed, of course, rather than resolved. And it may be that public policy educators—like congressmen—after wrestling with problems will have to conclude that no way of meeting them now appears both feasible and acceptable. But there is no substitute for the intellectual wrestling.

13. The writer has dealt to some extent with these issues. See above, chap. v, sec. 3; The Politics of Agriculture (Glencoe, Ill.: Free Press, 1952), p. 143; "The Farmer-Citizen's Participation in Politics," in the Farm Foundation, Increasing Understanding of Public Policies (Chicago, 1953); and "Economic Policy Formation in a Constitutional Democracy"(lecture delivered at the Economic Education Workshop, South Dakota State College [Brookings, 1954]). The quotation at the head of this section is from James Bryce, The American Commonwealth (New York: Macmillan Co., 1910), II, 271; Bryce's chapters (Part IV of this edition) are well worth adding to the literature on public opinion already cited.

14. See R. B. Tootell, Proceedings, LXIV (1948), 143-44.

15. B. F. Wright, Jr., "The Federalist on the Nature of Political Man," Ethics, Vol. LIX (January, 1949), Part II.

16. From the President's summary of the Republican policy conferences, New York Times, December 20, 1953.

16a. See Charles M. Hardin, "A Political Interpretation of Agricultural Issues," lecture, graduate school, USDA, December 8, 1954 (mimeographed).

17. Address to the Association of Land-Grant Colleges and Universities (cf. Proceedings, Vol. LXVII [1953]); see also above, chap. x and chap. xv, "Methodological Note."

18. Washington Post, December 15, 1953.

19. See his address before the Pennsylvania State Bar Association, January 16, 1953.

20. Annual Address of the President of the AFBF (Chicago: American Farm Bureau Federation,1951).

Chapter XVII

1. Irwin Edman (ed.), The Philosophy of Plato, trans. Jowett (New York: Macmillan Co., 1927), p. 77.

2. The Public and Its Problems (New York: Henry Holt & Co., 1927; Bloomington, Ind.: Principia Press, 1946), p. 59.

3. Nature and Needs of Higher Education (New York: Columbia University Press, 1952), p. 159.

4. See chap. iii, n. 26.

5. Further evidence of college efforts to decentralize government in agriculture is provided in the soil conservation phase of agricultural politics (see Charles M. Hardin, The Politics of Agriculture [Glencoe, Ill.: Free Press, 1952]).

6. Ibid.; see also above, e.g., the conclusion of chap. ii; see also the writer's article, "A Rounded Land Conservation Program," in the Annals of the American Academy of Political and Social Science for May, 1952.

7. Examples in other areas might include state control of social security programs, including the publication of lists of persons eligible for unemployment insurance; state control of offshore petroleum resources; decentralization of governmental employment services to states; federal "fair trade practices" legislation; decentralization of rent control; decentralization to the states of legislation to inhibit discrimination in private employment on grounds of national derivation, religion, or color; and the preference for handling regional resource-development programs through interstate compacts rather than through valley authorities.

8. See above, p. 188.

9. See above, p. 188.

10. H. F. Lionberger, "Low-Income Farmers in Missouri . . ." (Missouri Agricultural Experiment Station Research Bull. 413 [Columbia, 1948]); D. DeLany and V. A. Caulum, "Farm Women Look at the Home Bureau" (New York Agricultural College, Cornell Extension Bull. 754 [Ithaca, N.Y., 1948]); "The Lubbock County Study . . . " (Texas Agricultural College Extension Bull. R-11 [College Station, 1948]); cf. also the citations in Philip Selznick, TVA and the Grass Roots (Berkeley: University of California Press, 1949), pp. 121-23.

11. II, 472.

12. Pp. 58-59, 64-66.

13. The last direct consideration of the problem by the association occurred in 1941; cf. M. C. Wilson's paper and subsequent panel discussion, Proceedings, LV (1941), 179 ff.

14. From "Low Incomes in Southern Agriculture" (unpublished manuscript, department of economics, University of Chicago).

15. The writer has seen careful notes on this unreported speech by one who heard it; interestingly enough, the dean was answered by none other than Charles W. Holman, of the National Cooperative Milk Producers Federation.

16. Proceedings, XXXIX (1925), 27.

17. See above, p. 141.

18. Proceedings, XLVI (1932), 333 ff.

19. Proceedings, LVI (1942), 119.

20. For the 1920's see F. B. Mumford, of Missouri, Proceedings, XXXIX (1925), 188-93; P. F. Trowbridge, Proceedings, XXXIV (1920), 126-28; H. J. Webber, Proceedings, XXXIV (1920), 149-58; F. D. Farrell, Proceedings, XXXIX (1925), 114-18; and the remarks of A. R. Mann, C. E. Ladd, and E. W. Allen cited elsewhere; for recent criticisms see chap. xi above.

21. Cambridge, Mass.: Harvard University Press, 1948.

22. The New Leviathan (London: Oxford University Press, 1942), chap. xxvii.

23. The motion led to the appointment of a select committee, chaired by Senator Watkins (Republican, Utah), which unanimously recommended censure on several counts. On December 1, 1954, after extended debate, the Senate voted 67 to 20 to censure Senator McCarthy on the first count of the Watkins Committee report: for McCarthy's contemptuous treatment of the Senate subcommittee investigating his financial affairs in 1951 and 1952.

A Note on Abbreviations and Terms

AAA—Agricultural Adjustment Administration (occasionally referred
to as the "Triple A"); became the Production and Marketing
Administration (PMA) in 1945

ACP—Agricultural Conservation Program of the AAA to 1945; of the
PMA, 1945-53; renamed the "Agricultural Conservation Program Service" in 1953

ARA—Agricultural Research Administration; formed in 1942, consolidating most of the physical, biological, chemical, and engineering research of the USDA; changed to ARS in 1953

ARS—Agricultural Research Service; formed in 1953 by combining the
ARA with certain research hitherto carried on by the BAE, the
SCS, the Forest Service, and the PMA

AFBF—American Farm Bureau Federation; sometimes referred to as
the "Farm Bureau"

AMS—Agricultural Marketing Service; formed in 1953, chiefly out of
the BAE and the PMA

BAE—Bureau of Agricultural Economics; abolished in 1953, its functions
being divided between the ARS and the AMS

CCC—Commodity Credit Corporation

FHA—Farmers Home Administration; before 1946, the Farm Security
Administration (FSA)

FSA—Farm Security Administration

NFU—National Farmers Union; sometimes referred to as the "Farmers
Union"

OES—Office of Experiment Stations

PMA—Production and Marketing Administration; replaced the AAA in
1945; abolished in 1953

SCS—Soil Conservation Service

TVA—Tennessee Valley Authority

USDA—United States Department of Agriculture

The Annals—The Annals of the American Academy of Political and Social
    Science

APSR—American Political Science Review

JFE—Journal of Farm Economics

Proceedings—Proceedings of the Association of Land-Grant Colleges
    and Universities

The term "colleges of agriculture," or sometimes merely "colleges," refers to colleges or schools of agriculture which are part of land-grant colleges or universities. The term "Extension" usually refers to the Extension Service in one or more of the forty-eight states; occasionally it refers to the Cooperative Federal-State Extension Service. "Farm Bureau" is used to designate both particular state Farm Bureaus and the American Farm Bureau Federation. It is believed that the connotations will be clear in the context and that the usage in this book reflects the common employment of these terms.